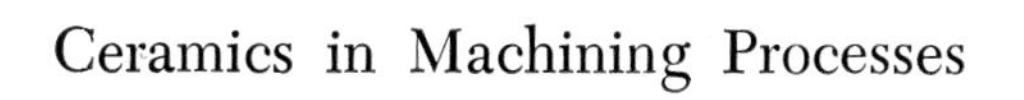
Ceramics in Machining Processes

Ceramics in Machining Processes

ALAN G. KING
Zirconium Corporation of America
Solon, Ohio

W. M. WHEILDON
Norton Company
Refractories Division
Research and Development Department
Worcester, Massachusetts

1966

ACADEMIC PRESS

New York and London

ACADEMIC PRESS INC.
111 Fifth Avenue, New York, New York 10003

United Kingdom Edition published by
ACADEMIC PRESS INC. (LONDON) LTD.
Berkeley Square House, London W.1

LIBRARY OF CONGRESS CATALOG CARD NUMBER: 66-29042

PRINTED IN THE UNITED STATES OF AMERICA

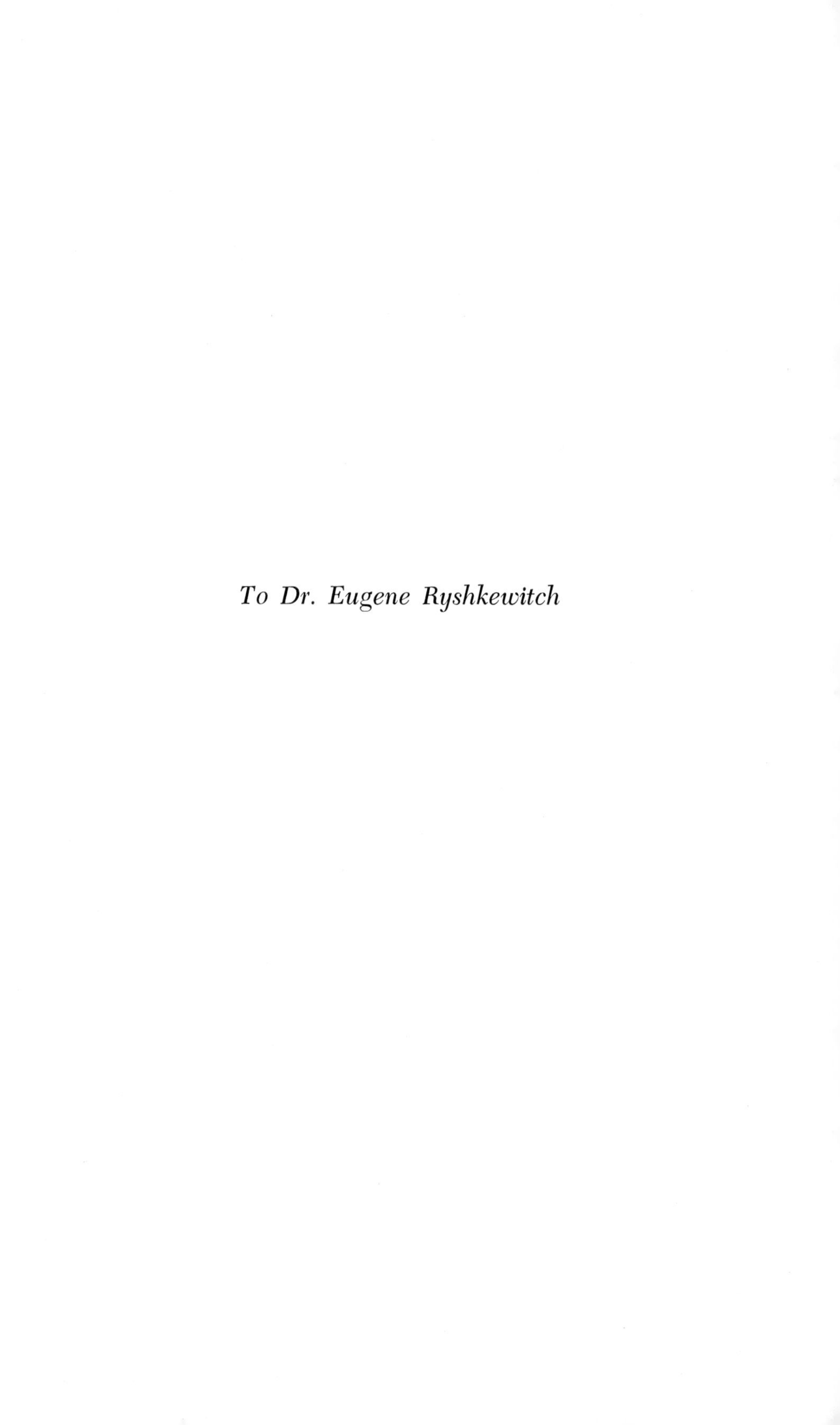

To Dr. Eugene Ryshkewitch

Preface

The development of a new structural material with unique physical and chemical properties presents a challenge to the engineer to fully explore its nature and applications. This is a stimulating endeavor of both hands and mind.

Progress in ceramic technology has improved the physical properties of alumina-based ceramics to such an extent that these ceramics could be considered for uses involving heavy mechanical loads and shocks. This is not merely an extension of a material into a new usage. Ceramics were always considered uniquely weak and brittle materials which fractured unpredictably under only modest service conditions. Therefore, it was necessary to bury a prejudice and pursue learning with an unencumbered mind before new experiments could be contemplated. The prejudgment of failure was so strong that only the naive or the visionary would have had the freedom of intellect to proceed along directions that were obviously ridiculous. After success was amply demonstrated, the reverse became obvious; materials with these physical properties would predictably function under these service conditions. Such is the belittlement of progress.

There is a need for a new cutting-tool material. The tendency is toward higher speeds and lower production costs, machining increasingly more difficult materials. The requirements of industry continually place ever-increasing demands on the tools with which metals are shaped. The ultimate properties of materials are invariably pushed to failure limits. Pre-existing cutting-tool materials such as tool steels and cemented carbides, while strong enough at room temperature, were not amply inert or refractory or wear-resistant to withstand some of these conditions. Their deficiencies were inherent, as they resulted from the basic composition and structure of the materials themselves. The possibilities of gross improvement were not especially attractive without radically departing from existing technology and composition. One approach taken was that toward alumina-based ceramics. For this approach to succeed, it was necessary to develop tooling systems capable of accommodating the demands of metal-cutting forces. Part of this problem was solved by evolving tool geometries which fully utilize the high compressive strength common to ceramic materials, and part by increasing the strength of the material itself. The research approach to this problem had to be multidisciplinary, drawing knowledge and technique from such diverse fields as mechanics, solid state physics, ceramics, physical chemistry, and tool engineering.

This monograph details this development and is as comprehensive as possible. There are, of course, areas not adequately covered due to appalling gaps in our knowledge and an understandable reluctance to part with proprietary information concerning research in active progress. Our desire is to be as liberal with information as possible. We have attempted to present systematically that information which has previously appeared in the literature and that which we have obtained from the generosity of others engaged in ceramic tool research. The subject is discussed from its earliest conception, through current technology, to future predictions, from the science of the crystalline state to machine shop practice, from how it fails, to how well it works. It is written primarily for the cognizant user and practical investigator of ceramic tooling with the hope that a deeper understanding of these remarkable materials and the forces acting on them will aid him in developing the utility of ceramic tooling and broaden its applications, and stimulate research into the many attractive areas not yet adequately explored.

We have also gathered together from many disperse sources the current state of the art, so that a comprehensive bibliography is available to guide further reading and future research; this information is usefully and systematically summarized.

Perhaps our primary impression of the ceramic tool is its seemingly inexhaustible supply of stimulating surprises. Experiments have given us glimpses into a yet untapped future and suggest possible radical departures from current tool design and usage. There seems no limit to the resourceful and imaginative investigator of experiments in tool design and use which can produce these surprises. Only the unexpected is predictable. The ceramic tool is a test and a challenge. Its use and improvement demand creative ingenuity and cognizance of the materials, properties, and factors affecting it. It is our sincere hope that our efforts may stimulate others to pursue novel and imaginative studies into the many areas of interest which have not yet been adequately explored.

ALAN G. KING
W. M. WHEILDON

September, 1966

Acknowledgments

We would like to acknowledge the assistance we have received from a great many people in the preparation of this work and in the execution of the research work which preceded it. On our own staff we have had the continued support of Norton's research management: W. L. Howe, N. W. Thibault, L. Coes, and N. N. Ault. Without their understanding and active encouragement, it would not have been possible to maintain a successful research program, nor would it have been possible to take the time and resources necessary to consolidate into this volume the information gained.

We would like to thank particularly O. J. Whittemore, Jr., who was the central researcher associated with the original discovery and early development of the successful VR97 tool. The importance of original discovery cannot be overemphasized.

We must also acknowledge John C. Logan, whose active interest and dedication to the idea far transcended what normally would be considered his obligation or normal staff participation, John Sjogern and L. P. Jensen, whose contributions were made early in this work, and G. Hague, E. F. Reiner, and C. R. Newell, whose assistance was invaluable in the later stages of the volume.

The generous help we have obtained from others, outside of Norton Company, who granted us permission to use published materials has been acknowledged in each instance in the text. Beyond this we would like to call special attention to the research staff of the Carborundum Company and M. S. Day and Donald P. Hunt who provided needed information about their CCT-707 tool and helped editorially in the preparation of the manuscript. Dr. E. W. Goliber of General Electric Company was very helpful in supplying information and photographs of his O-30 tool material. Mr. B. J. Naden and Richard C. Bradt of Vascoloy Ramet Wesson Corporation were very helpful in supplying information about VR97.

We have enjoyed a continued association with the staff of the Watertown Arsenel Rodman laboratory. Their interest in ceramic tools and their active cooperation have been extremely valuable in carrying out the test work that was used in this book. In particular, we would like to acknowledge the contributions of W. B. Kennedy under whose direction the test work was performed which led to the initial widespread interest in ceramic turning tools. Also of the Rodman staff, we wish to acknowledge P. A. G. Carbonaro, Harold McNamera, and David Thornton. Many tests reported in the subsequent pages were performed with the active cooperation of this staff.

We have had an active partnership with professors H. D. Moore and D. R. Kibbey at Ohio State University. The test methods which were developed at OSU were very valuable in developing an understanding of tool behavior as it was related to tool geometry and ceramic technology.

Their methods should be more generally applicable to machining problems than just the limited application to ceramics reported here. We are dependent on their results for many of the conclusions reported herein.

Contents

Chapter 5 / Tool Life and the Mechanism of Tool Failure

Chapter 6 / Tool Design

Chapter 7 / Tool Evaluation

Chapter 8 / Industrial Experience

Chapter 9 / The Future

Introduction

Why should we try to use ceramics as tools for the chip removal of metals? What real and potential advantages do ceramics have over cemented carbide or tool steel cutters?

A ceramic, as it is commonly known, is not the sort of object we would think of using for machining steel. Characteristically, ceramics have transverse rupture strength from only 10,000 to 30,000 psi; they fail readily by brittle fracture, and often will not even stand modest thermal shock. They are weak, notch sensitive, chip readily, and shatter under impact. They are also hard, refractory, chemically inert, retain their strength and hardness at high temperatures, and are among the most wear resistant materials known.

The mechanical properties of ceramics are generally poor. The chemical and thermal properties are generally excellent. The strength depends on variables which can, to a certain extent, be experimentally controlled. The chemistry, hardness, and refractory character depend upon the composition and crystal structure, and are inherent properties.

The use of ceramics in machining is, then, an attractive approach to solve some of the problems of modern chip removal processes. The inherent advantages provide the impetus and interest that exist in ceramic tool research.

The research problem at the outset was and, to a certain extent continues to be finding ways to improve the strength of those ceramics suitable for use as tools.

If we exclude borides and carbides from the term "ceramic," all of the ceramics currently used for metal chip removal are based on aluminum oxide with the corundum crystal structure.

All currently available ceramic tools are dense polycrystalline aggregates of very fine grain size, averaging from 2 to about 5 microns. Small amounts of other ceramic materials have been added to either refine the grain structure or promote sintering. They are all manufactured by either sintering or hot pressing, and their strength depends upon the alumina-alumina grain-boundary adhesion rather than an alumina-cement-alumina bond.

Alumina is unique among the oxide ceramics in its combination of high hardness, chemical inertness, and resistance to degradation at elevated temperatures.

The technology of alumina article manufacture was well advanced, prior to extensive ceramic tool application, and only relatively modest gains in strength were necessary to adapt this ceramic to machining purposes.

Currently, commercially available ceramic tools have transverse rupture strengths of from 80,000 to 120,000 psi and uniaxial compressive strength from 250,000 to 600,000 psi.

Practice has shown that this is strong enough to turn even the hardest steels at impressive stock removal rates. Practice has also shown that this is not strong enough to perform all of the severe chip removal processes that modern industry demands from a tool material.

At present, ceramic tools have an area of application where they perform advantageously because of properties arising from the inherent properties of alumina and, thus, are not excluded by their lesser strength.

The more an investigator works with ceramic tools, the more he realizes that there isn't anything particularly different in their behavior from other tool materials. The processes by which they are made are similar to those used in powder metallurgy or cemented carbide manufacture. They are used in much the same way as cemented carbides; they wear by similar processes, and fracture by similar processes. The conditions that are adverse for ceramic tools are also adverse for carbides. They are different—either better or worse—only in degree rather than in kind.

Those ceramics that are used for tools are a specific and special type developed especially for that discreet purpose. Only by careful control of raw materials and process parameters is it possible to maintain the high quality necessary for a tool material. Our own experience is that even minor changes in the purity or microstructure of the tool can have profound effects on its function—i.e., usually bad.

Ceramic tool manufacture is a precision industrial process in which great pains are taken to assure that product-purity, mixing, firing, and grinding all conform to exacting standards which have been proven necessary by experience. In some cases these requirements are more stringent than those used for cemented carbide manufacture. Alumina ceramics, which superficially have the strength, density, and microstructural requirements for use as a tool, often do not function well as a tool in an actual test. Obviously, we have not measured the pertinent properties—and just what these properties are in detail, remains obscure.

The tool materials that are used have been selected because they work. Actually, the situation is not quite this empirical. Certainly a material with a high transverse rupture and uniaxial compressive strength would be expected to out-perform a material with significantly lower strength values. What remains obscure, is why two materials with the same strength values perform so differently in a machinability test. The solution to this question should aid in the search for better ceramics because a more basic understanding of critical parameters tells us where to look for them and how to evaluate them.

As would be expected, ceramic tools have found their immediate utility in those applications where cemented carbides or tool steel cutters do not function satisfactorily. The high hot hardness and wear resistance of alumina is primarily responsible for extensive applications in machining abrasive cast iron and hardened steels, where higher cutting speeds are economically advantageous. The inertness of alumina to iron at high temperatures prevents welding of the tool to the workpiece, and is partially responsible for better workpiece finishes, which have, in some cases, eliminated subsequent grinding. The high wear resistance of ceramic tools has been utilized in machining long diameters where excessive taper cannot be tolerated. These are specialized uses where the ceramic's inherent properties give it an immediate advantage over cemented carbide. More generally, modern ceramic tools can be used advantageously for general machining of steel in those applications where heavy interrupted cuts are not encountered or where the part shape does not exclude the use of the negative tool geometries that are generally required with ceramics.

Everything, from tungsten to wood, from other ceramics to graphite, has been machined successfully with ceramic tools. High-nickel stainless steels or nickel-titanium bearing alloys present the primary exception. Ceramic tools have been used for milling of cast iron and steel with success. They have been used for boring. Usually, they are used in clamp type holders with negative tool geometry, but they have also been successfully brazed onto shanks, bonded with resins, and taken impressive cuts into hardened steel with a positive rake angle. They are used with sharp edges, Chamfered edges, and edges containing a small radius. While the volume usage of ceramic tools is at present largely confined to those few areas where they offer the greatest savings, the future applicability of ceramics will broaden to include a wider variety of machining problems.

The ceramic will supplement rather than replace cemented carbide and tool steel cutters. Cemented carbide is truly a remarkable material with a well advanced technology. A wide variety of materials are available to the tool engineer to help solve his machining problems. The extremely high strength of cemented carbide enabled the synthesis of diamonds to become a commercial reality. No other material has the strength necessary to achieve and sustain the high pressures used in this process.

Machining metals at high speeds requires some of the same physical properties in the tool material that are also required in ultrahigh pressure research. Localized pressures on the tool cutting edge can easily attain 100,000 psi in practice, and temperatures up to at least 800°C. Cemented carbide can have transverse rupture strengths up to 200,000 psi, and uniaxial compressive strength to 700,000 psi. Any new tool material that competes must be very special indeed. With typical transverse and compressive strengths of 90,000 and 500,000 psi, respectively, the ceramic is almost in the running, strengthwise, and with its other advantages it can compete in many instances.

The practice has been to design tool geometry which compensates for the ceramic's relatively low transverse rupture strength. Of course, these strength figures do not take into account the way strength varies with temperature. The ceramic retains most of its strength to 1200°C while carbide does not. In a high speed machining application, the ceramic might well resist fracture while the carbide tip shatters. This does prove to be the case. Both ceramics and low-cobalt-content cemented carbides are brittle materials. The carbide is stronger at low temperatures (slow cutting speeds), and the ceramic is stronger at high temperatures (high cutting speeds). Under machining conditions of fracture failure—rather than wear failure—we would expect the carbide to fail shortly after entering the work, as opposed to the ceramic which fails on entry. These factors are particularly acute when dealing with milling cutters, where many tens of thousands of entries must be made into the work by the cutting edge.

At present, the cemented carbide enjoys severe entry and severe mechanical-shock machining applications, without fear of encroachment by ceramic tools.

There are two parallel approaches available that are being taken to overcome the ceramic tools limitations:

1. Making stronger tools
2. Designing machining parameters and tool geometries that enable the tool engineer to machine economically with lower strength materials

The first approach is being undertaken by ceramists and materials scientists, and the second by mechanical and tool engineers. Both approaches have, to date, been partially successful and neither has been exhausted. We can expect improvements.

The interest in ceramic tools is worldwide with significant work being conducted in the U.S.S.R., Hungary, Germany, France, England, Sweden, Japan, and the United States. The introduction of a new tooling material proposes stimulating questions to the tool engineer and if he is of an inquisitive nature, he will try to answer some of these questions.

The number of companies, universities, and individual investigators that have worked with ceramic tools does indeed constitute an impressive list. The enthusiasm and optimism appears to be almost universal, and no one believes that the possibilities of this new art are by any means exhausted.

History

The ceramic cutting tool can hardly be considered new, if we adopt a tolerant view of definitions. Egyptian artisans, 25 centuries before Christ, used flint tool bits rotated with forked sticks to bore the insides of vases. Even before this, prehistoric man used stone tools as knives, axes, drills, and weapons. The bow drill with a flint tip used in upper paleolithic times may well be the first simple machine using ceramic tools. The progress in ceramic tool technology suffered a hiatus from this imaginative start until early in the twentieth century. Although we do not seriously propose a "deliberate" return to the stone age, we cannot help observing that history does have a way of returning to its origins for very old ideas are often revived.

The first real lathes may have been developed in the Bronze Age, in Mesopotamia and the Indus Valley (1). These pole lathes rotated the wood log between centers with a rope wound around the workpiece, and attached at the upper end to a horizontal pole, which was anchored at the other end. As the rope was pulled, the workpiece revolved and the pole bent elastically. The rope could then be slowly released and the stored elastic energy in the pole would rotate the workpiece as a cut was taken by a hand-held tool steadied on a rest. This simple lathe was used throughout the middle ages generally, and up to the industrial revolution in isolated areas.

During this time some improvements were made with the "treadle lathe" used for light work, and in the "Great Wheel" lathe used for heavier machining. The rotational energy in both cases was supplied by man power (Fig. 1).

Leonardo daVinci was perhaps the first and certainly among the most distinguished of the great machine inventors. He is credited with the invention of the first practical screw cutting machine and the first application of a lead screw to traverse a tool in a lathe.

The progress that produced the prototypes of modern machine tools did not occur until the start of the industrial revolution.

The first plateau in development was reached by a group of ingenious English inventors who developed a wide variety of machine

FIG. 1. Great wheel lathe (courtesy of Science Museum, London).

tools within a relatively short time in a form recognizable by modern standards.

Wilkinson, Bramah, Bentham, Brunel, Maudslay, Clement, Whitworth, Roberts, and Nasmyth invented, built, and improved machine tools to the point where large scale industrialization could become a reality. They gave to civilization the means to build. The development of steam power in the early nineteenth century provided the motive power, thanks to the pioneering of Wilkinson's boring machine, which made the machining of large cylinders with accurate inside diameters possible. Maudslay's slide rest and perfection of screw cutting were major advances, and Whitworth's industry in building a diversity of machine tools permitted widespread application of precision metal shaping. Although machines were previously built employing milling type cutters, it was Eli Whitney in 1818 who perfected the prototype of the modern milling machine. Carbon steel cutters were used on these early machines and, according to the standards of these times, performed well.

During the last quarter of the nineteenth century hardenable tool steels were developed in England and by the early 1900's high-speed steels were developed in this country, which allowed cutting speeds to increase fourfold.

Cemented carbide (Widia) was introduced in the 1930's from Germany and machining speeds again jumped severalfold. The early difficulties in using carbide cutters, the complaints about its brittleness, unpredictability, and chipping are heard only as a distant echo of the same complaints we now hear about ceramics. People found "alloying" elements to toughen cemented carbide, perfected manufacturing procedures, and suddenly "discovered" the negative tool geometries which the Egyptians inadvertently used with ceramics, for boring vases 45 centuries earlier. Machine tools during this period were steadily improving in power, speed, accuracy, and versatility to take advantage of these cutting materials as they developed.

The invention of the electric motor provided each machine with its own independent high speed, and tailored power source, and the modern machine shop, as we now know it, was possible.

The aluminum oxide tool was considered for machining as early as 1905 in Germany, and patents were issued in England (1912) and Germany (2) (1913). Ryschkewitsch conducted his research on pure oxide ceramics at Degussa, Germany during World War II. An outcome of this research was the first commercially produced ceramic tool, Degussit. A U.S. patent was issued on this material in 1942 (3).

In the Soviet Union in 1943, first attempts to make ceramic "cutting" tools were begun at the Institute of Chemical Technology in Moscow (4). Cutting tests with materials manufactured from aluminum oxide proved that ceramic tools could be useful as cutting tools. Extensive work was pursued to develop this material, and it was not until the manufactured variation, 322, that the super strong cutting tool Microlit was developed (Fig. 3).

Some work on ceramic tools in the United States (5) started as early as 1935, but it was not until 1945, after examining the Degussit material and hearing favorable reports from Europe, that ceramic tools were given serious consideration.

The early investigations included evaluation of boron carbide, silicon carbide, and aluminum oxide in competition with cemented carbide for machining of metals. It was established that the aluminum oxide would machine metals, but the particular ceramic tool of that time did not perform as well as cemented carbides.

Modern ceramic tools were simultaneously developed during the mid 1950's by several independent groups, and pioneering work at the Rodman Laboratory of Watertown Arsenal developed procedures for utilizing these materials for cutting metals (6). These materials and procedures placed the ceramic tool, for the first time, on a competitive level with cemented carbide.

The rate limiting factor that controls chip making progress today is the cutting tool material. Machine tools and procedures are designed around the maximum capabilities of new tool materials as they are developed and follow, rather than lead, progress in metal cutting.

The trend has been toward higher cutting speeds as each new material is developed because of the economies inherent in higher production capacity per unit of capital expenditure and man-hour labor. The advances from carbon steel to high-speed steel, to cemented carbide, to ceramics, each produced new chip-making capabilities and spurred machining tool manufacturers to develop new, faster, and more powerful machines.

Figure 2 shows the increase in accuracy from Wilkinson's boring machine to the present technology (7). The development of machine tools and methods of size measurement have been refined to the point where additional accuracy will be increasingly difficult to achieve—if it is at all required.

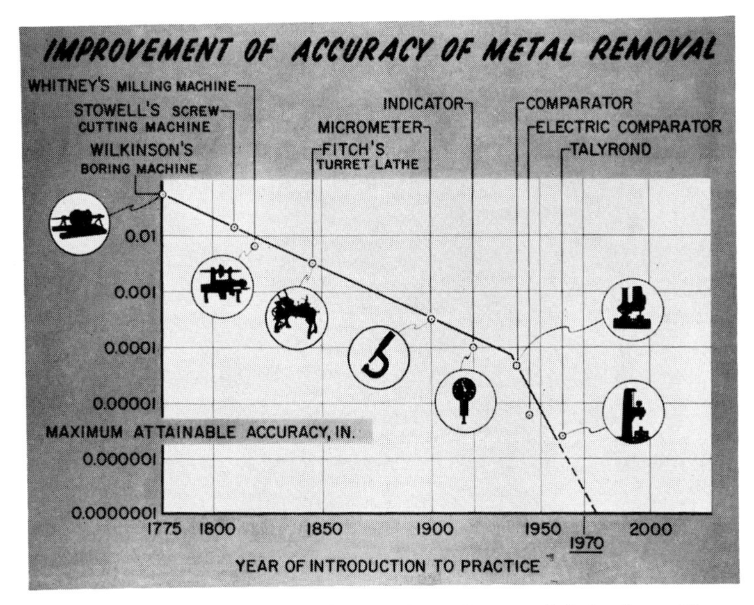

Fig. 2. Improvement in accuracy of metal removal (Merchant, 7).

Methods may be devised to achieve these tolerances more easily, and more automatically. This would make it possible for parts in general to be produced to a few microinches, which would allow more widespread utilization of increased precision. It is not likely, however, that machines will be developed that give precision much beyond that attainable in specialized instances.

Other machining processes will undoubtedly be developed that will produce certain shapes, more precisely than is now possible, on a wider diversity of materials.

In the foreseeable future, these developments are likely to receive only specialized utilizations and will not have any large immediate effect on machining in general.

Figure 3 shows the effects of improved tool materials on the maximum permissible cutting speeds (7), with approximately a twofold increase in speed for ceramics as compared with carbide.

Experimental indications suggest that ceramic tools have potentialities even beyond this increase. Eventually a problem will be associated with revolving massive workpieces at these high speeds that might require extensive innovations in machine design. It might, for example, become expedient to rotate the tool rather than the workpiece to machine large cylindrical shapes at very high speeds.

The main body of the book is divided into two sections: The first five chapters are concerned with the ceramic itself, its properties, and how it is made.

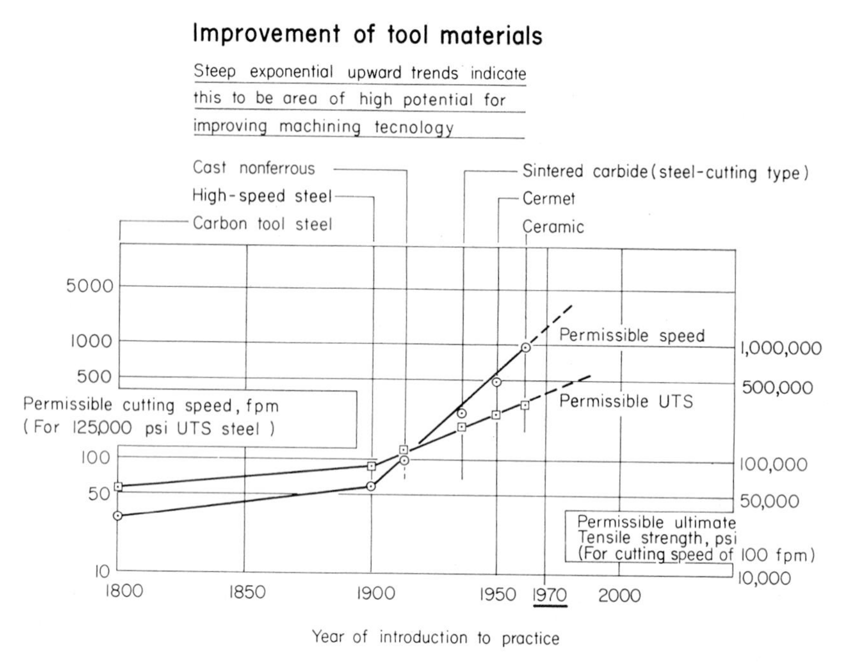

FIG. 3. Improvement of tool materials (Merchant, 7).

This background material has been included in the hope that ceramics will not be quite so mysterious to a tool engineer after he has read it, and some of this is directly pertinent to qualitative predictions of tool behavior. To the first approximation, at least, ceramic tool behavior is understandable and it is our desire to disseminate this understanding. It was not possible in all cases to illustrate processes with data on ceramic tools, and it was necessary to include examples of other materials. In general terms these illustrations are valid.

The remainder of the book is concerned with use of ceramic tools, their design, evaluation, and industrial applicability.

Chapter 1

The Properties of Ceramic Tools

At the time of its widespread introduction during the mid 1950's, the idea of using oxide ceramics for metal cutting was startling. It is not the sort of application we normally think of being suitable for ceramic materials. Some of the strongest engineering materials known are used as cutting tools. Cutting-tool applications require high-strength materials, and, even then, some environments are so severe that catastrophic tool failures still occur. In the past ceramics were characteristically thought of as brittle materials with low tensile strength and little impact resistance. However, these cutting-tool ceramics have transverse rupture strengths up to 122,000 psi which is the highest average value known. These ceramics commonly average 500,000 psi uniaxial compressive strengths with individual values as high as 700,000 psi. These figures are indicative of the real challenge ceramics are making in competition with other structural materials.

Figure 4 shows a ceramic tool turning a large gun barrel of heat treated steel hardened up to 500 bhn.

The ceramic replaced cemented carbide because the ceramic, under the conditions imposed on it at the cutting tip, had the superior physical properties. The machinist is using ceramics for cutting because it saves him money to do so.

Figure 5 is a photograph of a ceramic tool turning a 200 bhn steel log at 1500 fpm (8). This material would ordinarily be machined with cemented carbide at about 500 fpm. If we compare these two facts we can say that the ceramic can outperform the carbide 3 : 1.

At these high cutting speeds the metal-cutting process impresses upon the tool, high temperatures, steep stress gradients, and impact conditions. Up to a few years ago ceramics had been used for applications of modest stress, uniform shallow-stress gradients, and only gradual changes of stress or temperature with time. In metal cutting we often heat shock the cutting tip from room temperature to 800°C in a fraction of a second. This same tool tip is subjected to mechanical shock from zero load to full load in less than $1/10$ of a second during

FIG. 4. Turning a large gun tube at Watervliet Arsenal with ceramic tools (John W. Rodd).

entry of the tool into the workpiece. Pressures as high as 200,000 psi are estimated to occur at certain locations on the cutting edge. When we consider the superposition of machine-tool vibrations and irregularities in the mechanical properties and contour of the work piece, it is easy to see that very extreme conditions of service are attained during metal cutting, and it is no surprise that materials such as high-speed steels or the remarkable cemented carbides are usually specified for cutting tools. In order for ceramics to compete, it was first necessary to improve the physical properties of the ceramics to where the material could withstand these severe conditions. As we predicted from basic considerations of strength and microstructure, we found that dense- and fine-grained ceramics offered the improvements necessary to allow their utilization in this application.

FIG. 5. High-speed machining of steel using ceramic tools.

A. Comparison between Ceramic and Other Tools

Table I lists some pertinent physical properties of ceramic and other cutting tools materials. This table represents typical value of the physical properties for each type and grade of tool material. There are of course variations between manufacturers.

Inspection of the data presented in Table I shows that the ceramic tool has certain advantages and conversely, certain disadvantages.

TABLE I

PHYSICAL PROPERTIES OF TOOL MATERIALS

Measurements	High speed steel	C-2 Carbide	C-6 Carbide	TiC	Ceramic
Transverse rupture (psi)	50×10^4	23×10^4	25×10^4	17.5×10^4	9×10^4
Compressive (psi)	60×10^4	65×10^4	61×10^4	45×10^4	50×10^4
Modulus of elasticity (psi)	32×10^6	100×10^6	80×10^6	60×10^6	60×10^6
Microhardness (R_A)	85	92	91	93	93
Microhardness (Knoop[a] 100)	740	1800	1410	—	1780
Melting point[a] (°C)	1300	1400	1400	1400	2000
Density (g/cm³)	8.6	14.9	12.7	6.0	3.98
Grain size (microns)	10	2	3	3	3

[a] Variable depending on composition.

1. HARDNESS

The ceramic tool is harder than cemented carbides, and much harder than tool steels. In general, a harder material is more wear resistant than a softer material. Many of the present applications of ceramic tools are in the machining of abrasive metals such as cast iron, where the advantage of superior hardness of ceramic over most carbide grades results in increased tool life over that which was previously obtained. This advantage in wear resistance of ceramics over carbide is also shown in the machining of high shear-strength metals such as steel—particularly at higher cutting speeds. Microhardness measurements are customarily made by indenting the specimen with a ball or cone (Rockwell), or the point of a pyramid (Vickers or Knoop). In each case material in the high-stress region beneath the indenter is plastically deformed. The depth of penetration will be related to the yield strength of the test specimen, possibly an orientation factor, and the rate at which the material work hardens. Wear can also occur by a deformation mechanism and a correlation between microhardness and wear resistance during machining is not particularly surprising. Knoop microhardness indentations in aluminum oxide usually are not fractured for normal test loads. The normally brittle ceramic plastically deforms, under the severe stress conditions, at the pyramidal tip. The stress conditions on asperities between two sliding surfaces are at least this severe. Plastic deformation is to be expected on wear surfaces and the rate of wear should bear some relationship to microhardness as long as the wear process is not taking place under test conditions where wear by chemical reaction is favored. Alumina's advantage over cemented carbide and tool steel as a harder material can be translated into a real advantage in a metal cutting operation.

2. Compressive Strength

The compressive strength of commercially available ceramic tools is very high and well into the strength range of cemented carbides. Individual test specimens have shown a uniaxial compressive strength as high as 700,000 psi, and these materials commonly have average strengths of 500,000 psi. These high strengths enable the ceramics to perform as cutting tools. As a ceramic tool wears, the loading forces on the tool tip increase. If this increase of stress is brought to bear uniformally over the wear-land surface, then pressures as high as 200,000 psi may well occur on the tool cutting edge when cutting steel. To the first rough approximation this value of about 200,000 psi is the minimum compressive strength that a ceramic can have and still be useful as a cutting tool material for steel. In practice all commercially successful ceramic cutting tools have uniaxial compressive strengths in excess of this value. Early ceramic tools which did not conform to this requirement could not function in these applications and would fracture immediately upon entry into the work piece.

3. Tensile Strength (Transverse Rupture)

The values of tensile (or transverse rupture) strength for ceramic tools are significantly lower than those of cemented carbide or metal tools, and they present a serious limitation on ceramic tool utility. The average value for transverse rupture of 90,000 psi for ceramics is well below 500,000 psi for metals, or 250,000 psi for cemented carbide. Because of this low tensile strength, a ceramic cutting tool with a high-angle positive geometry would not be expected to withstand entry shocks. With this type of geometry excluded, there are some machining applications where it is not reasonable to try ceramics. Still, positive-geometry ceramic tools have been used with success for turning steel at moderate stock removal rates.

Efforts to increase the tensile strength of polycrystalline alumina have met with considerable success. These successes are, in part, the commercially available ceramic tools. The relatively low tensile strength can, to a considerable degree, be compensated for by the use of tool geometry, which places the tool tip under compressive loading and suppresses tensile crack formation.

4. Modulus of Elasticity

The modulus of elasticity is perhaps more important in an indirect way than a direct one to machining, in that it reflects bonding strength between atoms in the crystal lattice. In a very rough way, a high modulus is more desirable than a low one since the tool tip deforms less under stress, and materials with high moduli have the capacity of greater strength. A modulus of 60×10^6 psi for ceramic tools is two or three times that of steel and only slightly less than that for most grades of cemented carbides.

5. Melting Point

The melting point of a cutting-tool material is in itself not of prime importance, as tool temperatures are below the melting points of materials we might use as tools. The melting point of alumina is very high—much higher than cemented carbide or steel. This suggests that alumina will be refractory in character and retain many of its advantageous properties at high temperatures. This retention of strength and hardness at the high cutting temperatures is one of the most important properties of ceramic tools, and constitutes one of their greatest advantages over the less refractory materials such as tool steels or cemented carbides.

6. Density

There is no particular virtue in a high-density tool of one type over a low one of another. When comparing materials of the same class, however, density is a measure of residual voids or pores in the material, and a ceramic tool with low density contains more defects in the form of pores than one fabricated to near the maximum theoretical limit of density. The General Electric O-30 tool has a higher density than other ceramic tools because of inclusion of other phases in substantial amounts, rather than that it contains fewer voids. All successful ceramic tools manufactured in the United States have less than 2% residual pores.

7. Grain Size

In general, tool materials have shown a trend of greater strengths and uniformity of strength with finer grain sizing. In practice it has been determined that a certain optimum grain size exists for each material, and a narrow range around this optimum value is used by manufacturers for product control limits.

8. Behavior during Machining

The only justification for using ceramic tools is that they can machine more economically than other tool materials. Ceramic tool use is at present well entrenched in at least cast-iron machining. Ceramic tools are more economical because they have longer tool life and can operate at higher cutting speeds than other materials.

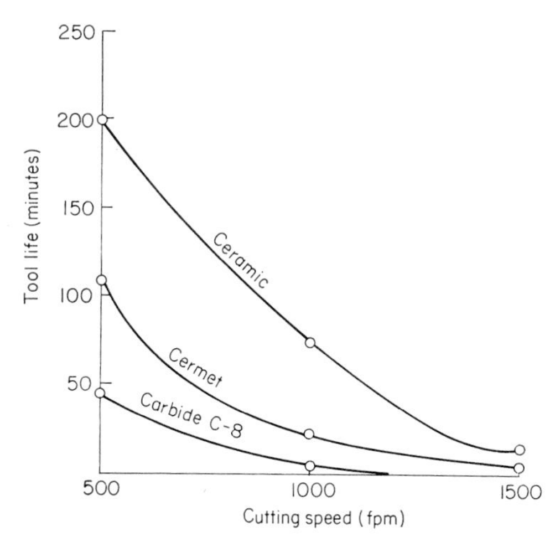

Fig. 6. Ceramics compared with other cutting-tool materials cutting steel 0.100-inch depth of cut, 0.005-inch feed/rev, —5° side rake, —5° back rake, 15° side and end-cutting angles (Krabacher and Haggerty, 9).

Figure 6 shows the relation between tool life and cutting speed found by Krabacher and Haggerty (9) comparing ceramic tools, cemented carbide grade C-8, and a TiC·Ni cermet. Tool life was determined by the occurrence of 0.020-inch flank wear, turning AISI 81B45 steel.

This indicates that ceramics are much more wear resistant than other cutting tools at these machining conditions, and at all speeds up to at least 1500 fpm. The ceramic used in this test was one of the better ones available. If this were the whole story, then ceramic tools would have no difficulty in replacing cemented carbide for the machining of steel. Since this has not occurred, there must be other criteria and, as Krabacher and Haggerty point out, ceramics often fracture before the end point of 0.020-inch land wear occurs. We have then another tool life criterion—fracture. This is not normally taken into account in the literature when comparing tool life—speed relationships, and an element of caution must be used in determining the significance of these data. On the basis of wear, the ceramic tool is in most cases markedly superior to carbide. Figure 7 shows their data on machining cast iron, with the same tools as used in the previous illustrations and under the same conditions.

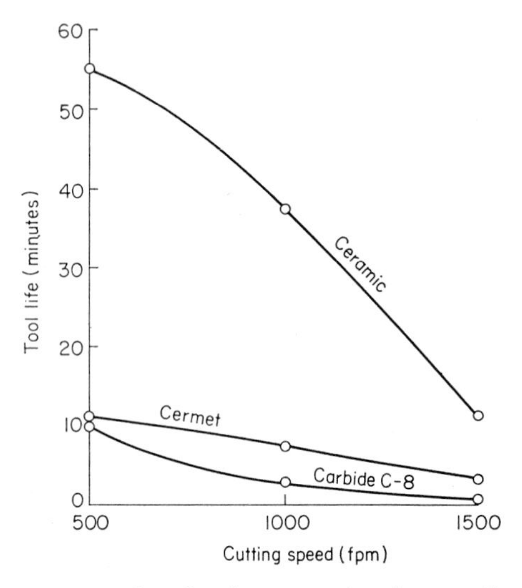

FIG. 7. Ceramics compared with other cutting-tool materials cutting cast iron. Conditions are the same as for Fig. 6 (Krabacher and Haggerty, 9).

For cast iron the wear advantages of ceramic tools are even more markedly evident than for machining steel. At 500 fpm the advantage of a ceramic tool over a carbide tool for steel was about twofold; with cast iron the advantage is about fivefold. Since cast iron has a low shear strength compared to steel, tool-tip fracture is less troublesome, and ceramics have been used to good advantage. In both cases the cermet was intermediate between ceramics and cemented carbide.

Siekmann's ten machinability studies on the O-30 ceramic tool as compared to other materials are presented in Fig. 8 (10). These data, which are based on a 0.015-inch flank wear, when plotted on the same scale as used by Krabacher (Fig. 6), agree with his data, except for the few differences in the slope of the ceramic curve. Siekmann obtains longer tool life for O-30 at higher speeds than Krabacher, and shorter tool life at lower speeds. Some differences can be expected due to different test steels, tool geometry, or the ceramics used. However, in essence the two sets of data are similar. Siekmann's data show that potential advantages of ceramics constitute an advance

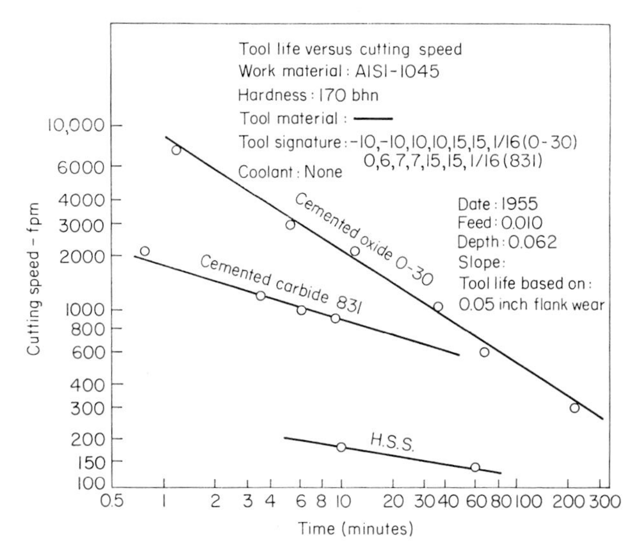

FIG. 8. Machining comparison between ceramics, carbide, and high-speed steel tools (Siekmann, 10).

in machining comparable to that which was made in the change from high-speed steel cutters to cemented carbide. Siekmann's data, like Krabacher's, do not consider fracture.

While wear is a reasonably well-behaved phenomenon, fracture has the perverse nature of occurring unpredictably, necessitating extensive test replication to produce reliable data on total tool life. Also, ceramics under some conditions are so durable that very long test runs are required. The difficulties account for the sparsity of data on total tool life.

Kibbey and Moore (11) indicate that machinability information on ceramic tools is more pertinent to the tool engineer if total tool life is measured rather than some intermediate end point. With ceramics their end point on straight turning is usually a fracture. Figure 9 is plotted from their data comparing ceramic VR97 with two grades of carbide. Kibbey and Moore's data predict ceramic tool behavior markedly different from that predicted by Krabacher or Siekmann. This sharp contrast results from selection of test end-point criteria. When wear failures occur in a machining condition, rate of wear measurements on the tool will constitute a more appropriate test criterion. When fracture failures occur, total tool life more correctly predicts tool behavior.

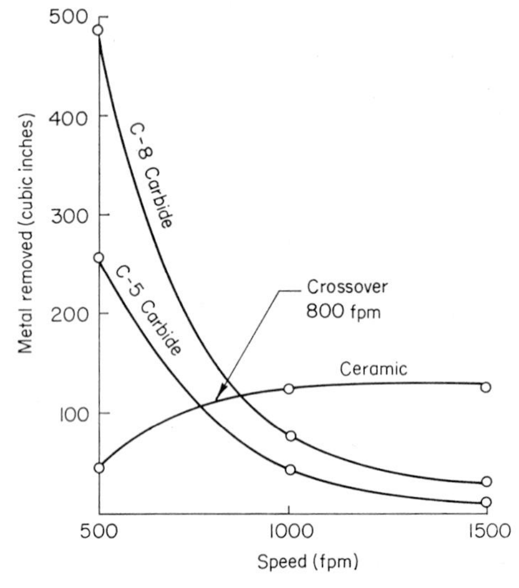

FIG. 9. The relative performance of ceramics compared with carbide using total tool life criteria. Machining conditions: 1045-annealed steel, 0.100 depth, 0.011 inch/rev, tool ½ inch × ½ inch × 3/16 inch, 1/16-inch nose radius. Side and front cutting edge angles −10°, side and back rake −5°, side and front relief angles −5° (Kibbey and Moore, 11).

Kibbey and Moore's data indicate that the life of ceramic tools (VR97 in this case) is insensitive to speed, and the curves for carbide and ceramics cross at a cutting speed, under 1000 fpm. At cutting speeds below this crossover, the cemented-carbide tool has the advantage when turning steel. At cutting speeds above this crossover, ceramic tools are more efficient. The crossover speed for different machining conditions is a variable which must be determined in each case. These problems of tool testing are discussed in much greater detail in Chapter 7. Kibbey and Moore's data on total tool life for carbide are consistent with data on the same materials by the other investigators, indicating a wear-controlled failure mechanism.

Tool manufacturers are faced with the marketing enigma of not being able to place ceramic tools in those steel-machining applications where the advantage of higher speed can be exploited. With the exception of hardened steels where the speed crossover is at a much lower speed, ceramic tools have not been widely used for machining steel by industry. Test data indicate potential utilization for this purpose beyond that now employed.

B. Comparsion between Ceramic Tools

In the United States three makes of ceramic tools dominate industrial utilization, while in Europe a greater variety of materials are marketed as ceramic cutting tools. These various materials, while predominately alumina, have different compositions and structures, and are made by a variety of processes. The physical properties and machining utility of these tools do vary as would be expected, and any generalization about ceramic tools has to carry with it the tacit recognition that a diverse performance between makes does occur. The range of physical properties and machining-performance characterizes the present state of the art of ceramic-tool manufacture, and the purpose of this section is to depict this range. Thirteen varieties of ceramic tools were collected from all over the world, and the physical properties and machining behavior of each type were evaluated.

1. Description of Various Ceramic Tools

All of the tools which were collected were tested for density, compressive strength, transverse-rupture strength, Knoop microhardness, and composition. They were subjected to microscopic examination by both transmitted and reflected-light techniques to determine grain size and microstructure. The values which were obtained do not in all cases match those supplied by the manufacturers. The primary discrepancies are for transverse rupture strength and Knoop microhardness. The values of these properties are sensitive to the test method and the discrepancies which do exist are thought to arise from differences between the methods used here and those used elsewhere.

TABLE II

CERAMIC TOOL PHYSICAL PROPERTIES

Tool	Manufacturer	Density (g/cm^3)	Average grain size (microns)	Compressive strength ($\times 10^3$ psi[a])	Transverse rupture strength ($\times 10^3$ psi[a])	Knoop microhardness K100[b]	Additives
O-30	General Electric Co., Metallurgical Products Dept., U.S.	4.114	2	505	85	1665	Major additions of TiO
CCT-707	The Carborundum Co., Bonded Abrasives Div., U.S.	3.931	3	445	85	1570	MgO
VR97	Vascoloy Ramet Co., U.S.	3.973	4	570	87	1655	MgO
Ceroc	Compagnie Generale d'Electro Ceramique, France	3.885	3.5	310	70	1580	MgO
Widalox	Fried Krupp, Germany	3.965	10	430	63	1640	MgO, TiC, Cr
Titanit	DEW, Deutsche Edelstahl Werkes, Germany	4.232	6	458	60	1555	Cr_3C_2
Hypalox (SPK)	Feldmuhle, Germany	3.858	5	270	62	1515	MgO
Degussit	Degussa, Germany	3.881	3	248	66	1595	MgO
Diamonite	Diamonite Products Mfg. Co., U.S.	3.727	10	217	49	1405	Cr_2O_3 solid solution, glass bonded
Revolox	Soderfors Bruk, Sweden	6.861	7	435	102	—	Major addition of WC + Co
Microlite	U.S.S.R.	3.864	5	456	51	1525	MgO
Tungalox	Toshiba Tungalox Co. Ltd., Japan	3.943	7	401	78	1608	NiO, MgO
NTK	Nippon Tokushu Togyo Kaisha, Ltd., Japan	3.904	5.5	516	57	1515	MgO

[a] Average of 2 determinations. [b] Average of 10 determinations.

The transverse-rupture tests were made on a ⅓-inch span with samples $\frac{3}{16}$-inch square. The short length of this specimen was dictated by the size of available materials and is expected to produce results somewhat different than those obtained on longer spans. Previous experience on one of the tools indicated a standard deviation of 4250 psi for values averaging about 75,000 psi. Since the values reported in the table present an average of two specimens, the expected error should be somewhat less than this. The Knoop microhardness readings are lower than those generally reported in the literature for polycrystalline alumina, because of a change which was introduced in making the indentation length measurement. Some of the white tools, like the Degussit or Ceroc, have properties due to low reflectivity and internal reflections which make the measurement of the indentation virtually impossible. As a result of this difficulty, all of the polished sections were aluminized in a vacuum-metallizing unit, after indentation, to produce a more suitable optically reflecting surface. The coating was very thin and significant geometrical changes would not be expected. This treatment enabled the microscopist to determine more accurately the terminus of the indentation than was previously possible. Because of the nature of the measurement this resulted in longer readings and lower hardness figures. To provide a comparison with a standard material a Linde sapphire rod was polished and indented in three random directions. Values of 1670, 1690, and 1790 were obtained from averaging ten indentations at each orientation. These are compared with values around 2000-Knoop units utilizing conventional measurement methods.

The advantage of these data is that all of the tools have been tested by the same method, and a result can validly be compared with the rest for the purpose of assigning relative position.

Table II lists the measured properties for each of the tools studied.

a. O-30 Ceramic Tool

The O-30 material manufactured by the General Electric Company is the unique invention of E. W. Goliber and resulted from his studies on the $TiO \cdot Al_2O_3$ system (12). The O-30 composition can be characterized by its exceedingly fine and uniform microstructure and the addition of 10% TiO to the Al_2O_3. It is evident from the table that the O-30 material has high hardness and very good strength. The ceramic is used extensively for a wide variety of machining conditions and materials. Figure 10* is a stereo pair showing a fracture surface on the O-30 ceramic.

The function of the TiO is primarily to assist in the sintering process. The high sintering rates at low processing temperatures suggest liquid-phase sintering. Complete densification of a compact can occur in 10 minutes at 1600°C. The presence of TiO on the

FIG. 10. Fracture surface of G.E. grade O-30 ceramic tool showing fine uniform microstructure. The smaller particles are TiO and some occur on alumina-grain boundaries. Electron photomicrograph of a shadowed replica. 2500 × (courtesy of E. R. Stover and A. S. Holik, G.E. Research Laboratory).

alumina-grain boundaries suggests that it may also act as a grain-growth inhibitor (13). TiO itself is a hard material and large additions to the alumina does not detract appreciably from the overall properties of the ceramic. The use of the TiO sintering aid enables the O-30 tool to be manufactured by a sintering process to virtually theoretical density. Figure 11 is a conventional polished section of the O-30 tool viewed in reflected light.

* The stereopairs can be viewed with a simple inexpensive stereoscope such as the CF-8, Abrams Instrument Co., Lansing Michigan. The stereoscope should be kept square with page, rather than tilted at the angle of the photographs.

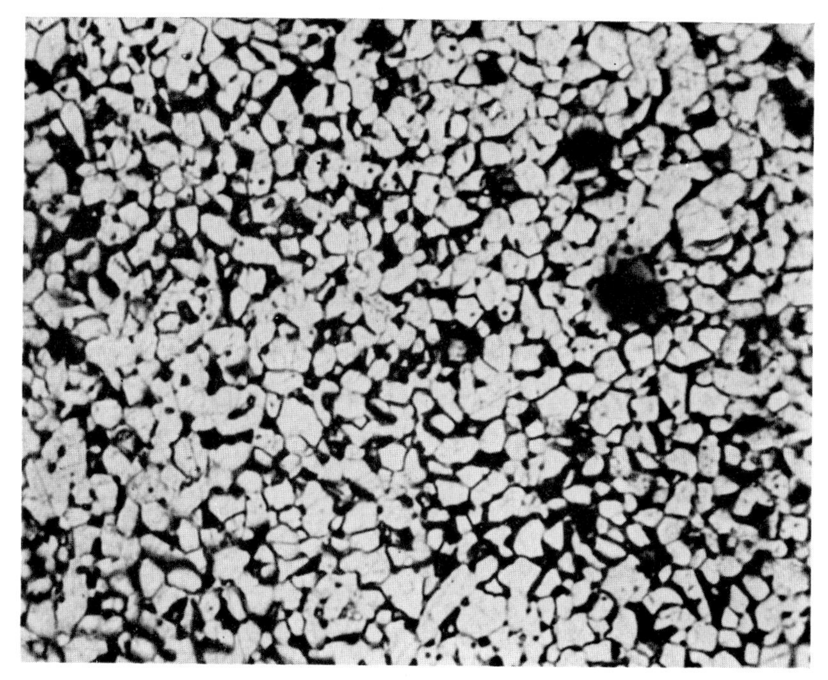

FIG. 11. Polished section of O-30 tool. Note the uniform fine-grained microstructure and absence of porosity. 1000 ×.

b. CCT-707

The CCT-707 (formerly called Stupalox) is manufactured by the Carborundum Company and is the most widely used ceramic tool in the United States today. This ceramic was developed by A. W. von Mickwitz who was their principal ceramic scientist associated with ceramic-tool research. It has very good physical properties, and can be seen in Table II, with a compressive strength in excess of 440,000 psi and a transverse rupture of 85,000 psi. While the CCT-707 tool does have, in general, a fine uniform microstructure averaging about 3 microns, some microneedles or prisms occur in the material with dimensions in a section averaging 2 × 15 microns. The composition includes only small additions of MgO which acts as a grain-growth inhibitor. The MgO addition to alumina is present as a solid solution in small amounts, or as a spinel $MgO \cdot Al_2O_3$ if larger amounts are used. Figure 12 is a polished section of CCT-707 showing the prisms.

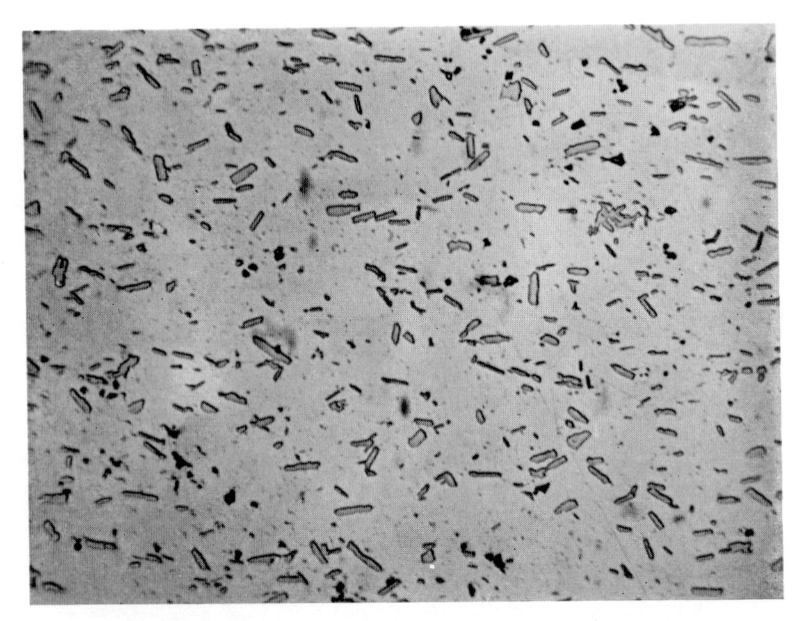

FIG. 12. Polished section of CCT-707 showing microprisms. 400 × (courtesy of Carborundum).

The density of CCT-707 is low for a hot-pressed alumina being only 3.93 g/cm^3. However, this density is adequate to provide sufficient strength and hardness for a wide diversity of metal-cutting applications.

c. *VR97*

VR97 is a dense hot-pressed tool material originally developed by Norton Company and now manufactured by the Vascoloy Ramet/Wesson Corporation. VR97 has the highest compressive strength of all the tools tested, and has as high or a higher transverse-rupture strength than all the other ceramics with the exception of the Revolox material which contains large amounts of cemented carbide. The density is close to theoretical and in metallographic examination pores are not visible. The high strength and hardness of VR97 have allowed this tool material to be applied over a very wide range of machining conditions on such diverse materials as cast iron to steels hardened to Rc 63.

Figure 13 is an electron photomicrograph of a VR97 fracture surface showing the grain structure.

The average grain size of VR97 is about 4 microns with some greater variation than the O-30 tool but less than with CCT-707. The only addition to the alumina is 0.5% MgO which acts as a grain-growth inhibitor. At this concentration small amounts of spinel, $MgO \cdot Al_2O_3$, are detected as a separate phase.

FIG. 13. VR97 fracture surface showing the grain structure. Stereo-electron photomicrograph. 2000 ×.

d. Ceroc

The Ceroc tool is a sintered alumina manufactured by Compagnie Generale d'Electro Ceramique, France. The tool can be characterized as having a fine uniform microstructure and an intermediate density. The strength of Ceroc is very respectable for a sintered alumina which does not contain sintering aids—other than MgO.

e. Widalox

The Widalox tool—manufactured by Krupp, Germany—contains additions of MgO, TiC, and Ti to the alumina. The microstructure is coarse with the alumina averaging 10 microns and the opaque phases averaging 2 microns in diameter. The alumina grains range in size up to 20 microns. The material is hard and dense and has moderate strength values.

f. Titanit

The Titanit tool is manufactured by Deutsche Edelstahl Werke, Germany and contains major additions of chromium carbide. It is finer textured than the Widalox tool with average grain diameters of 6 and 1 microns, for the alumina and Cr_3C_2, respectively. The grain structure is variable with the alumina ranging up to 20 microns in diameter.

g. Hypalox (SPK)

This material is a sintered tool manufactured by Feldmuhle, Germany. It has been extensively used in Europe in spite of the noticeably low compressive strength. The grain texture averages 5 microns which is appreciably coarser than other similar sintered aluminas. The density is slightly lower than that attained by comparable materials.

h. Degussit

Degussit is manufactured by Degussa, Germany, who pioneered some very early work on ceramic tools in the 1930's by Eugene Ryshkewitch, then of their staff. Their current tool has a fine but somewhat variable microstructure averaging 3 microns but ranging up to 20 microns in diameter. The density is average for a pure sintered alumina containing only MgO additions. The compressive strength is noticeably low and is comparable with the Hypalox tool.

i. Diamonite

The Diamonite material, manufactured by the Diamonite Product Manfacturing Company, U.S., is a glass-bonded ceramic. While it is perfectly usable for wear-resistant applications, it does not have sufficient strength or high temperature properties for extensive use as a cutting tool. The density is low, the grain texture coarse, and the strength too low for general use as a tool. Still, Diamonite will function under conditions of light service and was included for this reason.

j. Revolox

The Revolox tool is made by Soderfors Bruk, Sweden. It is markedly different from the other tools included in the study in that it is about half cemented carbide. This gives the material a much higher density than the other tools. Revolox is somewhat coarse grained with average diameters of 7 and 4 microns for the alumina and cemented carbide, respectively. The diameter of the alumina ranges up to 25 microns. The tool has very good strength which may be due in part to the large amounts of included carbide. Figure 14 shows the microstructure of Revolox.

FIG. 14. Metallographic section in reflected light of the Revolox tool. The white spots are carbide particles embedded in the alumina matrix. 820 ×.

k. Microlite

This tool originated in the Soviet Union and is of both practical and historical importance because it is still widely used there and was the first ceramic tool to receive wide application. It is a pure sintered alumina with only MgO additions. Microlite has a uniform grain structure averaging 5 microns and a moderate density compared with the other tools. The very high compressive strength is outstanding.

l. Tungalox

The Tungalox tool is manufactured by Toshiba Tungalox Company Ltd., Japan. It has high strength and density for a sintered alumina. The density has been achieved at the partial expense of grain size which is uniform but averages 7 microns. It is surprising that the strength is so high for this grain diameter. Presumably the NiO addition which forms a spinel contributes to the retention of strength at large grain sizes.

m. NTK

The NTK is a Japanese tool manufactured by Nippon Tokushu Togyo Kaisha, Ltd. The density is high for a sintered alumina without additions other than MgO. This has been achieved at the expense of grain size which averages 5.5 microns. The compressive strength is the highest value obtained for any of the sintered pure aluminas.

2. Machining Characteristics of Various Ceramic Tools

The thirteen tools described above were tested under a variety of conditions for their behavior during metal cutting. Two steels were used in the test: 4340 annealed steel 185 bhn, and Lo-Air type A-6 tool steel hardened to 350 bhn. The Lo-Air steel was furnished through the courtesy of the Universal-Cyclops Steel Corporation and Mr. Robert S. Morrow, whose assistance we wish to acknowledge. Lo-Air steel was used in preference to 4340 at the higher hardness because of its excellent deep-hardening properties.

The tools were tested on the two steels at each of three speeds, 500, 1000, and 1500 fpm, giving a total of 6 test conditions. The width of the flank-wear land was measured at five increments during the test—at 1000, 2000, 3000, 4000, and 5000 linear feet of undistorted chip produced. In other terms, the amount of sliding between the tool flank and steel was constant for each test with wear measurements taken every 1000 linear feet. Wear was measured by the use of a microscope which was mounted on a post attached to the lathe carriage. Figure 15 shows the microscope in position for taking a measurement. All tests were performed on a Jones and Lampson Turret Lathe at Watertown Arsenal which is instrumented for machinability studies.

FIG. 15. Tool post microscope used in machinability studies (courtesy of U.S. Army Materials Research Agency, Watertown Arsenal).

The measurements were made by translating the microscope with the micrometer dial shown at the top of the microscope assembly. The microscope assembly was lifted off the mounting post during machining and replaced each time for each measurement. Adjustable stops were used to determine the alignment and position of the microscope on the post. The entire operation of positioning the microscope, taking the measurement, and removing the microscope took only about 30 seconds. This procedure did not disturb the seating or positioning of the tool during the test as would have been done had the tool been removed for measurement. The tools measured approximately $\frac{1}{2} \times \frac{1}{2} \times \frac{3}{16}$ inch with a $\frac{1}{16}$-inch nose radius. Some of the foreign tools could not be obtained in the exact size needed for the test, and had to be reground so that the proper edge and radius geometry were obtained. The small differences between tool overall dimensions were not thought to be a significant factor in affecting the test results. A small land 0.006-inch wide was ground on the cutting edge at 60° to the top surface of the tool. The tools were mounted with a 15° lead angle, —5° side rake, and a —5° back rake. A 0.011-inch feed per revolution and a 0.080-inch depth of cut was used.

As the severity of the test increased due to a higher speed or higher hardness, some of the tools would fail by catastrophic fracture or by greatly accelerated wear as a result of a microfracture process. So in addition to wear data, information was obtained concerning the severity of the machining conditions within which the tools were able to function. Only four tools were able to cut for the full 5000 linear feet at the highest speed on the hardened steel.

First-order, least-square equations were fitted to the wear data. These equations had correlation coefficients averaging about 0.95, thereby confirming the adequacy of first-order equations for describing the wear behavior over the range studied. Table III lists the wear-equation parameters for each tool. No data indicates that the tool would not function. A number followed by an "F" indicates that while wear data was obtained, the tool failed by fracture before the full 5000 feet cut was taken. The equation is expressed as:

$$Y = AX + B$$

where

Y = the width of the wear land in thousandths of an inch
X = length of undistorted chip cut in feet
A = slope of the line
B = intercept of the line

A great number of individual conclusions can be drawn from the wear data in Table III relative to each tool's behavior in relation to the others, as cutting speed or hardness is changed. Rather, it is our purpose to draw more general conclusions relating to the overall

TABLE III

Least-Square Wear Equation Parameters Slope A, Intercept B

Type of ceramic tool	4340 Steel, annealed, 185 bhn						Lo-Air type A-6 tool steel, 350 bhn					
	500 fpm		1000 fpm		1500 fpm		500 fpm		1000 fpm		1500 fpm	
	$A \times 10^3$	B	$A \times 10^3$	B	$A \times 10^3$	B	$A \times 10^3$	B	$A \times 10^3$	B	$A \times 10^3$	B
VR97	0.92	1.68	1.59	3.17	3.60	1.95	0.35	2.16	0.35	3.67	0.15	3.91
NTK	0.79	2.05	1.70	2.82	3.01	3.60	0.18	3.50	0.33	2.91	0.30F	2.67F
Diamonite	1.16	3.20	—	—	—	—	—	—	—	—	—	—
O-30	1.00	1.54	1.93	1.67	3.53	2.75	0.15	3.83	0.28	3.52	0.18	3.46
Ceroc	1.18	1.42	1.55	1.63	2.80	4.05	0.26	2.52	0.28	2.88	0.27F	3.30F
Revolox	2.10	1.20	2.43	3.33	3.70	3.73	0.34	4.10	0.41F	3.95F	—	—
Widalox	1.05	1.15	1.69	2.15	3.02	3.55	0.51	1.89	0.32	3.72	—	—
Tungalox	1.00	1.68	1.44	2.78	2.53	4.60	0.40	2.62	0.15F	2.55F	—	—
Hypalox	0.98	2.66	1.33	3.27	2.50	4.06	0.51	3.83	0.11	4.13	—	—
CCT-707	1.10	1.96	1.47	2.33	3.39	2.65	0.37	3.99	0.28	2.42	0.33	2.13
Degussit	0.85	2.77	1.31	1.99	3.74	3.15	0.50	3.70	0.30	2.48	−0.12	6.60
Titanit	1.17	1.69	1.65	2.25	3.00	4.60	0.36	3.22	−0.04	3.00	—	—
Microlite	1.13	2.77	1.20	1.98	2.59	3.83	0.34	3.00	—	—	—	—

behavior and illustrate correlations between this behavior and other pertinent physical properties.

It should be emphasized that the wear data is only one criterion of overall tool utility and, often, a faster wearing tool might provide better total service in a particular application if it is more durable in terms of fracture failures.

a. Wear Rates

In general, the wear rates increased on the soft steel as the cutting speed was raised. This did not happen with the hardened steel as the wear rates were independent of cutting speed. Surprisingly, the wear rates on the hard steel were only $1/3$ to $1/10$ of those obtained for a lower hardness work piece. The explanation of this rather anomalous result is probably related to the details of stress distribution on the cutting edge, and how these distributions are affected by increases in the hardness, strength, or work-hardening characteristics of the work piece.

b. Fracture Failures

All of the ceramics except one were able to cut the soft steel at speeds up to 1500 fpm. Four tools failed to cut the hardened steel successfully at 1000 fpm, and nine tools failed to cut the hardened steel at 1500 fpm. Only four tools were able to function without failure over the entire range of testing conditions studied. Three of these four are the widely used tools of United States' manufacture. The fourth tool when subjected to the severest cutting conditions immediately generated a very wide wear land which significantly altered the edge geometry and assuredly altered the stress distribution on the cutting tip. The equation parameters clearly indicate an anomalous behavior when compared with the other curves. Since the geometry of the cutting edge was radically altered by initial wear, the proposition that the survival of this tool was fortuitous should be considered.

The other three survivors have in common both high-compressive and transverse-rupture strengths; these are the only tools that have both of these properties at high values. We conclude that both compressive and transverse-rupture strengths are important physical properties and that one without the other does not provide sufficiency for superior tool performance. This is consistent with the concept of fatigue damage which is discussed in Chapter 5. These three tools have also demonstrated superior resistance to failures when used by industry in a wide diversity of machining conditions. This is attested to by their widespread acceptance by industry. However, if a particular application requires very close adherence to a tolerance over a long continuous cut, one of the other more wear-resistant ceramics might be a better selection.

c. Effect of Speed on Wear Rate

The slope parameter "A" which appears in Table III represents the wear rate of the tools, and this is plotted against the cutting speed for the 4340-annealed steel in Fig. 16. Each curve represents the behavior of one tool over the speed range studied.

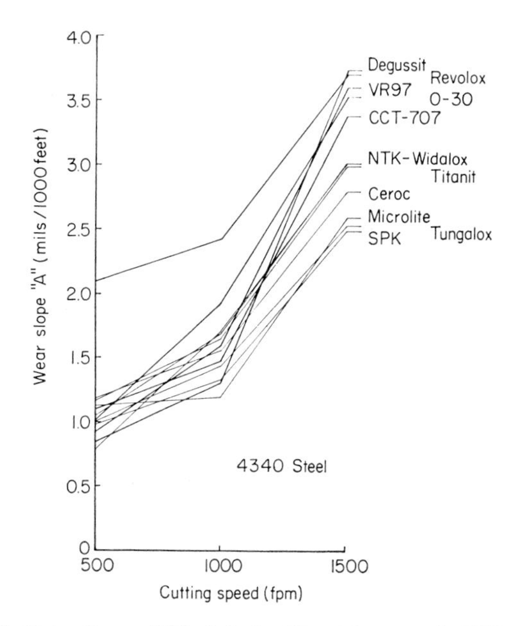

Fig. 16. Rate of wear "A" plotted with cutting speed, 4340 steel.

The plot shows that in general there are two types of tool materials; those that wear at unusually high rates at high speeds, and those that wear at relatively slower rates at high speeds. The most interesting observation in Fig. 16 is that the high wear-rate materials (except one) are those same materials which survived the most rigorous machining conditions; namely, the Degussit, VR97, O-30.

and CCT-707 tools. The remaining tool, Revolox, contains large amounts of cemented carbide and is a hybrid between a ceramic and carbide. Its high wear rate could be attributed to the thermal degradation of the carbide at the very high cutting temperatures and thereby really represents a different class of material.

The suggestion that comes to mind is that if microcracks are generated on the tool surface and propagate inward, at a velocity less than that at which the material wears, then crack nuclei will not form and the tool will be durable in fracture. Conversely, if the tool is very wear-resistant the cracks will grow, and when a critical crack dimension is reached, the tool tip will fail by a catastrophic fracture. In this sense, then, it may be desirable to have a wear rate higher than those of the lower group in the Fig. 16. A simple graphical solution to the 1500-fpm, 4340-steel case observed here, indicates that this wear rate should be about 7.5 microns per minute normal to the wear-land surface. This optimum wear rate should be variable depending upon the forces on the tool tip for different machining conditions and on the detailed configuration of the cutting edge which will distribute these forces on the tool surface.

d. Effect of Tool Microhardness on Wear

The thirteen tool materials in the test have a range of Knoop-microhardness values from 1665 to 1405. It was desirable to compare the microhardness with the wear behavior on the same tools. Since the total wear behavior contains two parameters, slope and intercept, it was necessary to assign a single qualitative ranking number to each tool for the purposes of making this comparison. These numbers are merely a linear progression from one to twelve (generally), with lower numbers being assigned to the tools which had the least wear. Figure 17 is a plot of microhardness against ranking number for the 4340 steel at 500 fpm.

The fact that a quite good correlation exists in Fig. 17 is somewhat surprising considering the diverse composition and microstructure of the materials in the test. This correlation shows that harder tools are more wear resistant at the slower speeds of soft steel. This correlation disappears at higher speeds and is not present for the harder steel.

The implications of these observations are that plastic deformation of the tool is the predominating wear mechanism at low speeds on soft steel (see Chapter 5). Competing wear mechanisms become more important at the higher temperatures at higher speeds where

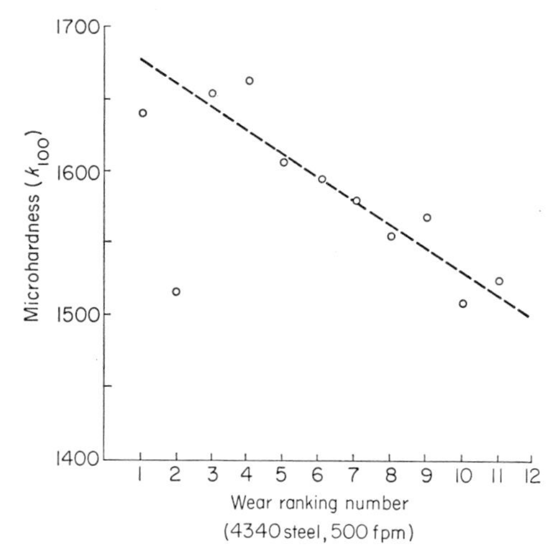

FIG. 17. Microhardness plotted against ranking number for 4340 steel, 500 fpm.

chemical reactions cause accelerated wear. This results in the disappearance of the correlation.

e. *The Effect of Strength on Wear*

The wear-equation intercepts indicate a zero-time wear of between 1 and 5 thousandths of an inch. Obviously wear cannot occur by fright alone, and a discontinuous wear process must connect the origin with the curve depicted by the equation. Questions relating to the nature of this process are of interest. The relationship between compressive strength and wear-ranking number for Lo-Air steel at 500 fpm is plotted in Fig. 18.

The correlation is fairly good, with only one point in serious disagreement. Certainly the correlation is good enough to require an explanation of a rather surprising relationship.

Wear quality being related to a strength parameter certainly suggests that a fracture process is responsible for the wear that occurs. This is not evident from observing the highly polished wear surfaces. The wear curves on the hard steel at the slowest speed are subparallel and differ from one another largely by the size of the intercept "B."

The quality ranking number in this case reflects the size of the

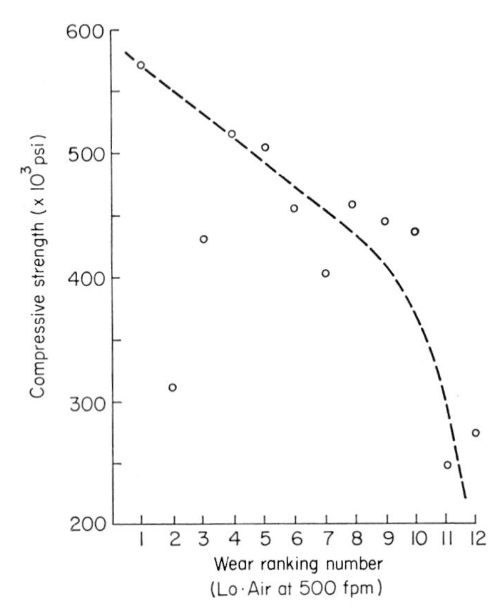

FIG. 18. Correlation between compressive strength and ranking number Lo-Air steel, 500 fpm.

original intercept, and the suggestion is that the initial wear which occurs in a discontinuous fashion, occurs by a fracture or crushing process. When a wear-land surface of sufficient dimensions is formed so that the compressive strength is not exceeded, the fracture process stops and smooth wear occurs by deformation or chemical reaction. This relationship between compressive strength and wear-ranking number was not seen for other cutting conditions. Excessive scatter in the test data and a greater divergence in slope parameters may account for this.

Chapter 2

Tool Manufacture

Ceramic tools are made by processes similar to those used in powder metallurgy, or similar to the production of cemented carbide. Essentially, very fine, high-purity alumina powder is mixed with whatever additives are required for a particular tool, pressed into a pellet and sintered, or hot pressed to effect shrinkage and promote the development of strong bonds between the alumina grains.

Commercial ceramic tools are made by both sintering and hot-pressing processes. These two methods are related but will be considered separately.

A. Sintering

When two particles are brought into contact at an appropriate elevated temperature, they grow together and form a bond between them. Surface tension forces produce a transport of matter by diffusion so as to minimize the surface area.

A pellet of finely divided alumina powder, which is pressed into intimate contact between particles, shrinks when raised to a high temperature due to the rearrangement of matter and the resultant shrinkage of pores. If conditions are judiciously controlled, the compact can be sintered to theoretical density.

Kuczynaski *et al.* (14) studied the sintering process in alumina by heating sapphire spheres which were held in contact. Figure 19 is a photograph of two sapphire spheres, that have formed a neck at the point of contact.

It can be visualized that if this process continues in a pressed compact, overall shrinkage of dimensions will occur. For a good general description of sintering phenomena see papers by Coble (15) and Burke (16).

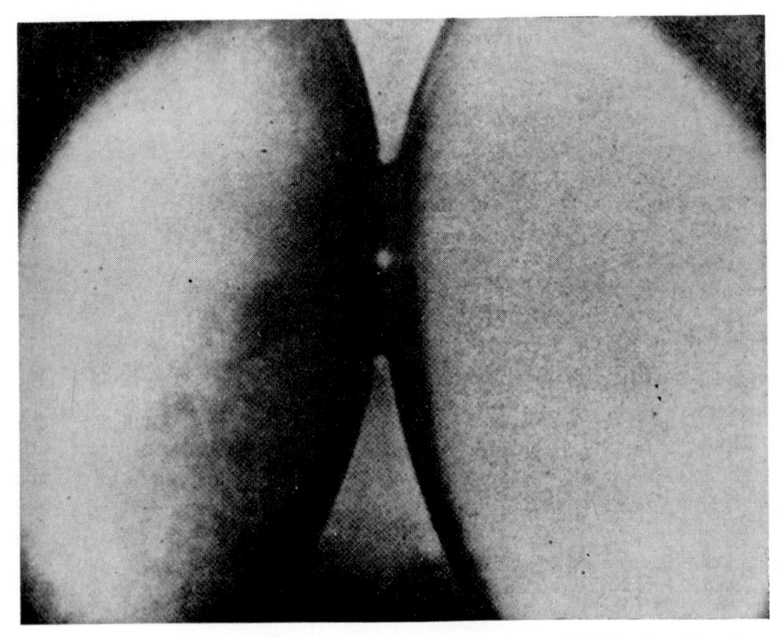

FIG. 19. Two sapphire spheres sintered together at 1950°C for 25 minutes. 400 × (Kuczynski *et al.*, 14).

1. EQUIPMENT

The apparatus used in mixing and otherwise preparing powders and compacts for sintering is not particularly unique. Comminution and mixing of alumina with additives is generally accomplished in an alumina-fortified ball mill, with an alumina-grinding ball to prevent unwanted contamination. In some processes cemented carbide or metal balls are used as these contaminants do not adversely affect these particular compositions. A water slurry of the constituents is milled for a short time in order to mix in additives uniformly and break up loose aggregates of the alumina particles.

The slurry after milling, is dried and mixed with a waxy, temporary binder which also serves as a lubricant during the pressing operation.

Figure 20 shows the pressing operation used to form pellets from the powder mix.

Since we wish to produce a sintered object with an average-grain size from 2 to 5 microns, we must obviously start with a powder finer than this. Generally, it is a more convenient and satisfactory

FIG. 20. Pressing of tool-bit preforms from powder mix (courtesy of Vascoloy-Ramet/Wesson Corp.).

procedure to produce powders by chemical or thermal decomposition of an aluminum salt, than by milling a fused alumina to the required size.

Powdered alumina made by decomposition is characteristically very fluffy and will not press readily into flaw-free dense compacts unless some milling is done to break up loose aggregates. It is also necessary to use proper types and amounts of wax binders and to follow certain pressing procedures. Our own experience has been that hydraulic presses are more satisfactory than mechanical ones because the rate of densification in the die can be better regulated and thus layering cracks can be prevented.

It is necessary to heat aluminum oxide to a very high temperature to sinter it to a high density. These high temperatures, and in some cases, special atmospheres, require specially designed furnacing equipment. These furnaces can be either gas fired for oxidizing atmospheres, or resistance heated for hydrogen atmospheres or vacuum.

The resistance furnaces are generally similar to those described in *Cemented Carbides* by Schwarzkopf and Kieffer (17) for the production of cemented carbides. Gas-fired kilns for sintering alumina in oxidizing atmospheres are generally constructed from alumina refractories and enclose the pressed shapes in saggers to assure more uniform heat distribution. Furnacing facilities used by European manufacturers have been described by Agte *et al.* (18).

2. Effects of Temperature

The properties of the sintered tool bit will depend very strongly upon the temperature at which it is fired, and the time the tool was soaked at that temperature.

Alumina powder compacts start to shrink above about 1200°C, but do not achieve a high density unless sintered at about 1700°C or higher. General Electric's O-30 will sinter at somewhat lower temperatures, because of the addition of the TiO-sintering aid.

Figure 21 shows Jones *et al.'s* (19) information on the end density of pressed compacts of alumina after firing for 1 hour at the specified temperature.

Little shrinkage occurs below 1200°C. At higher temperatures the end-point density is strongly dependent upon temperature. If these data are extrapolated to theoretical density (4.00 g/cm^3), this density is achieved at about 1650°C.

In actual practice the curve does not extrapolate with the same slope, but the slope begins to decrease at a density of about 3.80 g/cm^3 so that for these conditions theoretical density is not achieved at any temperature below the melting point. Sintered high-density compacts of alumina commonly have densities ranging from 3.85 to 3.92 g/cm^3. Higher densities can be achieved only at the expense of undesirable microstructural changes.

As the compact sinters and the pores shrink, a point is reached where the residual porosity no longer inhibits grain growth (20). Continued heating at a high temperature will progressively coarsen the grain structure with deleterious effects on the physical properties of the tool material. The driving force behind this grain growth is the surface tension of the grain boundaries. The grain boundaries tend to migrate toward their centers of curvature. This results in large grains becoming larger at the expense of the smaller ones.

Figure 22 is a photomicrograph, by Burke (16), of alumina which shows the migration of such a boundary. The small grain in the center of the photograph is shrinking and the large grain at the top is growing. In this sample, much of the residual porosity is entrapped within the grains and only a relatively small amount on the boundaries. When this condition occurs, it is extremely difficult to remove residual porosity by continued heat treatment.

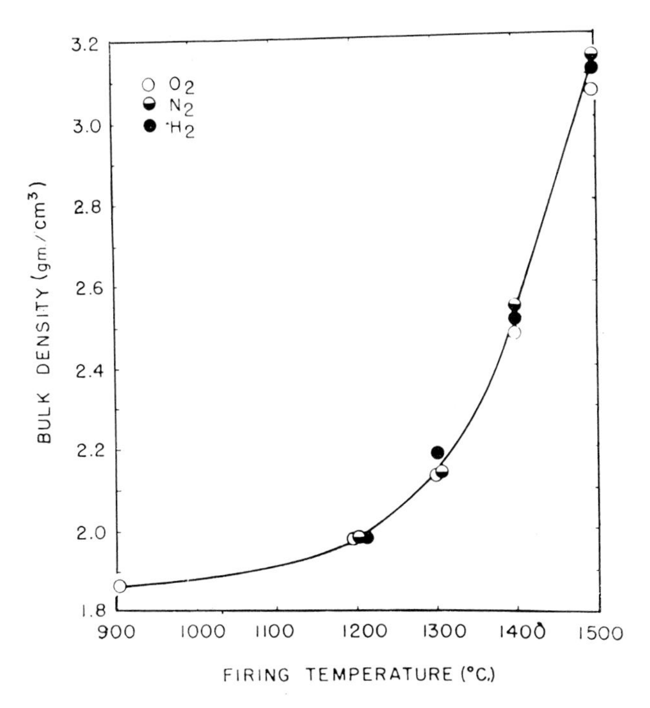

Fig. 21. Bulk density of alumina compacts plotted with temperature (Jones *et al.*, 19).

In the photograph, areas free from porosity can be seen through which the boundary moved. In some manner the boundary swept the alumina free from pores as it moved through the specimen.

The motion of boundaries through materials can purify them, as in zone refining, or reduce their defect concentration as in recrystallization of metals. The transparent sintered aluminum oxide, Lucalox, discovered by Coble probably takes advantage of moving boundaries, which sweep out the last vestiges of residual porosity and result in a pore-free ceramic object.

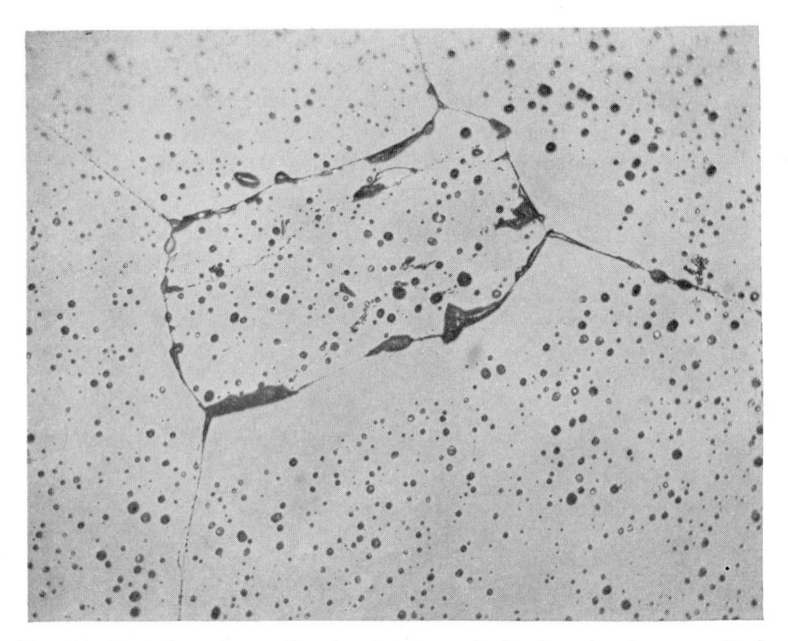

FIG. 22. Grain-boundary migration in sintered alumina showing porosity-free areas through which the grain boundary has moved. 500 × (Burke, 20).

The rate of grain growth is related by Burke to grain size by the relation:

$$D - D_0 = Kt^{1/2}$$

where D is the grain diameter at any time t, and D_0 is the starting-grain diameter at $t = 0$. In practice Burke points out that the exponent is often closer to $\frac{1}{3}$ than $\frac{1}{2}$. This equation usually holds during early grain growth. In practice, a limiting-grain diameter is reached, due to the extreme slowness of boundary motion during later stages of heat treatment.

The rate of grain growth, in single phase systems, is related by Fullman (21) to temperature with an equation of the type:

$$dD/dt = Ae^{-Q/RT}$$

where Q is the activation energy of the process, and R is the gas constant. The relation has satisfactory agreement with experiment and predicts a strong dependence of grain-growth rate upon temperature.

In order to produce a good ceramic tool by a sintering process a high density and a fine-grain size are required. To produce the high density, a high temperature and long sintering times are favored. To produce a fine microstructure, low temperatures and short sintering times are required. These two sets of firing conditions conflict.

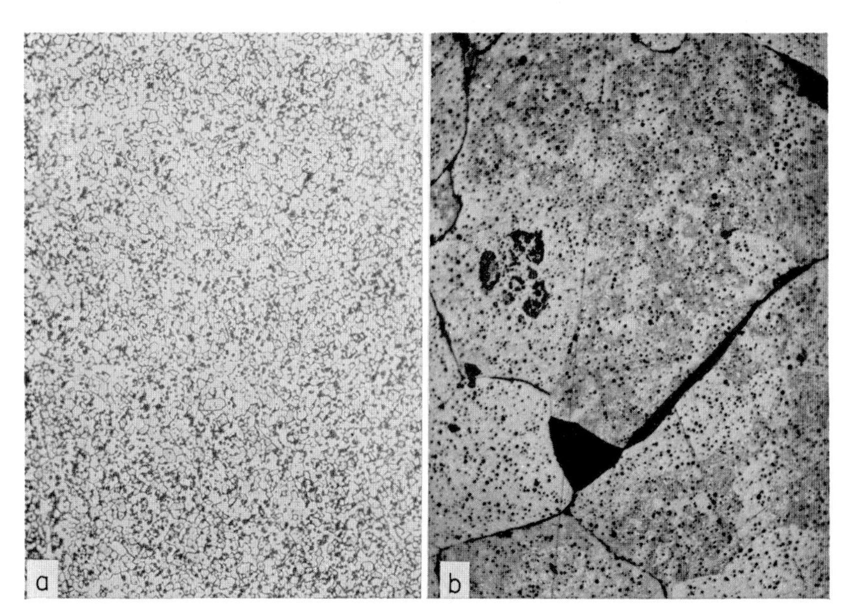

FIG. 23. Exaggerated grain growth that occurred in alumina specimens (*a*) when the temperature was raised from 1800°C to (*b*) 1900°C. 100 × (Burke, 16).

As a result of these contradictory requirements, sintering conditions have to be very carefully controlled and grain-growth inhibitors judiciously selected to prevent recrystallization. Figure 23 by Burke shows an exaggerated case of secondary recrystallization in which tremendous grain growth has occurred. The trapped pores within the grains cannot be removed effectively, and further heat treatment will not increase the density of this specimen. In ceramic tool technology much more subtle changes in microstructure than those shown here will have pronounced effects on tool performance.

Exact sintering schedules which are commercially used are not available; but, experience with alumina, containing a small amount of magnesia, indicates that it will have to be sintered in the vicinity of 1700°C in order to obtain a high density. Temperatures much above 1700°C will cause extensive grain growth and a resultant degradation of physical properties.

Hot-pressing temperatures will be of the same general magnitude as sintering temperatures in the vicinity of 1700°C.

Ceramic tools which contain sintering aids such as TiO can be sintered to a high density at lower temperatures. Carboloy's O-30 tool can be sintered to a high density at 1600°C with only 30 minutes sintering time.

In general, sintering or hot-pressing times will have to be short to prevent grain growth.

3. Effects of Raw Material

Control over the raw materials for ceramic-tool manufacture is necessary to obtain each type of tool at the exact specifications. Many of these specifications are the result of empirical trial and error, and the details of why they are needed remains obscure. Many different sources of alumina, many different formulations, and many different treatments have been tried. Only a few combinations result in satisfactory ceramic tools.

Raw materials can have pronounced effects because composition can effect shrinkage rates, density, and grain growth of alumina-sintered compacts. The particle size, shape, and surface activity of alumina powders are other factors that have to be controlled in the production of alumina-cutting tools to produce optimum properties.

4. Composition

All successful ceramic-tool formulations start with high-purity alumina powders, which are made by the decomposition of aluminum compounds. Since sintering proceeds by a bulk diffusion process, any impurities affecting the active-lattice vacancies would be expected to have effects on the sintering of alumina. Only certain impurities seem to have pronounced effects, for reasons that have not yet been expounded on in detail.

Diffusion proceeds in crystals by atoms jumping from occupied lattice sites to vacant lattice sites. If jumps of this kind are predominantly in one direction due to a concentration-, a pressure-, an electrical-, or a thermal-gradient, the net effect of this process is a transport of matter through the crystal. Impurities dissolved in the crystal, which have a valence other than that of the host atom they are replacing, must have additional charges associated with them to preserve electrical neutrality.

Under certain conditions, a lattice vacancy will satisfy these electrical requirements. And under certain conditions, it is likely that these vacancies will participate in the diffusion process. Kingery (22) discusses, in greater detail, some of the factors relating to diffusion in oxides; it is evident from his discussion that all is not yet understood. A number of investigators (19, 23, 24, 25) have studied the phenomenological effects of impurity additions on sintering and grain growth of alumina. Smothers and Reynolds (24) divide impurity additions into three categories; those which promote grain growth, those which have no effect on it, and those which retard grain growth.

It is difficult to conceive of any impurity which will not fall into one of these categories, and it must be concluded that this classification has sufficient breadth to encompass all contingencies. These are listed in Table IV.

TABLE IV

THE EFFECT OF IMPURITIES ON GRAIN GROWTH IN ALPHA ALUMINA[a]

Increased growth	No effect	Retarded growth		
Ti	Ga	F	Sr	V
Nb	Y	Cl	Ba	Mg
Mn	P	Br	La	
Cu	Fe	I	Cr	
Ge	Th	Sb	Si	
	Ce	K	Su	
	Zr	Na	Ca	

[a] Smothers and Reynolds, 24.

Figure 24 shows their data on porosity of the specimens at different firing temperatures.

We note that those impurities which promoted grain growth (Ti, Nb) also promoted sintering, and those materials which retarded grain growth (NaF, Sb) also retarded sintering. Jones, Maitra, and Cutler (19) studied the effects of oxidizing and reducing environments on the sintering of alumina with 1 mode % titania additions. Fig. 25 is a replot of their data.

The curves again show that titania is a very effective sintering aid for alumina and that there is also a pronounced atmosphere effect on densification. The authors conclude that the atmosphere is interacting with the impurity to affect the vacancy concentration, and diffusivity of the alumina.

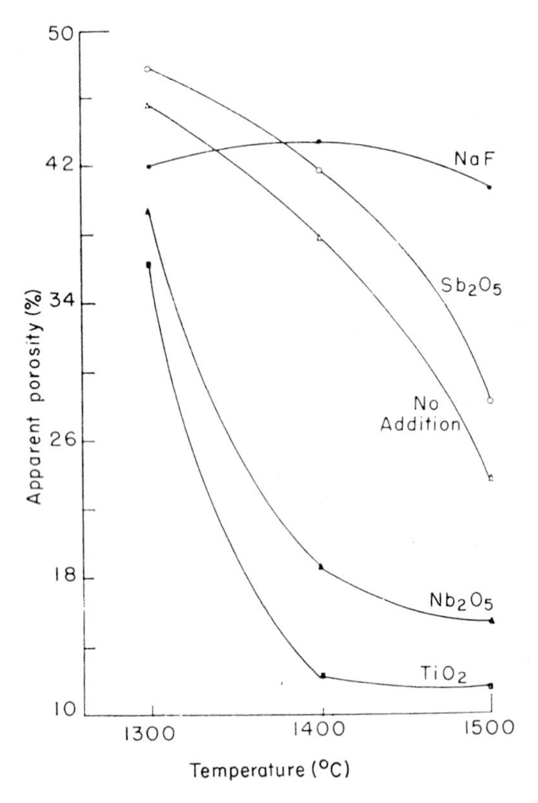

FIG. 24. The variation in apparent porosity of sintered-alumina compacts with temperature and 1% impurity additions (Smothers and Reynolds, 24).

Ceramic-tool bits commonly have additions of TiO or MgO to aid sintering and retard grain growth. The problems inherent in obtaining a high-density and fine-microstructure tool caused Goliber (26), of the General Electric Company, to experiment with suboxides of titanium as additions to alumina. TiO evidently promotes densification during sintering without the deleterious grain growth that is encountered using TiO. He was able to sinter essentially pore-free objects and retain a uniform microstructure, with an average-grain size of 2 or 3 microns. This remarkable material has excellent mechanical properties and is the basis of Carboloy's O-30 ceramic tool.

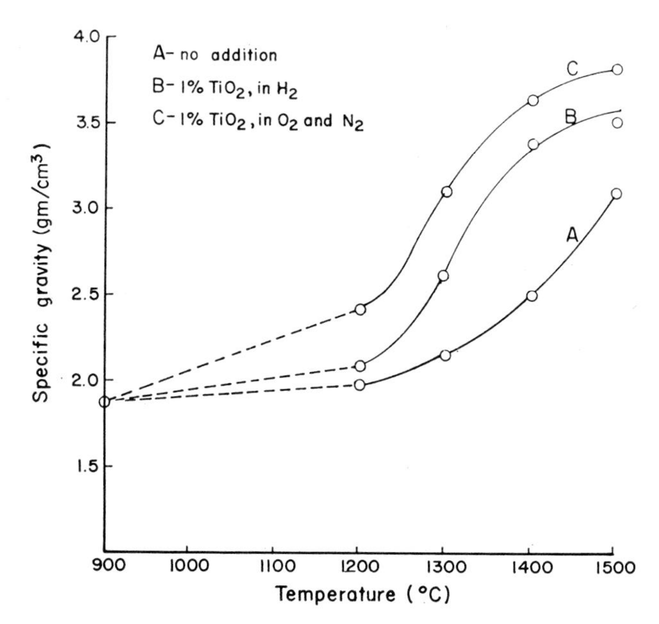

FIG. 25. The effect of TiO additions and firing atmosphere on the specific gravity of sintered-alumina compacts (Jones *et al.*, 19).

Additions of a magnesium compound to alumina prior to sintering has become a common practice wherever a fine microstructure is required (27). Magnesia, or a magnesium compound, is the most effective grain-growth inhibitor for alumina that is known, and is effective in concentrations as low as 30 parts per million. Generally, in ceramic tools a few tenths of a percent are added to alumina to inhibit grain growth. Magnesia reacts with alumina at sintering temperatures to form spinel ($MgO \cdot Al_2O_3$). Small additions of MgO to alumina will not appear in the fired product as spinel, but rather will occur in solid solution. Jorgensen and Westbrook (28) have shown that the MgO tends to segregate at grain boundaries and cause a local-boundary hardening as determined by microhardness measurements. Coble and Burke (29) have considered that the higher MgO concentrations at the grain boundaries may cause a reduction of boundary mobility and subsequently an inhibition of the grain-growth process. For larger concentrations of MgO, such as, those commonly used in ceramic tools some spinel is formed as well.

Burke has explained that the spinel forms small second phase inclusions that retard grain-boundary motion in much the same manner as pores during earlier densification. Just why some included second phases are more effective than others remains obscure.

It has been shown that the end-point density of a sintered compact is to the first approximation determined by its firing temperature and time of firing. This explanation does not consider the process by which pores are removed from grain interiors through grain-boundary motion. Referring back to Fig. 23, it is evident that under certain conditions of grain growth the pores do not disappear on the boundary as it moves past them. This leaves pores included within the grains, that cannot be removed by further heat treatment. If a grain-growth inhibitor such as MgO is added, the boundary motion is retarded and pores have the opportunity to collapse on the boundary before it moves away. Certainly, with slower boundary motion, the gases within the pores would have more time to diffuse along the boundary and escape from the system.

Sintered compacts of alumina which contain magnesia additions characteristically have higher ultimate densities than those which do not. This small increase in ultimate density may well be important in determining optimum ceramic-tool properties. Magnesia additions, then, have the dual effect of producing fine uniform microstructures and promoting greater ultimate densities. Both properties are desirable in ceramic tools. Coble (30) has shown that the atmosphere surrounding an alumina compact in a furnace can have a considerable effect on the density obtained. Alumina sintered in the H_2 or O_2 with MgO additions can be sintered to theoretical density. Alumina sintered in nitrogen or inert gases still retains some porosity. He attributes this behavior to differences in solubility of the gases in alumina which influence the rate at which they can diffuse out of the compact.

5. Particle Size

It is not uncommon to find that the particle size of the powder used to form ceramics has a large effect on the properties of the sintered objects. At first this may seem surprising, since these particles invariably grow during the latter stages of sintering. It would seem that fine particles with the more rapid sintering rates would overtake the coarser materials, act similarly to them, and ultimately produce similar objects.

This is not the case, however. Sintered ceramics made from fine powders often show the surprising result of a coarser grain size than ceramics made from coarser starting materials. Figure 26 is a composite photograph of sintered alumina specimens by Cahoon and Christensen (25), showing the effect of milling time and firing temperature on microstructure.

The specimens on the upper right were made from finer-milled powders and recrystallized at lower temperatures than the lesser-milled and coarser-alumina powder on the lower left. Any attempt to make finer microstructures by starting with finer powders would be manifestly preposterous, but, of course, it has been tried. Various investigators have studied this effect, and it turns out not to be uncommon with a variety of materials. Duwez *et al.* (31) show a similar phenomena with BeO for example. Wilder and Fitzsimmons (32) measured the grain growth on a variety of powders with different original sizes. Figure 27 is their data showing original diameter of the powder particles plotted against the ratio of fired-grain size to original diameter.

No grain growth occurs with their firing conditions if the starting material is coarser than 10 microns. If the starting material is about 1 micron, however, the fired-grain size increases a hundredfold, resulting in a 100-micron average grain size.

Particles of a very small size contain large amounts of surface energy in relation to their volume, and when pressed into intimate contact, sinter readily at low temperatures. These powders are more sinterable than the coarser materials. Figure 28 shows Cahoon and Christensen's data for the porosity of sintered-alumina specimens plotted against firing temperature for six powders at increasingly finer size (longer milling time).

As can be seen in Fig. 28, higher-density objects are obtained at lower temperatures with the finer powders. Since a ceramic tool requires both a high density and a fine microstructure, it is no surprise that they are made from very fine and sinterable alumina powders. The use of a sinterable alumina and the addition of magnesia for microstructure refinement enables these two conditions to be fulfilled.

The powders used for the manufacture of ceramic tools are pre-

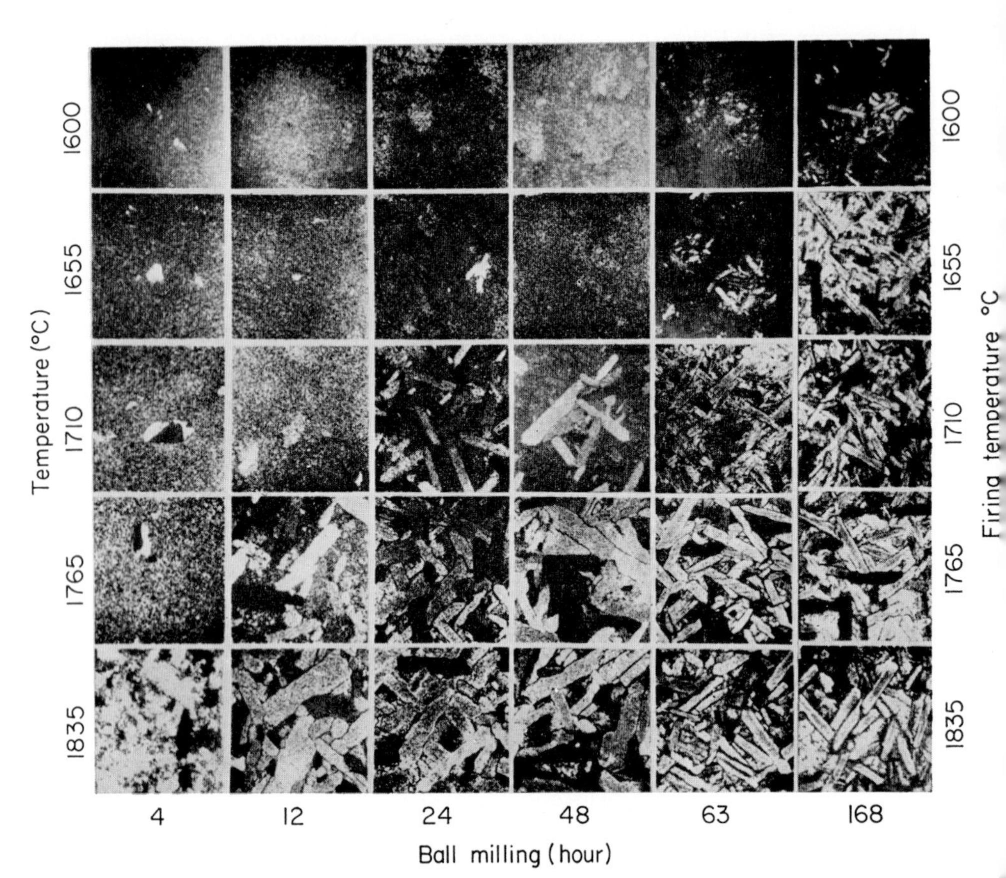

Fig. 26. The effects of milling time and firing temperature on the microstructure of sintered alumina compacts. 38 × (Cahoon and Christensen, 25).

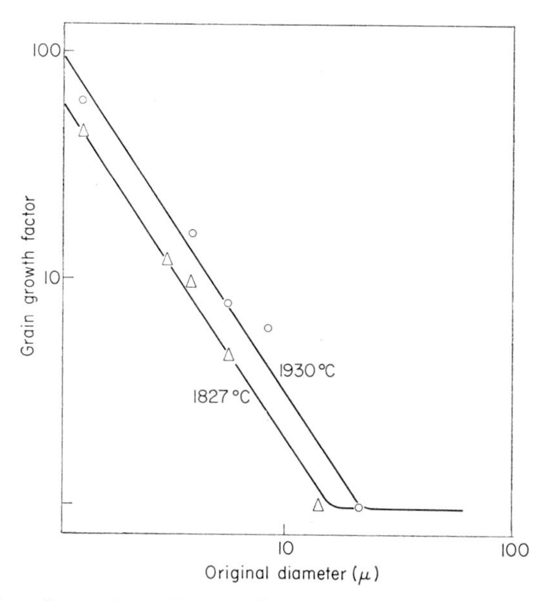

FIG. 27. The effects of powder-particle size on alumina-grain diameter in sintered compacts (Wilder and Fitzsimmons, 32).

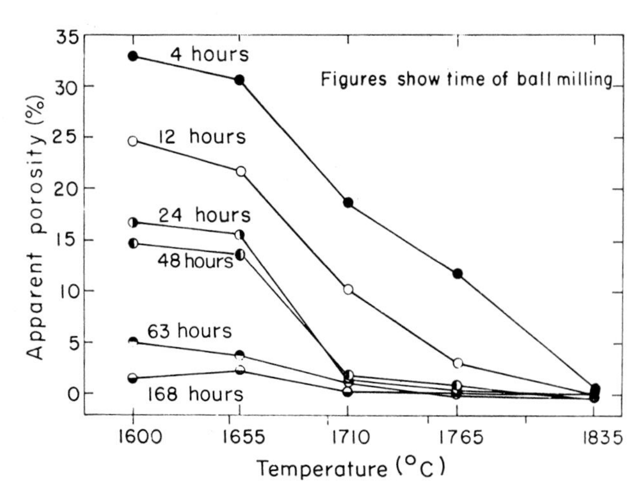

FIG. 28. The effects of milling time (particle size) on the density of sintered-alumina compacts (Cahoon and Christensen, 25).

pared by the thermal decomposition of an aluminum salt, usually the hydroxide or ammonium alum. The temperature of this calcination has an influence on the particle size of the powder and its subsequent sinterability. Figures 29 and 30 are electron photomicrographs of alumina powder, calcined to approximately 1000°C and 1250°C.

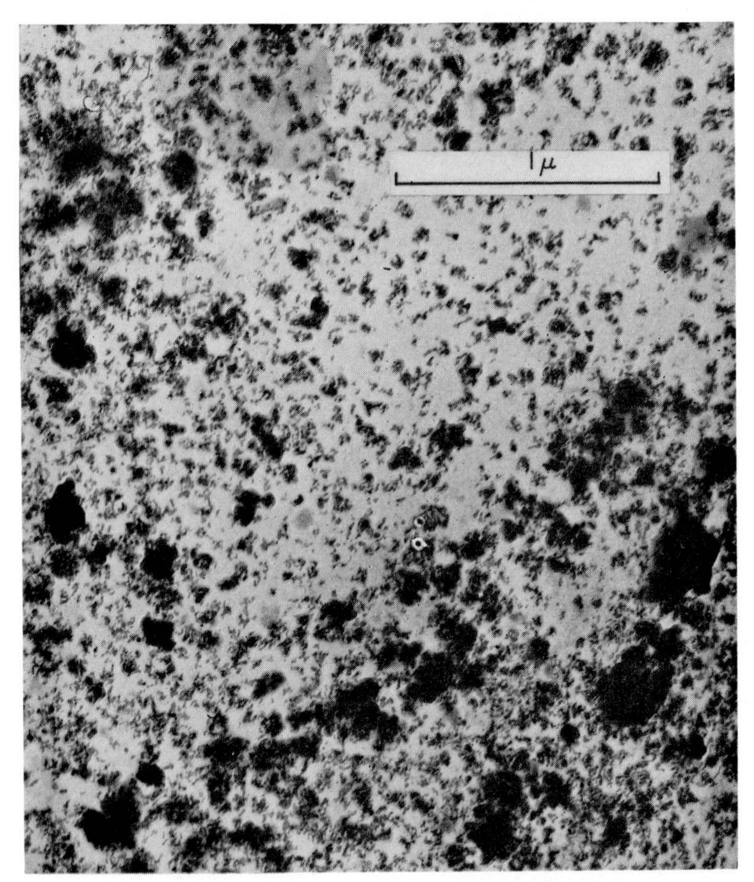

FIG. 29. Aluminum-oxide powder derived from the 1000°C calcination of ammonium alum. 60,000 ×.

The particle size has increased from about 0.04 to about 0.3 microns with the additional calcination. When dealing with these very fine powders, the surface area is sometimes a more convenient measurement and is expressed in square meters per gram. These two materials have surface areas of 70 and 15 m^2/g, respectively, as measured by nitrogen-adsorption methods.

A fine sinterable alumina powder can be produced from the hydrolysis of aluminum isopropoxide by water vapor and subsequently calcined to decompose the aluminum hydroxide (33). The tempera-

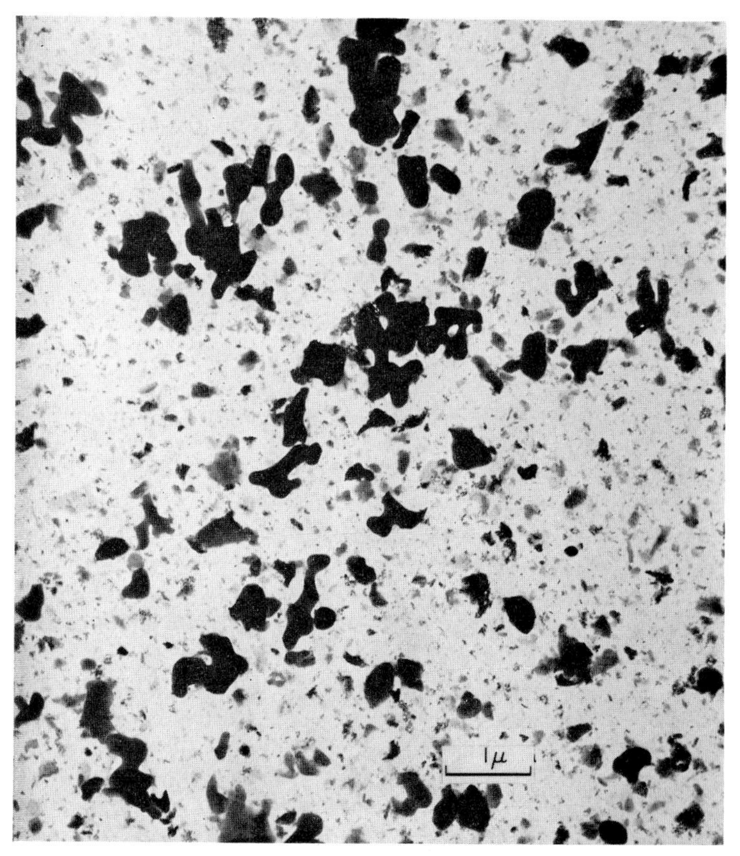

FIG. 30. Aluminum-oxide powder calcined to approximately 1200°C. 20,000 ×.

ture of calcination can have a pronounced effect on the sinterability of the powder, and a pronounced effect upon the density of a hot-pressed compact, especially if low hot-pressing temperatures are utilized. Figure 31 shows the end-point density obtained on aluminas calcined at three temperatures.

The density of the compact increases with decreasing calcination temperature over the range studied. A very large and sharp change in sinterability occurs between 1000° and 1200°C. Since these powders are exceedingly finely divided, they have a large surface area in proportion to their volume. The amounts of adsorbed materials on the surface can represent a significant impurity contribution. When this adsorbed material is gaseous, it is released during sintering.

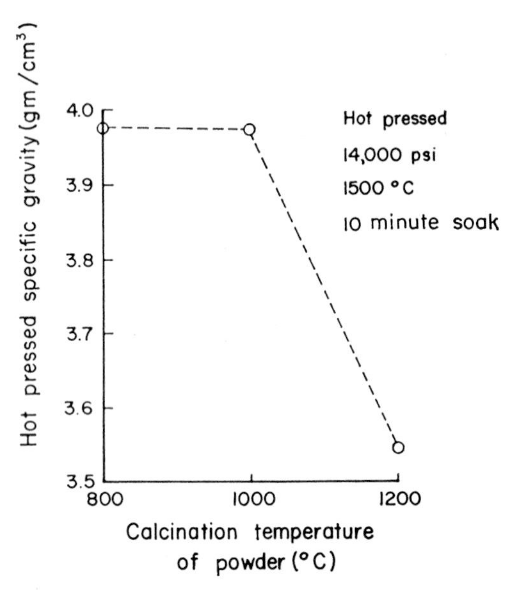

FIG. 31. The end-point density of hot-pressed alumina derived from aluminum isopropoxide calcined at various temperatures. Conditions of hot pressing: 1500°C, 14,000 psi.

On alumina the gaseous species is probably water, and as a result, it would be difficult to sinter in a perfectly dry atmosphere. Experiments in our laboratory indicate that this adsorbed layer is not completely removed below about 1400°C.

Other materials can be adsorbed on alumina during processing such as Na_2O from calcining furnace atmospheres, or impurities dissolved in the water used in ball milling.

Processing of alumina powders for ceramic tools is a meticulous procedure, requiring unusual cleanliness in all of its aspects. One tenth of 1% of certain impurities can have undesirable effects on the properties of the tool, and this amount can easily be adsorbed unless precautions are taken.

6. PRESSING

Obviously, two particles cannot sinter together unless they are touching. When dealing with fluffy loose powders, it is necessary to apply pressure so that a large portion of the particles are in intimate contact. This process is accomplished in a die, so that the article is also shaped into whatever size and configuration is required. The die, of course, is oversized to allow for shrinkage during sintering. A temporary organic binder of some sort is added to the powder to hold the compact together after pressing, to provide internal lubrication between the powder particles during pressing, and to facilitate stripping of the pressed compact from the die.

The pressing of fluffy powders, in particular, involves some know-how in order to maintain uniform densification without layering cracks developing in the preform. The rate of pressing is important because too fast a rate does not allow entrapped air to escape and the preform will disintegrate during stripping.

The die itself must have a fine finish and comply with the proposed dimensions to a high degree of accuracy. This will prevent the preform from being subjected to excessive lateral pressure during stripping, by forcing it into a narrower constriction than the size of the cavity where it was pressed. Our own practice has been to use hot-pressed boron carbide for a die material, because it does not wear rapidly or add contamination to the sample. Figure 32 shows a die lined with boron carbide that is used in producing preforms.

FIG. 32. Powder die lined with hot-pressed boron carbide (courtesy of Vascoloy-Ramet/Wesson Corp.).

The amount of pressure used in forming alumina ceramics determines the initial bulk density of the preform. As would be expected, higher pressures yield denser pieces. The proportionate increase in bulk density becomes smaller at higher pressure levels, and practically, most pieces are pressed at about 20,000 psi.

B. Hot Pressing

Hot pressing is similar to sintering except that pressure is applied to the sample as it is heated in a furnace. This allows more rapid densification and generally results in higher densities. The technique is particularly useful in producing fine-grain-sized specimens, as the temperatures and time needed for complete densification can be substantially less than those used in sintering. Because of these advantages both the CCT-707 (34) and VR97 ceramic tools are hot pressed.

There are a number of processes by which pressure can aid in densification. These include grain-boundary sliding, particle fragmentation, plastic deformation, and accelerated diffusion.

Aluminum oxide will plastically deform above 1000°C. Small amounts of deformation at the points touching between particles would allow some of them to slip past each other to form a more closely packed body. The combination of deformation and grain rearrangement with some particle fragmentation are probably the predominant processes active in early stages of densification.

Coble and Ellis (35) have described the hot pressing of powder compacts to occur in four progressive stages: repacking, plastic flow, grain rearrangement, stress enhancement of diffusion, and a final stage of stress enhanced diffusion related to a creep model of deformation.

The pressure tending to close a pore according to Murray *et al.* (36) is $2\pi/r$ where π is the surface tension and r is the pore radius. The effect of an external pressure is to add an additional term $2\pi/r + P$. With greater pressures acting on the pore to force it closed, increased rates of densification are expected. Figure 33 is their data obtained on the densification rates of BeO for hot-pressed and sintered samples. The curves show much faster densification, and much higher end-point densities for hot pressing than for sintering. Walker (37) has shown that at least a good part of this rapid densification was due to sintering effects of the carbonaceous furnace atmosphere.

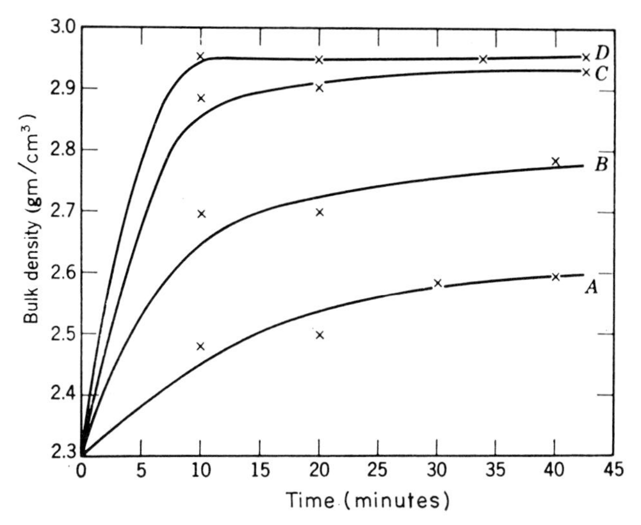

FIG. 33. A comparison between the sintering and hot pressing of BeO. Curve *A* sintered in a graphite-tube furnace at 1600°C. *B*, sintered at 1800°C. Curves *C* and *D* are hot pressed at 2000 psi at 1600°C and 1800°C, respectively (by Murray *et al.*, 36).

However, in a technological sense, more rapid densification can be routinely achieved by hot pressing. Mangsen *et al.* (38) investigated the relations between temperature, pressure, and time for hot pressing of Al_2O_3 in connection with the development of the CCT-707 tool. Their data for hot pressing–26 minutes–appears in Fig. 34. This

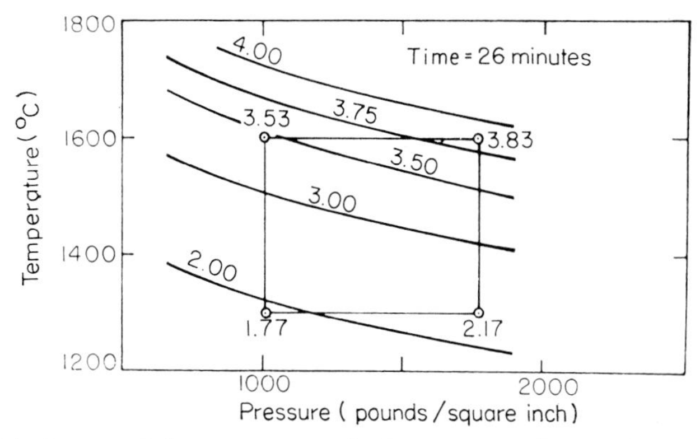

FIG. 34. Computed density contours for hot pressing alumina (Mangsen *et al.*, 38).

family of curves, plus those obtained for different times, predict the density of a hot-pressed sample that is achieved under any temperature and pressure conditions. These curves are not valid, of course, for materials of other compositions or particle size.

The alumina used for hot pressing is essentially the same as that used in sintering. Either alumina powder or a lightly sintered preform is placed in a graphite die, and then placed in the hot-press furnace. As the sample is heated, pressure is applied with a graphite plunger. This pressure is slowly increased during the run as the sample shrinks. A typical run may take an hour, using a maximum pressure of about 3000 psi, and a temperature of about 1700°C. The soak time at maximum temperature is usually just a few minutes. After the furnace cools, the mold is removed and the piece pushed out of the die.

1. Equipment

Two types of molds are currently in use by different manufacturers. The Carborundum Company CCT-707 molds large plates which are sliced and ground into ceramic tools. Vascoloy Ramet (VR97) molds each tool independently in a compartmented die. Figure 35 is a photograph of a production die used in the manufacture of VR97.

All die parts are made from mold-grade graphites and are machined to close tolerances. Commercial grades of graphite are not especially strong, limiting the amount of material which can be molded and the pressures used during hot pressing. Since the strength of graphite increases with temperature, the maximum pressures are not applied to the die until the furnace is at its soak temperature.

Commercial furnacing equipment is not available for this type of application, and special furnaces have to be designed. Figure 36 is the type of furnace used by Vascoloy Ramet/Wesson Corporation in the production of the VR97 tool.

The furnace is of graphite construction and heated with graphite-resistant elements. The power leads through the metal-furnace shell are flame sprayed by the Rokide coating process to provide additional oxidation resistance and electrical insulation. The furnaces are transferable from cooling stations to the hydraulic press. Temperatures are measured by optical pyrometry. Two graphite dies, ready for hot pressing, can be seen on the right of Fig. 36.

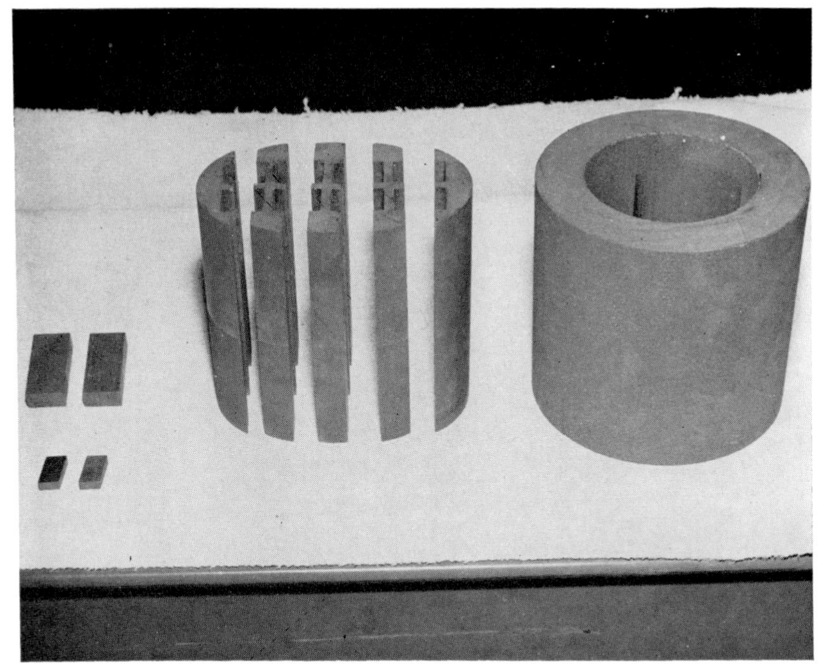

FIG. 35. Graphite hot-pressing mold (courtesy of Vascoloy-Ramet/Wesson Corp.).

2. FURNACE ATMOSPHERE

In hot pressing, the furnace atmosphere is different from that normally encountered in sintering, due to the presence of graphite. Carbon or carbon-containing gases can and are adsorbed on the sample during hot pressing, resulting in a gray color which is imparted to the tool. Walker has shown that carbonaceous atmospheres enhance the sintering of alumina. His information appears in Fig. 37. With these atmospheres normally present in graphite molds, the alumina sinters more readily in hot pressing than it does in normal sintering procedures. This carbonaceous atmosphere will penetrate by diffusion into the alumina compact as it is heated in the furnace. Figure 38 is a photograph of a section cut through a VR97 tool. The diffusion of the carbonaceous atmosphere into the alumina can be seen as an outer-gray zone which encapsulates the white interior.

FIG. 36. Ceramic tool hot-pressing furnace in operating position on the hydraulic press (courtesy of Vascoloy-Ramet/Wesson Corp.).

This adsorption occurs before the alumina achieves a high density by gaseous diffusion through connecting pores. Tools cut from the white interior do not perform as well in machining tests as those cut from the gray zone. This is thought to arise from better bonding in the gray zone due to the sintering enhancement from the furnace atmosphere as explained by Walker.

A chemical reaction occurs between aluminum oxide and carbon at high temperatures forming aluminum carbides and oxycarbides. Foster *et al.* (39) show eutectic at 1850°C which represents an absolute top temperature where Al_2O_3 and C can occur in intimate contact without reaction. There is evidence that solid-state reactions occur at even lower temperatures and, practically, it is not generally advisable to hot press alumina much above 1750°C.

Hot-pressed alumina differs from sintered, in that structural damage by plastic deformation can cause the formation of strains in the hot-pressed article. These residual strains have effects on the hardness

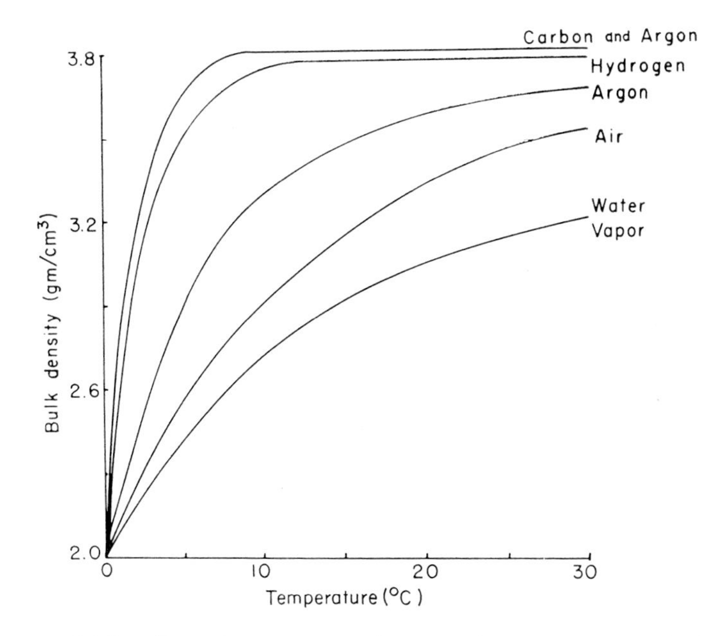

FIG. 37. The effect of various atmospheres on the sintering rate of alumina at 1650°C (Walker, 37).

FIG. 38. The diffusion of the carbonaceous atmosphere causes a discoloration around the tool-blank exterior.

and strength of the ceramic tool. For certain types of machining it is possible that these strains are beneficial.

It is possible to produce almost transparent objects by hot-pressing ceramics. George F. Scott (40), Norton Company, hot pressed transparent MgO in 1958. Shortly thereafter, this was duplicated with alumina. In both cases, the samples had a gray color and a degree of transparency.

3. Finishing

VR97 and GE O-30 are individually molded or sintered to shape so that only surface and cam-grinding procedures are necessary. Carborundum CCT-707, being molded in large blanks, must also be sliced with diamond wheels to form the rough shapes desired. Figure 39 shows the hot-pressed disks of alumina being mounted onto plates for surface grinding and slicing.

After mounting, the disks are sliced with a multiple cutterhead into the desired configuration. The disks are not sliced all of the way through as this often produces chips on the tool blanks. Figure 40 shows the slicing operation on the disks.

The disks are then surface ground on a rotary table grinder with diamond wheels, inverted, and ground on the opposite surface. The blanks are demounted from the work plates and the corners ground on the surface grinder so as to minimize the cam grinding which produces the desired tool geometry. Figure 41 shows a tool blank mounted in the cam grinder.

Fig. 39. The setting of alumina disks to work plates (courtesy of The Carborundum Co.).

FIG. 40. Multiple slicing of alumina disks (courtesy of The Carborundum Co.).

FIG. 41. Tool-blank ready for cam grinding (courtesy of The Carborundum Co.).

In some cases, it is desirable to strengthen the edge of the tool. This is commonly done by the user, by hand honing the edge. The manufacturer does this either by tumbling the tools in an abrasive medium so as to produce a small radius on the cutting edge, or by grinding a chamfer on the edge. Figure 42 shows a photograph of the fixture used by us to produce this chamfer.

FIG. 42. Chamfer-grinding fixture for ceramic tools.

The fixture during use is held onto the table of a grinding machine and located by the cross-feed so that the tool edge which protrudes through the slot will touch the flat face of a cup wheel. The position is adjustable so that a chamfer of the proper width is produced. The tool is held square against the internal surfaces and rotated by hand. One must be careful to maintain contact with the alignment fixture. Once set, the fixture assures that a uniform chamfer of the width selected will be ground on the tool-cutting edge. The angle of this chamfer is set by the construction of the fixture with only two choices available, 60° and 30° with the tool-flank surface. Fixtures of this type can, of course, be made for any angle, or can be made adjustable, if so desired. The properties of aluminum oxide make it more difficult to grind than cemented carbide. The ceramic is harder, more notch sensitive, and more susceptible to thermal shock. If careful grinding procedures are not followed, the tools are apt to have chipped edges. Grinding finish can adversely affect the impact strength, with coarse scratches weakening the ceramic.

The procedures necessary to grind ceramic tools, successfully, can readily be accomplished on available equipment without the necessity of any elaborate precautions. The grinding machines should be in good shape, and not vibrate excessively. A slow feed and slow wheel speed should be used, if possible, and the tool should be flooded with a suitable coolant.

Manufacturers recommend resinoid-bonded diamond wheels for grinding ceramics. Typical wheel specifications are D220 N100 B for general purpose grinding and D320 N100 B for finishing. The tool is flooded with coolant during grinding with the wheel in-feed, at about 0.001 inches for roughing, and 0.0002 inches for finish grinding. Chipping can be reduced by slowing the wheel speed to 3000 fpm. Taeyaerts (41) has shown that the economics of diamond-wheel usage also favor speeds between 2000 and 3000 fpm.

Chapter 3

Strength of the Ceramic and Tool Usage

As was pointed out in the first chapter, the ceramics used as cutting tools have the disadvantage of having lower tensile strengths than cemented carbides. This lower strength is the primary reason that ceramics are not widely used in machining jobs requiring heavy interrupted cuts or in milling cutters. In these applications, the tool tip is subjected to very high-shear stresses or impact-loading conditions. Without sufficient reserve strength, too many unpredictable fracture failures will occur and user acceptance will be poor.

As an illustration of the importance of tool strength in machining practice, the data of Okushima and Fujii (42) are presented in Fig. 43.

As is evident from Fig. 43, strength not only limits tool utility in a go, no go sense, but it also is pertinent to tool life under conditions where the tool is operable.

Tool geometry has been modified with ceramics in the attempt to overcome part of this ceramic strength disadvantage: The cutting tip is placed under compressive loading with negative geometries, and special tool or edge configurations are used to redistribute machining stresses in a more satisfactory manner. These procedures, while they have increased tool utility, have not offered a general solution to the problem of machining with ceramics. Since ceramic-tool strength is marginal for these applications, each type of machining job has to be individually engineered and evaluated—this creates an unreasonable burden on the tool engineer.

Research dealing with strength problems of various materials is relatively new with ceramics. Many of the earlier techniques and theories developed by physical metallurgists are now being applied to ceramics in the effort to improve their physical properties. A new understanding of ceramics is rapidly being developed.

A goal of this research is to find ways of making stronger engineering materials. It is certain that this goal will be at least modestly realized. A modest (say twofold) improvement in tensile strength of alumina ceramics will have profound effects on tooling practices. This chapter is a summary of our current knowledge pertinent to the strength problem of alumina ceramics.

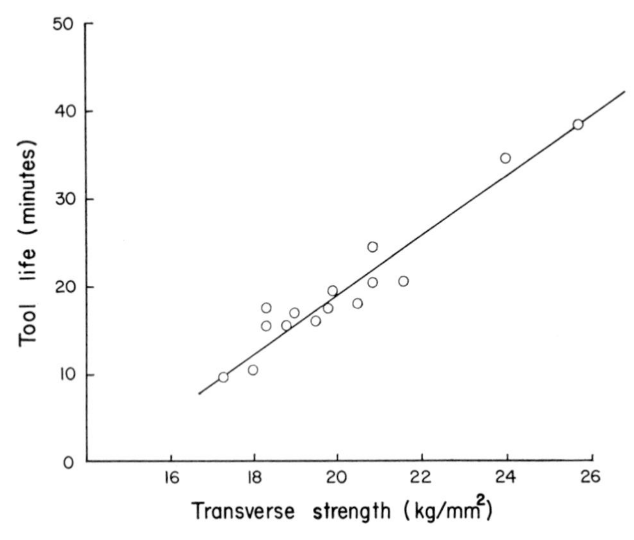

FIG. 43. The relation between transverse-rupture strength and tool life of ceramics (Okushima and Fujii, 42).

A. Strength and Tool Surface Finish

The physical conditions that exist on the surface of a ceramic, as it is being ground, are very severe. Local temperatures and forces are very high which imparts localized severe physical damage to the ceramic. This damage can be deformation damage, scratch notches, or crack nuclei formed in the scratch roots. We have found that this damage affects the strength of the ceramic tool.

1. GRINDING DAMAGE

A scratch, such as one produced by grinding, etches into an oriented line of polyhedral pits, which are probably evidence of dislocations in the alumina. This damage extends for some distance down into the ceramic, beyond the bottom of the scratch itself.

Films of VR97, which were ground and polished for thin section studies, sometimes developed curvatures due to different amounts of grinding or polishing damage on each side of the section. The maximum stresses necessary in the section to produce this amount of curvature must have been about 30,000 psi. This is an appreciable portion of the tensile strength of the specimen.

Residual stresses, resulting from surface finishing, can exist in alumina ceramics. These stresses or crack nuclei influence strength properties.

2. Impact Strength

Impact strength was measured on VR97 by dropping a ½-inch steel ball bearing from increasing heights onto the surface of a thin-disk sample, that was supported by a circular knife edge near its periphery (43). Figure 44 is a photograph of the apparatus.

The distance the ball drops in order to produce a fracture is plotted against the hot-pressing temperature of the specimen. All impact tests were performed at room temperature. Each point in Fig. 45 represents the average of four samples.

The two curves, 120-grit and 220-grit, represent the abrasive size used in the diamond-grinding wheels to finish the specimens. At a given temperature, considerable improvement in impact strength was found with the finer of the two finishes. Tool-bit ceramics that were hot pressed at lower temperatures were weaker in impact than those pressed at higher temperatures, as evidenced by the curves sloping off to the left. The anneal curve represents the effect of reheating the specimens to 1300°C after grinding, in the successful effort to heal some of the grinding damage. Annealing heals grinding damage and the decreased strengths with lower hot-pressing temperatures are not observed.

The point "*P*" on Fig. 45 represents the average impact strength of samples which were polished with diamond powders on lead laps, and represents the highest values observed. The type of surface finish certainly has a profound effect on impact strength, with average values varying as much as sixfold.

The fine-grained samples on the left side of the diagram broke into two pieces in each case, with the fracture paralleling the grinding scratches on the lower surface (the tensile surface). On the basis of

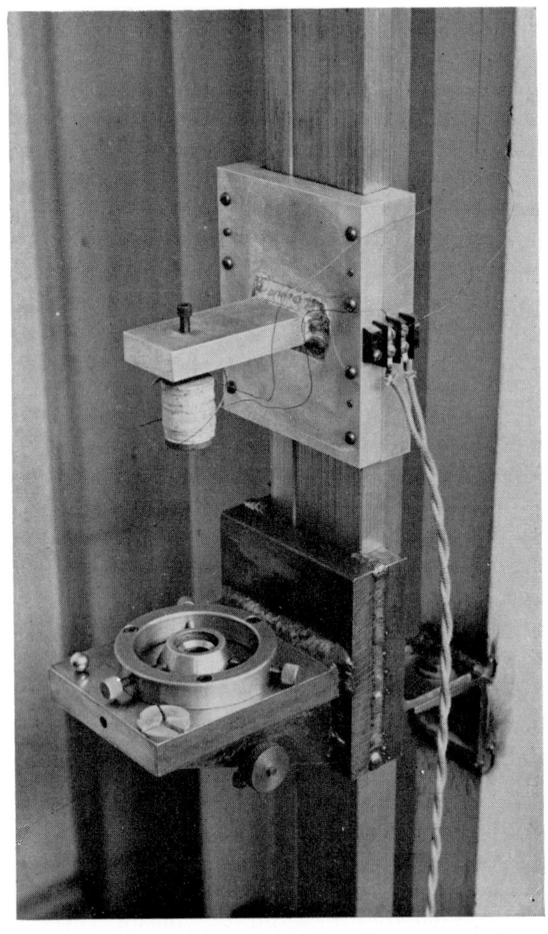

Fig. 44. Impact-test apparatus showing the electromagnet lowered from the operating position. The disk-shaped sample is held on the annular-knife edge contained within the alignment collar. A broken specimen is shown on the base plate.

fractography, it appears that the fracture was initiated on the top surface and propagated downward as part of a conical surface. When this conical fracture intersected the bottom surface, the fracture direction was controlled by the grinding scratches and, thereby, became a flat surface parallel to these marks.

The Carborundum ceramic-tool material (then Stupalox) was also tested by this method in 1958 with an average value of 93 cm as compared with 115 cm for VR97. The surface finishes were comparable but not identical, as grinding was done by each supplier. The difference between these two values is not considered to be particularly significant due to scatter in results.

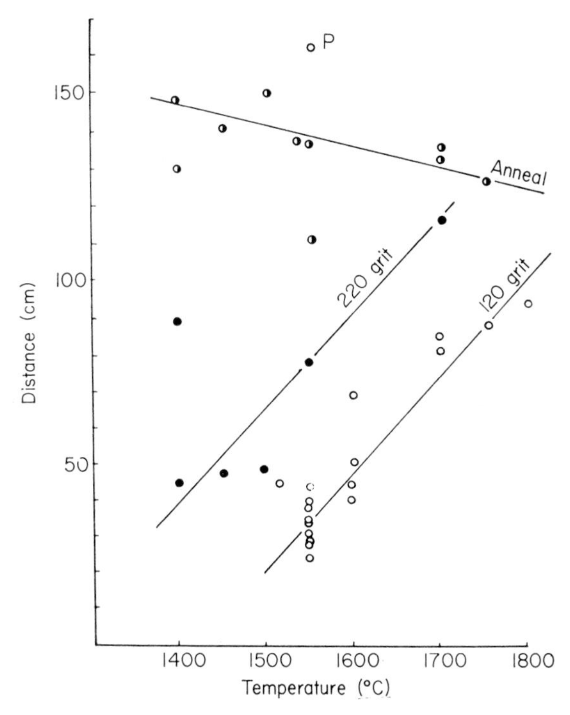

FIG. 45. The impact strength of hot-pressed alumina as it varies with the temperature of specimen fabrication.

The effects of annealing treatment on tool performance were enthusiastically tested under impact-machining conditions, turning a 200-bhn longitudinally slotted steel log. Surprisingly, the annealing treatment did not show any advantages. Since the increase in impact strength with annealing is a real enough phenomenon, it was concluded that factors other than impact strength alone were controlling tool failure.

The possibility remains, however, that under some machining conditions annealing the tool might have advantages. It will be necessary to control other tool-failure mechanisms first, before annealing treatments can assume much general importance in machining. Ryshkewitch (27) has summarized work of Pearson and Tomilovskii on annealing of alumina ceramics. Both authors reported beneficial effects of annealing, with improvements in mechanical strength up to 35%. This improved strength is attributed to the healing of flaws which could have acted as crack nuclei. This is probably true since an annealed sample, when rescratched, will again show the original lower strength value.

3. Crack Nuclei

The theoretical strength of most materials is much higher than the strength observed by actual test. Certain processes are acting which reduce the strength by factors of 100 or 1000. Griffith, in 1921 (44), described one process by which this can occur. This theory is known as the Griffith Crack Theory, and describes the behavior of many elastic structural materials. Griffith correctly assumed that crack nuclei preexisted in materials, and that an application of tensile stress would cause these nuclei to grow. The growth of these elastic cracks leads to a catastrophic fracture. His formula is

$$p = (E\pi)^{1/2}/c$$

where p is the tensile stress necessary to propagate a crack of length c; E is the elastic modulus, and π is the surface energy of the fractured faces. The force necessary to cause fracture is, then, inversely proportional to $c^{1/2}$. Once the minimum stress necessary to propagate the crack occurs, the crack will continue to grow at an accelerated rate, up to a limiting value, until either the stress is removed or the sample fractures. These crack nuclei can evidently be formed in tool-bit materials, with larger nuclei resulting from a coarser diamond abrasive. Annealing treatments can heal these nuclei by a sintering process.

4. Polishing

From the foregoing discussion, it would be desirable to remove crack nuclei and other grinding damage produced in ceramic tools. A common laboratory technique for accomplishing this is to dissolve off the surface with a suitable solvent. Some solvents dissolve uniformly, producing a polished surface, while others attack stressed areas—preferably dislocations or grain boundaries—and produce an etched surface.

Borax fusions at between 750°C and 900°C produce polishes on alumina, while $NH_4F \cdot HF$ or $K_2S_2O_7$ fusions produce etched surfaces. For strength studies the chemical polish is preferred. Figure 46 is a photograph of VR97 tool bits before and after being polished by a borax fusion.

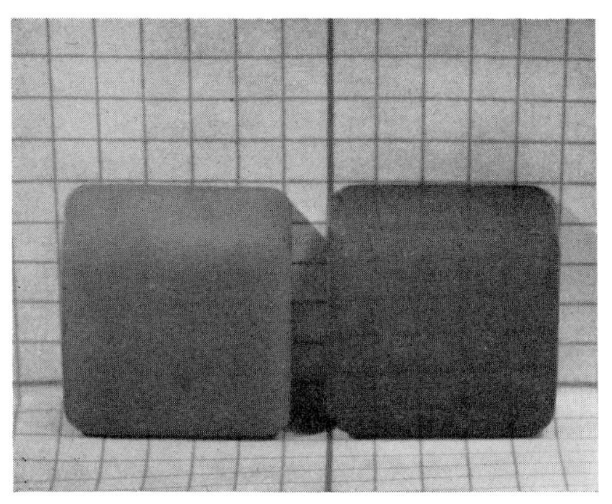

FIG. 46. The effect of chemical polishing on the surface finish of ceramic tools. The tool on the right has been polished by immersion in a borax fusion at 250°C for 5 minutes. The tool on the left is the same type of tool with a ground finish before polishing.

The cutting edges of the polished tools develop a small radius (0.001 inch to 0.003 inch) during polishing. This small radius increases the chipping resistance of the tool and acts similarly to a honed or tumbled edge.

Chemical polishing of alumina increases its transverse-rupture strength by about ⅓. The amount of material dissolved from the tool surface need not be great. This increase in strength is obtained by removing a layer of about 5 microns. Additional solution did not increase the strength further. Evidently, the grinding damage is stopped by grain boundaries in the tool. Only those crystallites, in the top layer that is in contact with the grinding wheel, sustain the damage. This layer is about 5 microns thick or slightly less than $\frac{1}{10}$ the thickness of this page. This thin film of damaged material has considerable deleterious effects on the impact and transverse-rupture strength of ceramic tools.

Machining tests have been performed with chemically polished tools (45). VR97 tools ½ × ½ × 3/16 inch with 1/16-inch nose radius were prepared by grinding a flat 0.006-inch wide on the cutting edge at a 60° angle to the top surface. Half of these tools were chemically polished. The tools were tested on AISI type A-6 tool steel at Rc 52, 1200 fpm, 0.015-ipr feed, and 0.080-inch depth of cut. The ground tools averaged 86 seconds and the polished tools averaged 222 seconds total tool life to failure.

These results were reproduced in a later test. The threefold increase in tool life stimulated other work in studying machining performance of chemically polished VR97.

An attempt to duplicate these results at Ohio State University, by Moore and Kibbey, failed to show an improvement in tool life with the chemically polished tools.

It appears that the factors governing tool life are more complex than first supposed, since both of these test results were reliable and reproducible. Chemically polished tools have been used experimentally for making heavy interrupted cuts on cast iron, under cutting conditions more severe than those possible with ground tools. The exact extent of usefulness has not yet been determined. Under some conditions the improved strength produced by polishing would seem to offer advantages.

B. Strength and Tool Microstructure

The strength of alumina ceramics varies with the amount of porosity and average-grain size, with stronger ceramics being dense and fine grained. Ceramic-tool research has naturally concentrated on these materials, and all commercially available ceramic tools are dense and have fine microstructures.

1. Porosity

Coble and Kingery (46) and Trostel (47) have measured the relationship between traverse strength and porosity. Coble and Kingery's data are presented in Fig. 47.

All ceramic tools are materials with less porosity than those shown in Fig. 47, but the trend toward higher strengths at lower porosity is clearly established. A trend of this sort would be expected just on the basis of having more solid material over which the load is distributed in a given cross section.

The behavior of ceramic tools, in practice, is not this straightforward, and relatively small changes in porosity can have effects. Brewer's (48) data (Fig. 48) shows a much steeper tool-life porosity curve than Coble and Kingery's data on strength would suggest.

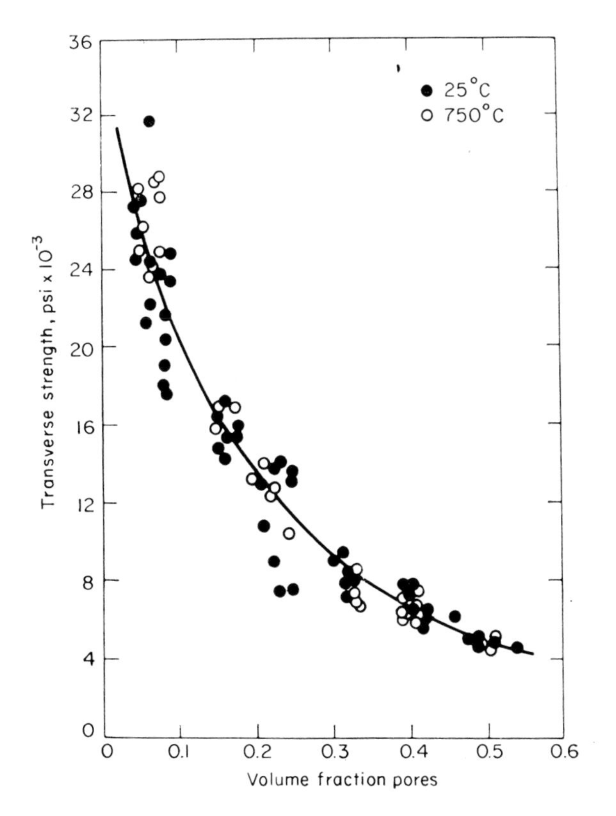

FIG. 47. The relationship between strength and porosity in alumina ceramics (Coble and Kingery, 46).

The change of density from 99.93 to 99.98% produced a tenfold increase in tool life at 1000-fpm cutting speed. This apparent discrepancy may be due to the way residual porosity is distributed, particularly those last vestiges of porosity in very dense materials. Ceramic-tool materials are up to three times stronger than the specimens used by Coble and Kingery, and at these strength levels other factors may well be more controlling of strength than overall porosity.

Voids that were distributed as microcracks at grain boundaries would be, for example, more deleterious than the same amount of void distributed as spherical pores within grains. Brewer's data probably reflects a change in wear mechanism, related to intergranular bond strength, resulting in microspalling of the less dense materials.

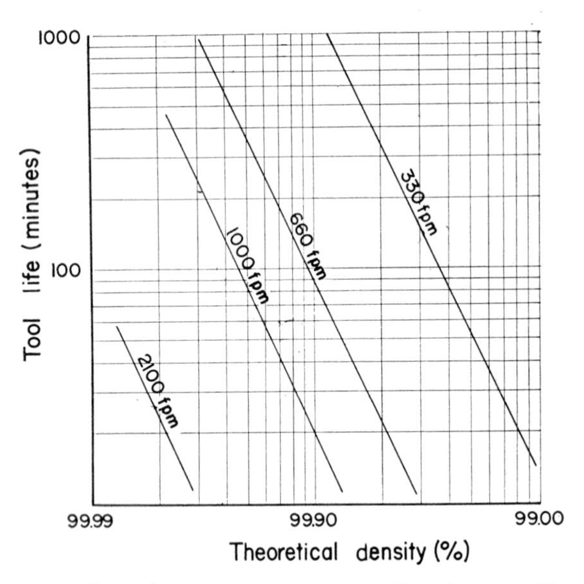

FIG. 48. The effect of porosity on ceramic-tool endurance (Brewer, 48).

2. GRAIN SIZE

If cracks occur at grain boundaries, and the length of these cracks are related to grain size, as would be expected, then fine-grained materials would be stronger than the coarser according to a simple application of the Griffith' theory. A unit crack length in a polycrystalline material, by this hypothesis, would be somewhat less than one-grain diameter and the strength would vary inversely as the square root of this dimension. In practice, this relationship has not been exactly followed with ceramics, and the exponent varies from 1 (49) to ⅓ (50). Figure 49 shows the relations between grain size, transverse-bend strength, and temperature for hot-pressed alumina by Spriggs *et al.* (51).

All ceramic-tool materials fall very close to the strength-temperature plane shown in Fig. 49, as a typical grain diameter is about 3 microns. It is particularly significant that the irregular surface sharply curves upward (higher strengths) as this plane is reached, and this curvature is present up to temperatures above 1300°C. Figures 50–52 are stereo-electron photomicrographs of fracture surfaces on experimental ceramic-tool materials of different grain size.

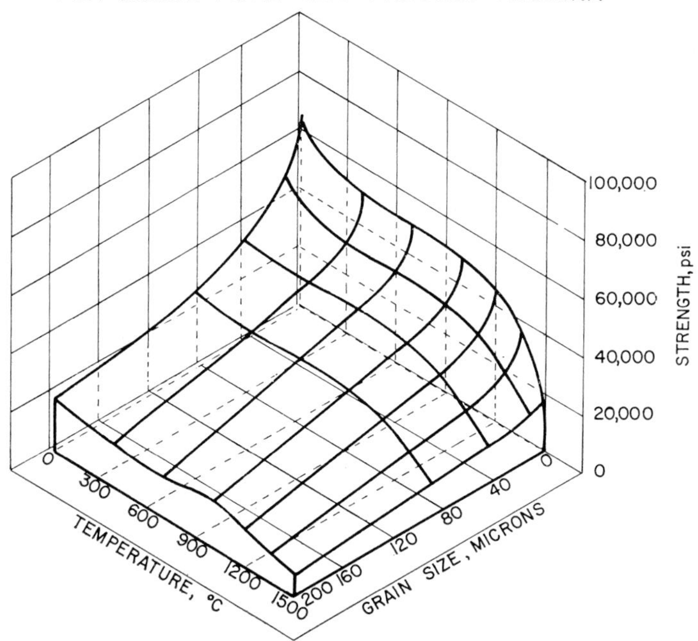

FIG. 49. Plot of strength, temperature and grain size for pure, dense hot-pressed alumina (Spriggs *et al.*, 51).

Fracturing can occur along grain boundaries or through intercrystalline or transcrystalline grains. There is an increasing tendency for transcrystalline fracture with the finer grained materials. Since the grain boundaries would be expected to be weaker than the crystals, increasing amounts of transcrystalline fracture might result in a stronger object. In any case, the change of character of the fracture surface with grain size would seem to indicate differences in mode of fracture propagation.

Fig. 50. Stereo-electron photomicrograph of a coarse-grained experimental ceramic tool on a fracture surface. Average particle size is 7 microns. 3000 ×.

Fig. 51. Stereo-electron photomicrograph of a 3-micron ceramic tool on a fracture surface. 3000 ×.

FIG. 52. Stereo-electron photomicrograph of a 1-micron experimental ceramic tool on a fracture surface. 3000 ×.

3. Grain Shape

Most polycrystalline single-phase ceramics have equidimensional grains arrayed and shaped much like the bubbles in a soap froth. This microstructure results from surface-tension forces at grain boundaries rather than a crystallographic control of shape. Figure 53 is a transmission-electron photomicrograph of a tool bit, illustrating this microstructure.

The section was prepared by lapping a specimen to a film, of approximately 20-micron thickness and, then, producing a hole in the center of this film by chemically polishing. The alumina at the periphery of this hole was less than one micron in thickness and was transparent to the electron beam.

The CCT-707 tool has a microstructure of fine equidimensional grains, averaging about three microns in diameter, with some larger prismatic crystals dispersed throughout the structure. The prismatic- or lath-shaped crystals are believed to be beta alumina. Figure 54 is a photomicrograph of this structure.

The mechanism by which the prismatic microstructure develops is thought to be controlled by small amounts of liquid phase which are present during sintering. This hypothesis has not been firmly established. The shape of the crystallites, in any case, is obviously

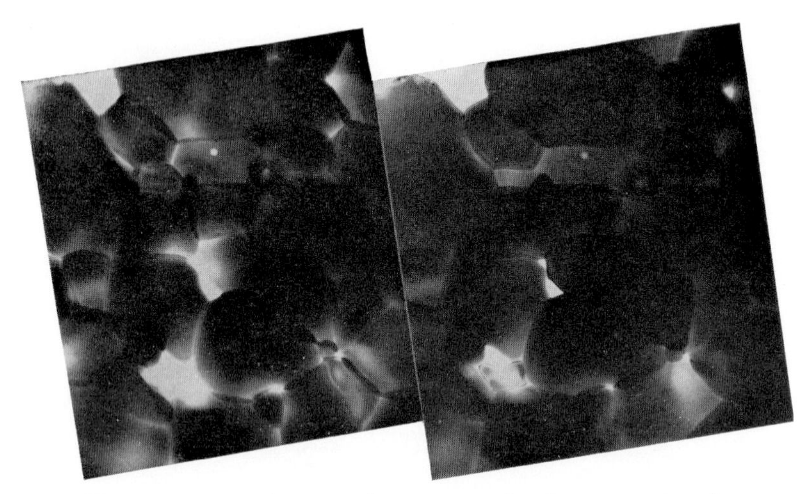

FIG. 53. Transmission-electron photomicrograph of a ceramic-tool section. 9000 ×.

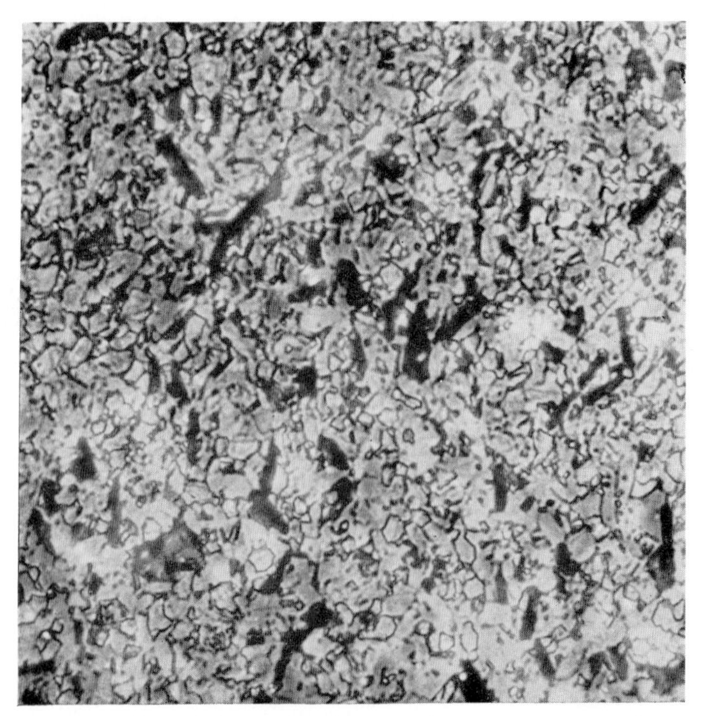

FIG. 54. Etched polished section showing the microstructure of CCT-707. 850 × (courtesy of The Carborundum Co.).

controlled by internal crystallographic orientation rather than by surface tension.

C. Strength and Temperature

By definition, strength is the unit stress necessary to cause a catastrophic fracture. A given material will fracture at different stresses, depending upon temperature. Generally, materials become weaker at higher temperatures, and this is true for cutting-tool materials. Since the tool tip is hot during chip removal, the strength at these temperatures is more pertinent regarding in-cut tool failures than room-temperature strength. Figure 55 is from Ryshkewitch and relates the tensile strength of sintered alumina to temperature.

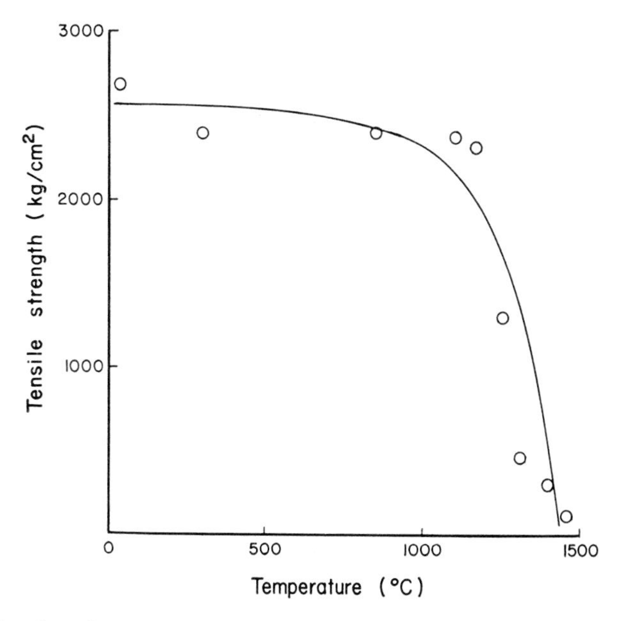

FIG. 55. The effect of temperature on tensile strength of alumina (Ryshkewitch, 27).

The data show a uniform strength up to about 1200°C, and then a sharp decline at higher temperatures. The decline in strength at about 1200°C has not been adequately explained. It could be related to plastic deformation processes, which begin to occur in alumina at about this same temperature. Small amounts of deformation could form crack nuclei which would then grow according to Griffith's criteria.

Orowan has modified this original concept by including other energy-absorbing processes in addition to the surface-energy term originally considered by Griffith. In the case where plastic deformation occurs at an advancing crack tip, this deformational energy must also be considered.

From semiquantitative considerations of the forces within crystals the theoretical maximum strength of an object is approximately one tenth of the elastic modulus. From Griffith's theory, the stress necessary to propagate a crack is proportional to $E^{1/2}$. Then, the effects of temperature on elastic modulus are pertinent. Figure 56 is

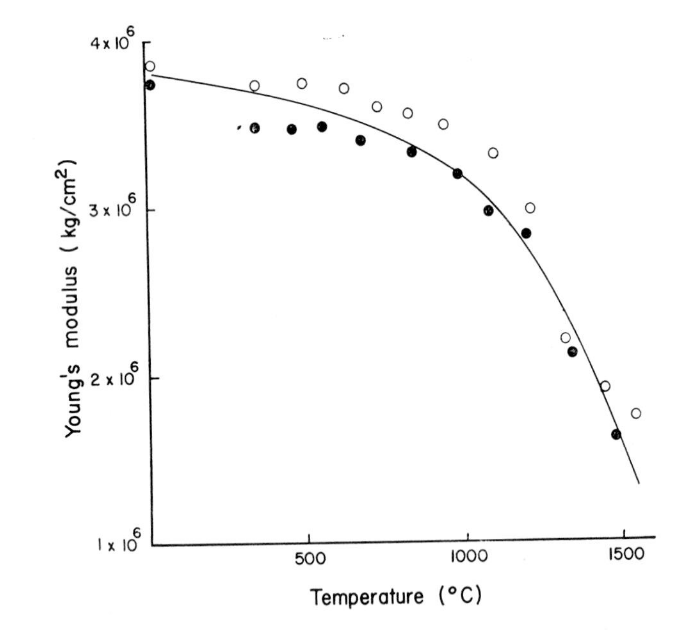

FIG. 56. The effect of temperature on the modulus of sintered alumina (Ryshkewitch, 27).

Ryshkewitch's data on the modulus of sintered alumina with temperature. Large changes in modulus do not occur at temperatures below about 1200°C. Similarly, Kingery and Pappis (52) have shown that the impact strength of alumina is fairly constant up to about 900°C as shown in Figure 57.

In general, ceramic-tool performance is expected to be satisfactory up to 1000°C or 1200°C (1800°F to 2400°F). Cook's (53) data (Fig. 58) on cutting-tool temperatures indicate, by extrapolation, that these temperatures will not be reached at any currently employed cutting speeds on steel, or any cutting speeds likely to be employed in the near future.

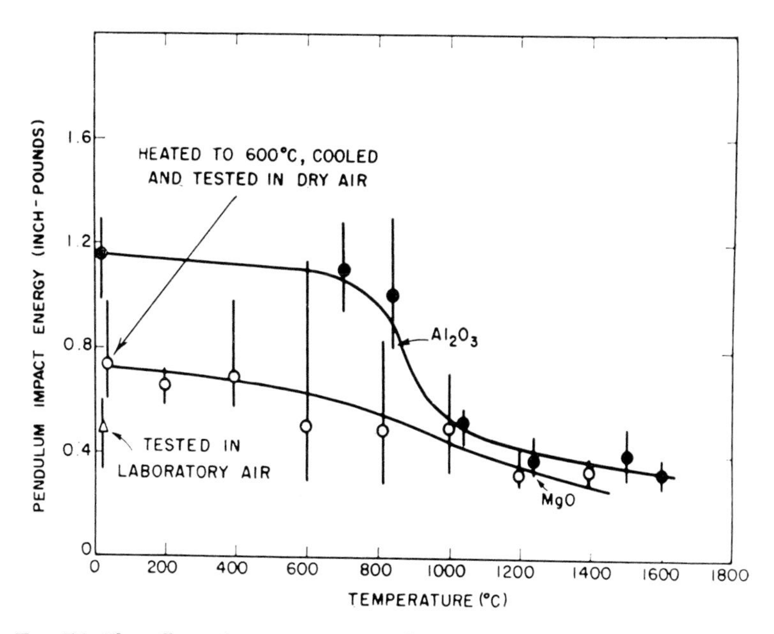

FIG. 57. The effect of temperature on the impact strength of sintered alumina (Kingery and Pappis, 52).

Experimentally, this conclusion has been verified by Siekmann (54) with O-30 tools on AISI 1045 normalized steel up to 18,000 fpm.

These conditions are far beyond those at which any other tool material can cut steel. The real significance of this discussion is that ceramics have capabilities in retaining strength at higher temperatures than cemented carbides, and any improvement in strength that is made will likely be retained at these temperatures. The largest benefits from this are in the future when machine tools are built to operate at higher speeds or in the hot machining of troublesome refractory alloys.

The point is that ceramic tools have potential applications at

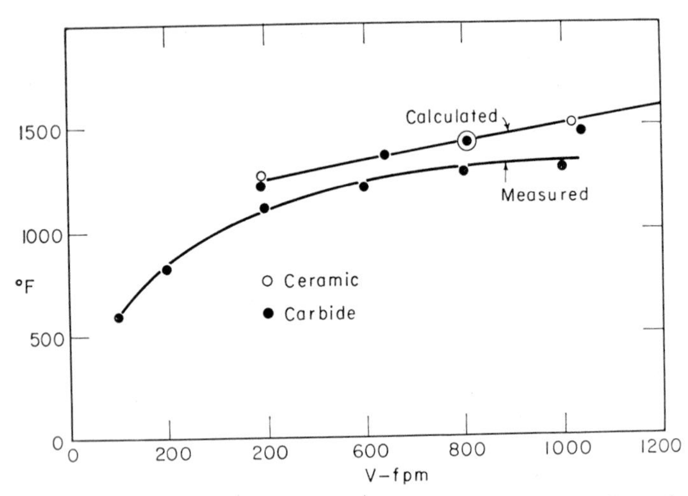

Fig. 58. Calculated and measured cutting temperatures. 1018 steel, 0.0052 inch/rev feed, 0.05-inch depth of cut (Cook, 53).

higher speeds and provide a motive for another surge of machine-tool research. The problems associated with rotating an off-balance work piece at higher speeds is likely to be more troublesome than developing a tool to cut at these speeds. The lack of degradation in strength or elasticity at high temperatures of alumina points to its use in machining where these high temperatures are involved.

Sapphire does not plastically deform at temperatures below about 900°C, according to Wachtman and Maxwell (55). Since this deformation involves only a one-slip system, a polycrystalline aggregate cannot deform even at temperatures higher than this unless other processes such as grain-boundary sliding, or creep are active. The importance of deformation processes in initiating crack nuclei is well established in metals, alkali halides, and MgO. The role of deformation leading to fracture in alumina is not yet clear. If this is a real problem in high-temperature strength of alumina, the solution to improve strength properties will most probably involve alloying with other materials to retard these deformation processes.

D. Strength and Pressure

The mechanical properties of materials under hydrostatic loading differ from those at atmospheric pressure. Bridgman has shown that strength can be increased and ductility enhanced, if testing is done under a superimposed hydrostatic high-pressure condition (56, 57). A tool tip-cutting steel is immersed in a plastic medium and subjected to high-pressure conditions on all of its surfaces in contact with the work piece. By using negative tool geometries these forces act inward upon the tool, placing it under compressive loading. Figure 59 shows schematically the restraining forces that act on the tool during cutting.

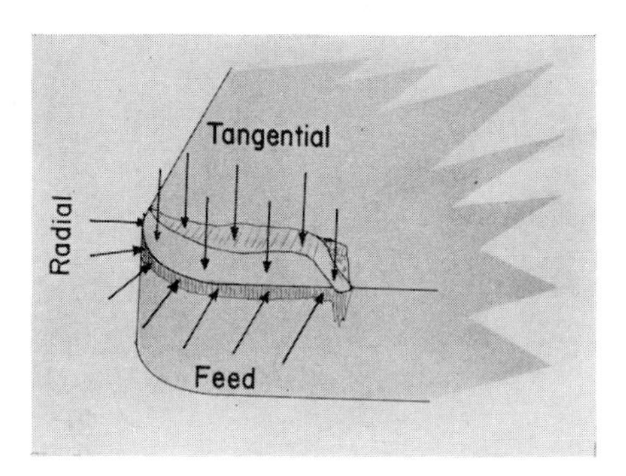

FIG. 59. Schematic view of tool tip subjected to restraining forces.

These compressive forces tend to retard crack formation in the tool and thereby increase its compressive strength beyond that measured in conventional test setups. Bridgman (56) has shown that the compressive strength of Pyrex increased from 20,000 to 670,000 psi when measured under a hydrostatic pressure of 400,000 psi. He has also reported a compressive strength of sapphire at 1,000,000 psi when supported by a hydrostatic load of 350,000 psi. Surprisingly, the compressive strength can be greater than the sum of the hydrostatic load and normal strength. There is a synergistic effect. This was not true for all of the materials Bridgman tested; but it does illustrate a potential enhancement of compressive strength if a material is restrained by lateral hydrostatic pressures. His research on brittle materials indicated that the surface condition affects the amount of increased strength, and here again we see a potential influence of surface finish on tool-bit properties.

One primary influence of hydrostatic loading is the greatly increased plasticity to the inhibition of cracks which would normally cause the specimen to fracture at lower stress levels, or at a smaller amount of distortion. One of the most striking results is that he was able to deform sapphire at room temperature (58). Figure 60 shows one of these crystals.

Ordinarily, sapphire will not deform below 900°C. The effect of hydrostatic pressure allows an increase in stress level without fracture to the point where deformation can occur at room temperature.

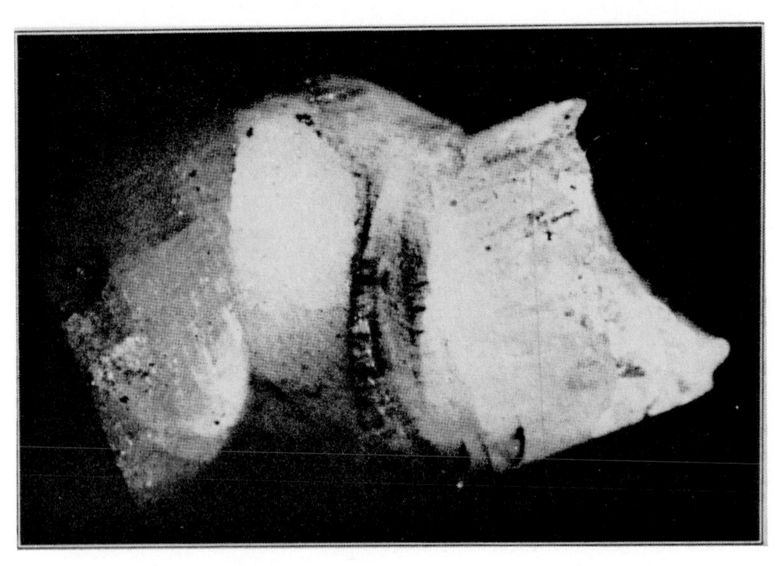

FIG. 60. A sapphire single crystal deformed at room temperature by a compressive stress with a superimposed hydrostatic pressure (Bridgman, 58).

In ceramic-tool usage the temperatures at which deformation processes can occur are somewhat lower than those normally expected. Since alumina normally has only one slip system, and it is a polycrystalline aggregate, the tool tip itself would not massively distort. Local distortions at free surfaces, however, could occur, and probably do occur, as will be shown later. These plastic-deformation processes are a source of wear and could lead to crack nucleation which ultimately causes tool failure.

Bridgman (57) has also shown that materials sheared under high-compressive loads will tolerate greatly increased distortions, without fracture, from those normally obtained. The metal sliding past the cutting-tool surface puts that surface under shearing stresses and the cutting forces superimpose a high-compressive load. Under these conditions the tool surface would be more apt to distort than it would at lesser loading stresses. This factor becomes pertinent in relation to wear phenomena discussed in greater detail in Chapter 5.

As the tool wears, the configuration of the cutting edge changes. While the total loading may not change appreciably, the distribution of these forces on the cutting tip can change. Figure 61 is a taper

FIG. 61. Section through the cutting edge of a used ceramic tool. 200 ×. The crater surface is cut at the top, the flank-wear land is the vertical surface cut by the section on the right.

section through a used ceramic tool which cut annealed 6150 steel at 1500 fpm.

Originally, the tip was square with a 0.006-inch wide land ground at an angle 60° to the top face. The taper section magnifies the curvatures actually produced. If we make the reasonable assumption that the force distribution is reflected in the wear pattern, greater forces occur short distances back from the cutting edge than at the edge. As wear progresses and the configuration changes the direction of these forces is altered. Due to elastic distortions in the tool, a tensile stress of increasing magnitude is produced which tends to produce cracks behind the cutting edge in the crater and below the cutting edge on the wear land. The propagation of these cracks will depend on the vectorial properties of the local forces on the tool tip. When dealing with brittle tool materials where the predominate failure mechanism is fracture, conventional machinability studies, relating tool forces, angles, friction, shear planes, and the like, do not adequately define the system to predict tool failure. Obviously, we are also concerned with pressure gradients on the cutting edge. The magnitude and distribution of these gradients is a function of cutting-edge geometry and machining parameters.

Commercial tools are offered with three-edge geometries: sharp, tumbled and rounded, and ground to an accurate-edge chamfer. Hand honing at the cutting edge is also a common practice. The best geometry for a particular application is that one which minimizes stresses and distributes these stresses so as to minimize fracture probability. This edge geometry is critical in some cases, such as in the machining of very hard steels. The detailed configuration and nature of the cutting edge can greatly affect tool life. For instance, the machinability test results were mentioned earlier for a 0.006-inch wide, 60° chemically polished chamfer where tool life was increased threefold. In this test the two effects of chamfering and polishing were tested independently and compared with a polished chamfer to determine their interaction. The cross section of the edge geometries are shown schematically in Fig. 62, drawn at 800 diameters magnification.

The machining tests were performed on AISI, Type A-6 tool steel hardened to Rc 52 at 1200 fpm, with 0.015-inch feed and 0.080-inch depth of cut. The results of these tests are shown in Table V, where the tool life in seconds is listed for 6 tests on each of the three-edge geometries.

The increase in tool life with the chemically polished lands is dramatic. This increase cannot be attributed to either the edge geometry or the chemical polish alone, but results from the combination of increased strength due to polishing and a more satisfactory distribution of stress due to edge geometry.

It should not be assumed that this geometry is by any means optimum. The shape of the wear surface on a tool, since it results from stress and temperature distribution and acts so as to relieve gradients, may be a better geometry with which to start. The difficulties of producing this geometry by conventional grinding techniques will probably preclude its usage. Some experiments with precision molding, using pressed-graphite-powder dies, have indicated

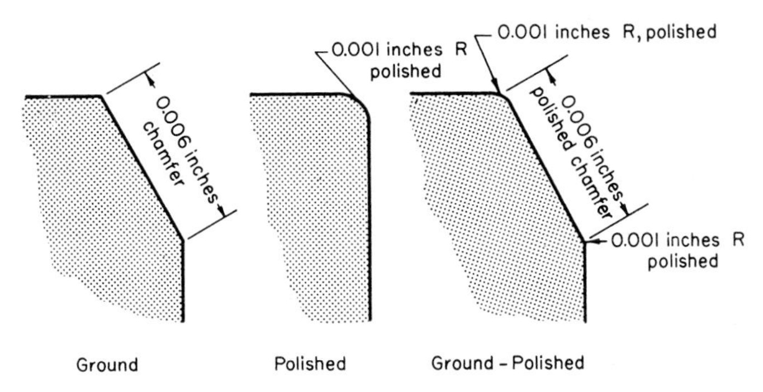

FIG. 62. Cutting-edge profiles, 800 ×.

a possible approach toward the solution of this problem. Some graphite powders will press into coherent objects, very near theoretical density, and retain, on the graphite, a faithful replica of the surface and shape of the mandrel around which it is pressed. These graphite pieces can then in turn be used as hot-molding dies for making alumina articles. Figure 63 is a photograph of an alumina specimen made by this technique.

TABLE V

TOOL LIFE WITH EDGE TREATMENT[a]

Ground chamfer	Chemical polish	Polished chamfer
53	57	267
66	106	116
116	78	404
90	27	188
76	51	167
117	62	193
Average 86	63	222

[a] Measured in seconds.

FIG. 63. Precision hot-molded specimen using pressed die technique.

This technique is by no means perfected; and commercial ceramic tools with novel-edge configurations are potential products of the future, rather than something in active development. Should such configurations become necessary by industry, potential methods of producing them can probably be developed.

E. Strength and Composition

Small amounts of impurities can have profound effects on the mechanical behavior of materials, as is evidenced by hydrogen embrittlement of steel, oxygen embrittlement of molybdenum, or by carbon in iron. Not only the type and amounts of impurities assume importance, but also the thermal and deformational history of the system have great influence on impurity controlled mechanical properties. The metallurgical development of heat-treatable alloys are evidence as to some of these factors.

Concerning ceramics, this type of study is in its infancy and any discussion of impurities on mechanical properties must be incomplete. The metallurgists have described phenomena which can occur in materials due to impurities. The ceramists have not yet applied this knowledge to ceramic systems, except in a few cases, and many of these are not directly pertinent to a discussion on ceramic tools. Still, the most attractive way to improve mechanical properties of ceramics is through detailed considerations of impurity content, distribution, and heat treatment.

Our own experience with ceramic tools indicated the necessity of starting with high-purity raw materials and following careful processing procedures to maintain this purity. Empirically, it was discovered that contamination was harmful to tool quality. This trend toward pure materials is true, of course, in metallurgy, where vacuum melting is assuming increasing importance and careful control of raw material composition is mandatory.

It is also true with mechanical characteristics of silicon and germanium semiconductors, where extremely small amounts of certain impurities weaken these materials drastically. Very pure defect free- and chemically polished-silicon massive single crystals have been reported to have tensile strengths up to 700,000 psi. Ordinarily, silicon is extremely brittle and notoriously weak and would not even be considered as an engineering structural material.

Satkiewicz (59) has shown that MgO crystals, containing about 0.5% Cr, have an impurity controlled yield point which is affected by an annealing heat treatment. The stress-strain diagrams for these materials are shown in Fig. 64.

The samples on the right portion of Fig. 64 were vacuum annealed at 1000°C prior to testing. This heat treatment precipitated a second phase in the crystals, which is thought to provide dislocation sources which are activated at lower stress levels, and hence the specimens show a twofold drop in yield point.

Ordinarily, pure MgO has a yield point of about 12 kg/mm. This yield point can be increased to 56 kg/mm by the addition of chromium and proper heat treatment.

The point is that ceramic systems have impurities and heat-treating behaviors related to those found in metals; therefore, alloying ceramics is a perfectly reasonable procedure in the attempt to improve mechanical properties.

Usually, impurity effects are related to such phenomena as yield point, precipitation hardening, dispersion hardening, phase changes, or creep processes. Since these processes are associated with deformation, and since the role of deformation in alumina as a crack nucleator is not known, the role of these processes is not yet clear in the strength of alumina ceramics.

Ryshkewitch has shown that solid solutions of chromium oxide in alumina are harder than pure alumina. Some early ceramic tools (Sintox) contained chromium in the attempt to improve tool hardness. Chromium has also been added to alumina abrasives for this purpose. Neither of these attempts were notably successful, since the

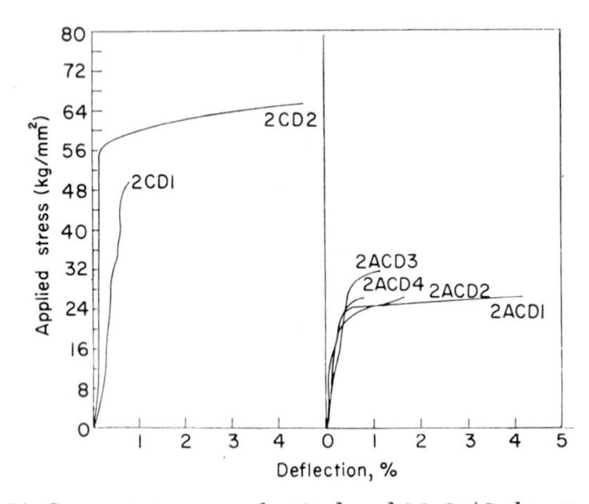

FIG. 64. Stress-strain curves for Cr-doped MgO (Satkiewicz, 59).

improvement was small and there was not a controlling parameter in service. The additives commonly incorporated in ceramic tools are more to control sintering and microstructure; they are not added specifically to increase strength beyond that obtained by a dense fine-grained material.

Cahoon and Christensen have found that soda is a harmful addition to alumina ceramics, through the formation of the beta alumina phase. Soda, empirically, has also been found to be harmful in ceramic tools and the soda content of VR97 is maintained well below 0.1%. Some experiments using thermally decomposed ammonium alum as an alumina source showed that residual sulfur in the powder can result in extremely brittle and weak tools.

Thus far, in our lack of adequate sophistication, pure alumina seems to work best with additions of only certain sintering and microstructural controls. Certain other impurities are deleterious and should be avoided in tool-bit manufacture. The deliberate alloying and heat-treatment procedures which likely will improve ceramic-tool performance are developments we must anticipate for the future.

Impurities can aggregate or disseminate in a solid solvent, depending upon solubilities and temperature. As was shown with chromium-doped MgO, by Satkiewicz, heat treatments can nucleate the impurities and cause precipitation. Second phases dispersed in a solid matrix can have large effects on mechanical properties; this fact is the basis of precipitation-hardening and dispersion-hardening techniques. Included solid particles can act as dislocation sources and increase ductility, or they can retard dislocation motion by pinning and decrease ductility. They can act as stress concentrators, because of different elastic properties than the matrix, and can introduce residual stresses because of differences in thermal expansion.

Electron microscopy of tool-bit-fracture surfaces has not disclosed the presence of precipitates within the alumina grains. The spinel ($MgO \cdot Al_2O_3$) that forms during fabrication of the CCT-707 and VR97 tools is present as separate grains. Differences of elastic modulus or thermal expansion between spinel and alumina could, under conditions of stress or nonequilibrium temperature, produce stresses within the tool. The thermal expansion of spinel and alumina are similar and stresses due to differential thermal expansion are not great.

At 1000°C Young's modulus for alumina is 3.22×10 kg/cm, while for spinel it is 1.6×10^6 kg/cm^2. An inclusion of spinel, surrounded by alumina under stress, will elastically distort more readily than the matrix. Since it will distort more readily than alumina, the inclusion will act similarly to a void (but less so) in concentrating stress

Whether or not these stress concentrations are sufficient to nucleate fractures is not known. If they are, then the size of the spinel inclusions would be of considerable importance in determining strength because of the Griffith theories.

This general subject of impurity and strength is currently an area of active research, with the really significant answers still unknown.

F. Strength Distribution

It is exceedingly difficult to manufacture objects which are perfectly clean or have perfect distributions of added impurities. Even if it were possible to start with ceramic powders, without concentration gradients in them, the act of sintering or hot pressing the powder by itself would result in the formation of concentration gradients by either differential sublimation or adsorption of furnace atmospheres. With concentration gradients of impurities a virtual certainty, strength distributions within a tool are not unexpected.

VR97 adsorbs furnace gases during hot pressing which give it a gray color. This color does not extend uniformly throughout the tool, as it does with the Carborundum CCT-707 material. In some cases (fortunately experimental), as many as six separate diffusion zones can be seen from the tool's outer surface to the center.

The rate of diffusion for each gaseous impurity through the porous alumina is different, and the visual presence of these zones is a chromatographic effect, reflecting these different rates. This should not be surprising as alumina is used by chemists in chromatographic columns for the separation of the different constituents in a solution.

A technique was developed to measure the strength distribution in such a material; it is based upon the presence of fractures accompanying Knoop microhardness indentations. This technique is similar to one developed by Palmour *et al.* (60). A rectangular matrix of Knoop indentations is made on the polished surface to be studied. Typically, the matrix is 20×20 indentations with a spacing of 100 microns between indentations.

Each indentation is observed under high magnification (the lighting is fairly critical), and the presence or absence of fractures is noted. The load on the indenter was chosen so that about half of the indentations fractured. A map of the matrix can now be contoured into areas with the same amounts of fracturing. The contour intervals relate fracture probability, under given and constant-loading conditions. Figure 65 is the fracture-probability map of a VR97 tool.

The top edge of the tool was as molded; normally about 0.015 inch is ground from this surface. The outstanding feature of the pattern is that an embrittled zone (high fracture probability) occurs about 0.020 inch in from the edge. The central part of the tool and the edge itself have significantly lower fracture probabilities.

Three visual zones appear in the material. The outer zone is black, very thin, and occurs by solid-state diffusion of carbon into the alumina. This zone roughly coincides with the strong outer skin. The middle zone is gray and coincides with the embrittled area. This zone probably results from gaseous diffusion of impurities into the alumina prior to densification. The solid-state-diffusion process has such low rates of mass transport that impurities could not be introduced to the depths of 0.040 inch as shown in Fig. 65, for the short time the sample was at significantly high temperatures. This gray zone can be excluded from the hot-pressed tool if a vapor barrier consisting of molybdenum or tantalum foil separates the alumina from the graphite. The inner zone is lighter gray and represents the pure alumina, without diffused impurities present. The central portions of the tool and the outer skin are significantly stronger than the middle zone.

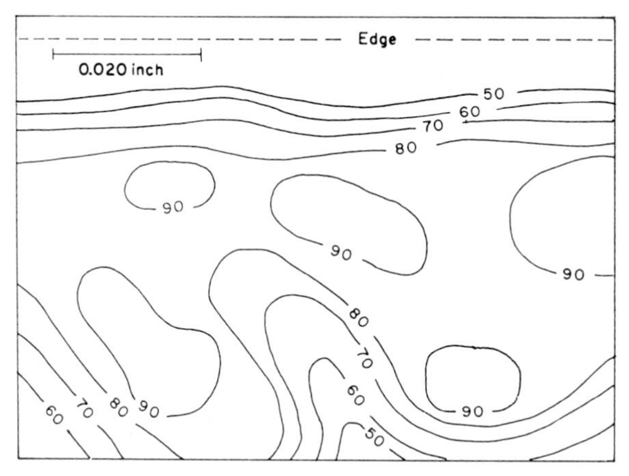

FIG. 65. Fracture probability contours on a section through a ceramic tool. The numbers refer to the percentage of indentations which fractured. Molded edge at the top.

An attempt was made to identify the impurities in the middle gray zone by spectrographic analysis. These analyses did not identify the impurities present. The gaseous species in a graphite furnace at about 1700°C will consist mainly of elements which ordinarily cannot be detected with the emission spectrograph, so the failure of this test was not surprising.

Figure 66 is another map of strength microdistribution on a similar tool, but with a more extensive matrix.

The pattern again shows an embrittled area about 0.025 inch in from the edge. It also shows a lack of homogeneity in the central portions that resisted our efforts to achieve uniform mixing. In this case, a high-strength protrusion extends about 0.040 inch into the weakened area. An embrittled spot occurs in the lower right corner, and may be due to a speck of included impurity. A spot like this on the cutting edge of the tool could easily lead to premature failure.

Another test was developed that is simpler to perform, and is based on impact abrasion of a sample surface. A high-velocity particle,

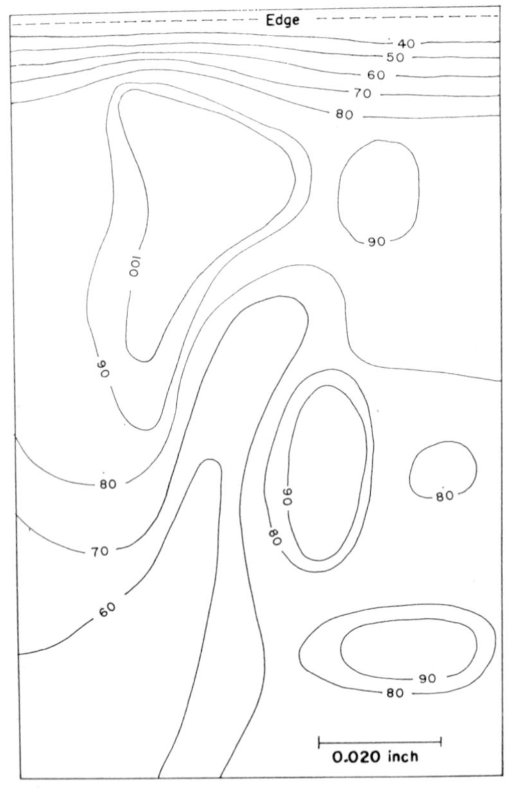

FIG. 66. Fracture probability contours showing a considerable lack of homogeneity in a carefully prepared specimen. Molded edge at the top.

impinging on the surface of a brittle material, removes pieces from the surface by a fracture process. The amount of material removed is in some way related to the strength of the material. In a sense, an impact abrasion process is, then, a relative strength test.

The test is performed by impinging a stream of fine alumina powder and water, driven with compressed air, onto the surface of the tool. The process is similar to grit blasting, except water is used as a vehicle. The configuration of the abraded surface is measured with a toolmaker's microscope, by a traverse across the tool, measuring at each point the depth of the surface below an arbitrary reference plane. The depth is simply measured by focusing onto the surface and recording this position on the vertical dial indicator which is connected with the focusing mechanism. A plot of the depth against lateral traverse gives an indication of the internal abrasion resistance across the tool. Such a plot is given in Fig. 67.

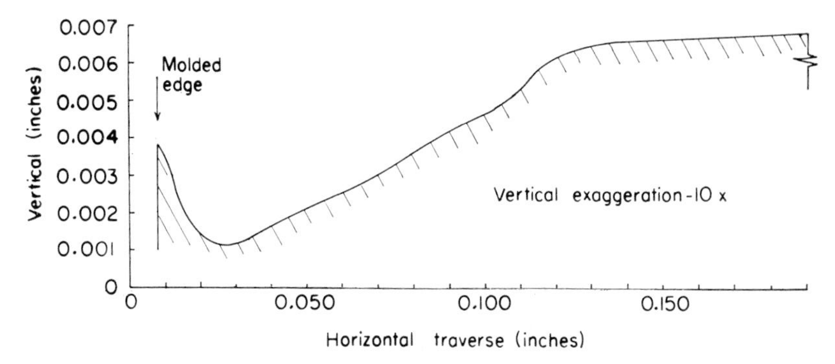

FIG. 67. Surface profile which developed on a ceramic tool due to abrasion.

Essentially, the same features are shown here as were shown in previous graphs. The edge of the tool is strong although it has a weakened zone between this edge and the central zone. The size of the weakened zone, in this case, is broader because this particular sample had greater permeability to the furnace gases. It would seem that our reasoning as to this test's validity is at least partially vindicated. The primary purpose, however, of this discussion is to afford the opportunity to present the following result.

In a number of cases, black spots were present in the section surface, indicating the inadvertent presence of contamination, probably carbon. Traverses were made across these inclusions—one example is shown in Fig. 68.

The surprising result is the presence of the moat around the hard spot. We must have one of two conditions in order to produce this result: The strength of alumina is strongly controlled by impurity concentration, being higher at high concentrations and weaker than pure alumina at low concentrations; when two impurities diffused at different rates from the contaminate particle, the slower strengthened the alumina and the faster weakened it. The identity of these impurities was not established. Topographical features of this type were not uncommon and were not always accompanied by visible inclusions.

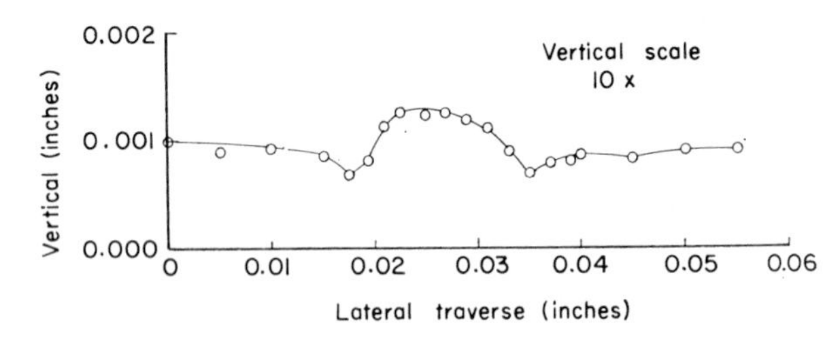

FIG. 68. Surface profile across an inclusion, abraded tool sample.

Certainly, impurities can have considerable effects on the mechanical properties of alumina tools. The control of these impurities is necessary to produce the high-quality ceramics required by tool engineers.

G. Strength and Initial Tool Wear

In Chapter 1 data was presented in Fig. 18 which indicated a reasonably good correlation between compressive strength and the degree of wear. The apparent explanation of this correlation is that the initial wear is by a crushing process which develops a flat surface with sufficient area to withstand the loading forces to which it is being subjected. The size of this initial surface should be related to the compressive strength of the tool.

This wear surface is analogous to the controlled-flank-area investigations of Kobayashi and Thomsen (61) and can be treated in the same manner. If the assumption is accepted that the size of the wear surface is a simple function of compressive strength, then it is possible to calculate the relative amounts of force which are proportioned to friction and which bear on the initial-wear surface and then to make a sizable correction in the calculated coefficient of friction.

The coefficient of friction in orthogonal cutting is expressed by the following relation (62):

$$\mu = (F_t + F_c \tan X)/(F_c + F_t \tan X)$$

where $\mu =$ coefficient of friction; $F_t =$ thrust force; $F_c =$ cutting force; and $X =$ rake angle.

By our reasoning, and following that of Kobayashi and Thomsen (61) or that of Albrecht (63) in his considerations of metal plowing, the thrust force F_t as measured with a tool-post dynamometer must be divided between that portion bearing on the flank-wear land and that portion which is due to chip-tool friction. Only the latter is pertinent to the calculation.

From Table III in Chapter 1, an average width of the "*B*" intercept is about 3 mils, and with a depth of cut of 0.080 inch the projected area of this initial wear surface is approximately 25×10^{-5} square inches. An average compressive strength is about 4×10^5 psi for all of the materials tested, and therefore the force which formed this surface by crushing the cutting edge is about 100 pounds. The feed force in this cutting experiment varied from 170 to 240 pounds, with an average taken at 200 pounds. Only about half of the total feed force is utilized in the frictional drag of the chip across the tool crater. The other half is utilized in compressing the flank-wear surface during the initial stages of cutting. Appropriate corrections in the calculation of coefficient of friction are compared with the result obtained without this correction as follows:

$$\mu = \frac{200 - 320\,(-\tan 5^\circ)}{320 - 200\,(-\tan 5^\circ)} = 0.51 \qquad \text{uncorrected}$$

$$\mu = \frac{100 - 320\,(-\tan 5^\circ)}{320 - 100\,(-\tan 5^\circ)} = 0.22 \qquad \text{corrected}$$

The measurements of friction coefficient which we made under conditions of sliding speeds, temperatures, and pressures, which approached those in metal cutting, yielded values between 0.17 and 0.24. The corrected value of 0.22 that was calculated from the cutting experiments is a more reasonable value than 0.51 which was obtained without the correction. We are assuming that the lack of orthogonal cutting conditions does not introduce a significantly large error.

The implication of this is that the crushing hypothesis is quantitatively reasonable and introduces a correction of the proper magnitude for computing the coefficient of friction or other parameters involving the thrust force.

Chapter 4

Properties of the Ceramic and Tool Usage

Physical properties other than strength also contribute to ceramic tool utility. Strength was considered separately in the previous chapter because of the extensive nature of the discussion. In this chapter the properties of hardness, chemical reactivity, frictional characteristics, and thermal shock are examined and their pertinence to ceramic tools is discussed.

A. Hardness

Hardness is a physical property which is easier to measure than to understand. Hardness is not a single property by itself, but depends upon a number of more basic properties such as strength of chemical bonding, crystal structure, and plastic deformation. Hardness values are relative and thereby depend upon the method of testing, such as those of Rockwell, Vickers, Brinell, Knoop, or Mohs. The first four of these tests depend on the penetration of a pyramid or ball into the test piece under controlled loading. Mohs' hardness depends upon the ability of one substance to scratch another. Each of these tests has its usefulness and in general the Knoop hardness measurement is preferred for hard, brittle ceramic materials. The Knoop indenter produces an elongated diamond-shaped depression in the sample. The hardness is calculated by measuring the length of the indentation with a microscope. This test is preferred on very hard materials because the length of the indentation is more sensitive to changes in hardness than the length of the more regular shape, such as a Vickers pyramid. The Knoop method also produces less chipping on hard materials. Thibault and Nyquist (64) and Tarasov and Thibault

(65) extended the usefulness of the test for these measurements on ceramics and defined the factors pertaining to obtaining measurements on ceramics. In order to give meaning to Knoop values, Table VI listing the Knoop hardness of various materials appears below.

TABLE VI

KNOOP HARDNESS DETERMINED AT 100-G LOAD FOR VARIOUS HARD SUBSTANCES[a]

	Knoop number 100 load (K_{100})	
Substance	*Average*	*Range*
Primary boron carbide (Norbide)[b]	2800	2670–2940
Molded boron carbide (Norbide)	2760	2580–2900
Gray silicon carbide (regular Crystolon)[b]	2460	2250–2680
Gray silicon carbide (regular Crystolon) (check)	2550	2320–2760
Green silicon carbide (green Crystolon)	2480	2230–2740
Green silicon carbide (green Crystolon) (check)	2480	2130–2620
Titanium carbide	2470	2350–2620
Tungsten titanium carbide	2190	2050–2320
Alpha aluminum oxide (38 Alundum)[b]	2050	1860–2200
Alpha aluminum oxide (synthetic boule)	1950	1680–2100
Primary (unbonded) tungsten carbide (WC)	1880	1570–2140
Cemented carbide (Kennametal K6)[b]	1800	1700–1940
Ceramic tool VR97[c]	1650	— —
Cemented carbide (Kennametal KM)[b]	1500	1390–1600
Cemented carbide (Kennametal K12)[b]	1410	1280–1500
Garnet (Barton Mines, New York)	1360	1240–1440
Topaz (Thomas Range, Utah)	1340	1240–1500
Synthetic blue spinel (Linde)	1270	1190–1460
Quartz	820	760–880
Hardened tool steel, Rockwell C-60.5	740	730–760

[a] Random crystal orientation. From Thibault and Nyquist (64)
[b] Trademarks.
[c] Added to table from later measurements.

One basic requirement of a cutting tool is that it must be harder than the material being cut. As can be seen from the table, aluminum oxide is considerably harder than cemented carbides and this is to its advantage. The hardness value for the VR97 ceramic is intermediate between the hard and soft grades of cemented carbide. The hardness shown here is lower than that shown by a single-crystal boule. Intergranular cracking of the polycrystalline ceramic allows the indenter to penetrate more deeply into the ceramic tool than it does for the single crystal, where grain boundaries are not available. This differential hardness would not be as noticeable if the loading method did not result in intergranular cracking or yielding. In terms of wear resistance where the loads are generally less concentrated than they are in hardness testing, the single-crystal hardness would be a more accurate estimate of the materials durability. This is not as true for cemented carbide because of the higher tensile strength or relatively stronger intercrystalline bonding.

Early hardness investigations on VR97 tools (66) disclosed that hardness was variable depending on the temperature at which the material was hot pressed (Fig. 69).

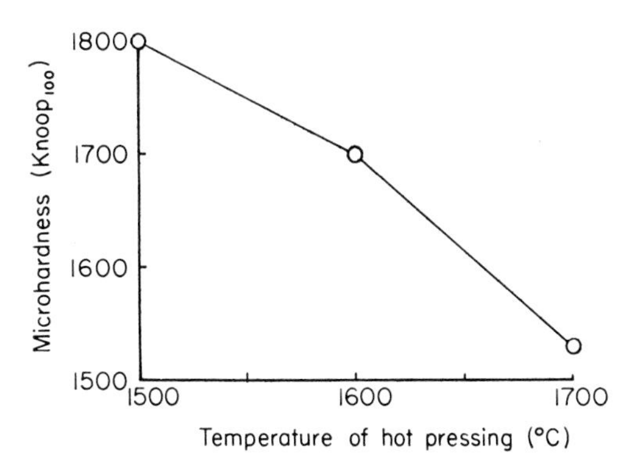

FIG. 69. Hardness variation with hot-pressing temperature. All hardness measurements were made at room temperature.

In general, the values are somewhat lower than those of single-crystal sapphire, and the hardness increases with lower hot-pressing temperatures. This increase is due to the finer microstructures developed at lower temperatures. As was shown earlier the brittleness of these harder materials also increased, so that the selection of a proper tool material depended on the relative merits of these two properties and an effective compromise needed to be established.

Metcalfe's data (67) shows the relation of hardness with temperature on several cutting-tool materials (Fig. 70). The particular ceramic tool in these data is G.E.'s O-30. Other ceramics would show similar curves where the hardness advantage is maintained at elevated temperatures. Since the temperature of the tool edge increases with cutting speed, the ceramic would again be expected to function at higher speeds than other materials. This has been found to be true.

The process of making a microhardness indentation requires that material under the diamond point is laterally displaced. This displacement is accomplished by plastic deformation of the material being tested. Brittle materials will flow under these high-pressure

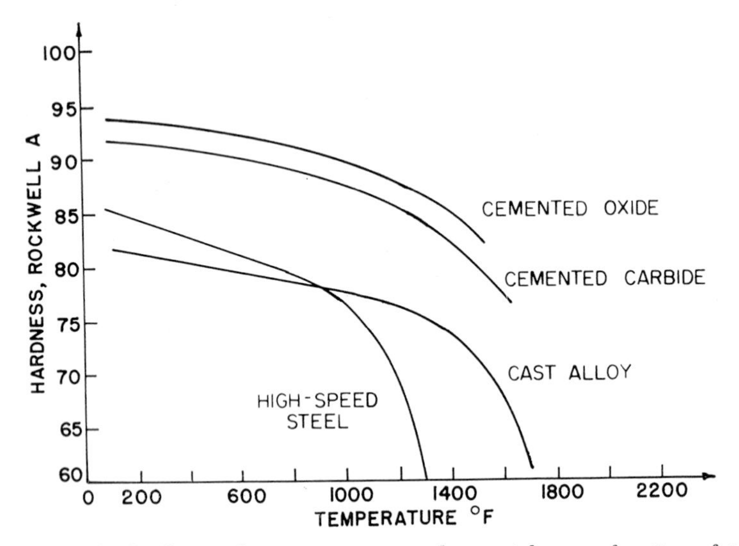

FIG. 70. The hardness of various cutting-tool materials as a function of temperature (Metcalfe, 67).

conditions because the indenter has a force component which tends to place the material under restraining pressures. As we have seen earlier, aluminum oxide will plastically deform under these conditions.

Ryshkewitch (27) has shown that an actual chip can be cut from sapphire using a diamond-tool point in exactly the same way a metal chip can be cut. Figure 71 shows such a chip.

It is not uncommon to see fracture-free Knoop indentations in a normally brittle material like aluminum oxide. Since the indentation is elongated, the hardness value measured is a function of the orientation of the crystal with the long axis of the indenter. It is not uncommon to see a systematic variety of hardness values on crystals, depending on which plane is tested and which direction is chosen on that plane. This is reasonable, of course, as the slip planes in the crystal will be more favorably oriented to receive maximum shear stress in certain directions than they would be in others. In testing a fine-grained dense material like a ceramic tool, the indentation length transects about ten or so crystallites and the measurement represents an average value.

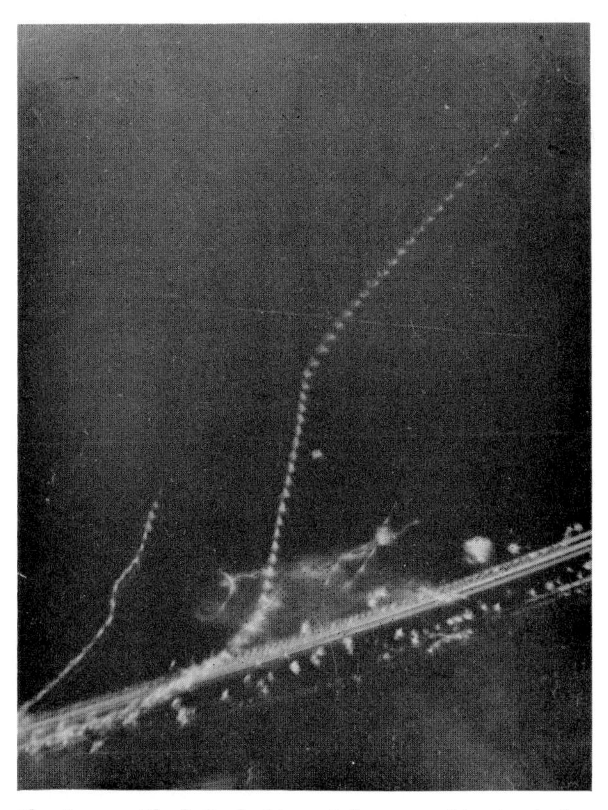

FIG. 71. Aluminum-oxide helical chip cut from sapphire boule by a diamond point (Ryshkewitch, 27).

Some hot-pressed ceramics show tendencies for the individual crystallites to line up in the same direction. Where this occurs, the "average" value obtained by the microhardness indentation will vary slightly depending upon the direction of this preferred orientation with the sample surface.

Aluminum oxide is a hard material because it is dense, has high-bond strengths, and does not have a variety of slip systems available by which it can deform. The crystal structure consists approximately of closely packed layers of oxygen atoms with small aluminum atoms placed in the holes between layers. This arrangement leads to a high density of 4 g/cm^3 which is high when compared with the low

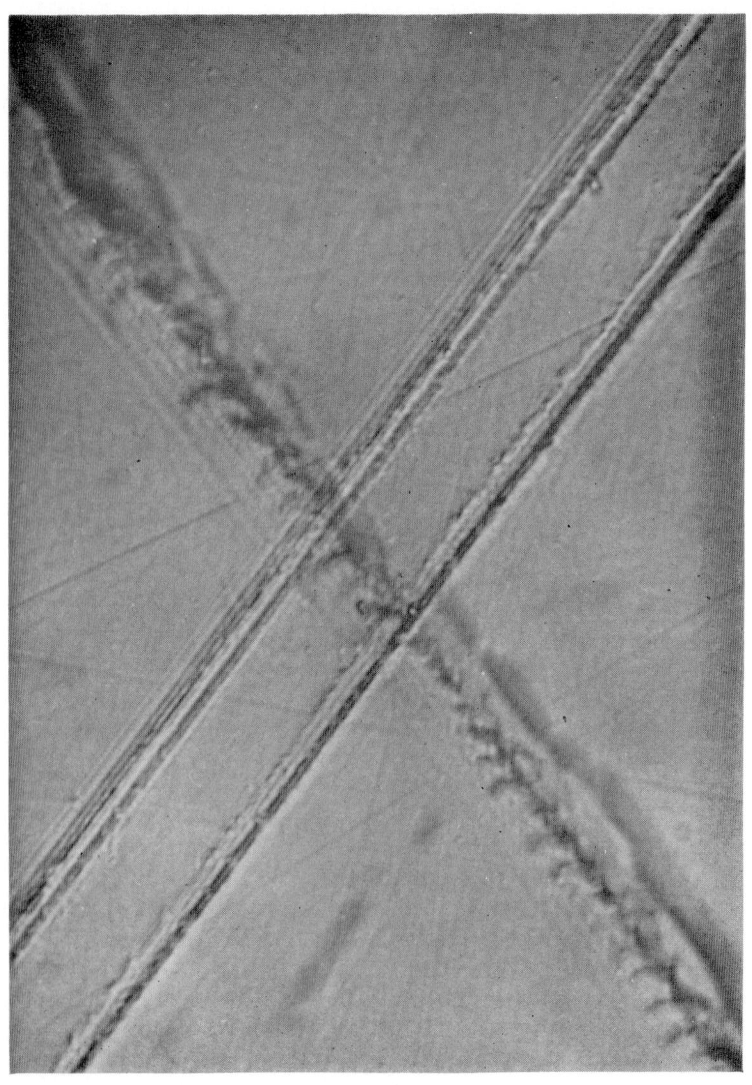

FIG. 72. Scratch in sapphire made by a harder ruby (Ryshkewitch, 27).

atomic weights of the atoms involved, and to other oxides, such as MgO and SiO_2. Aluminum metal has a very great affinity for oxygen and each of these bonds requires a large force to separate the atoms. The presence or absence of slip bands in a crystal is property dependent on the crystal structure. Alumina is so arranged that only one-slip system is easily available for deformation. There is no way to deform a randomly oriented polycrystalline aggregate utilizing a single-slip system because adjacent crystallites cannot compensate for changes of shape without forming accompanying voids. Alumina, then, is hard because it has lots of chemical bonds, each of them is strong, and they are arranged so they cannot easily move relative to each other. The hardness and the retention of this hardness at high temperatures depends on composition and structure, and is a basic property of the phase.

The hardness of a substance can be varied by either changing its structure or by changing its composition. In Fig. 72, Ryshkewitch (27) shows the increased hardness of ruby ($Cr_2O_3 \cdot Al_2O_3$ solid solution) over sapphire by a scratch test.

Hardness can also be varied by incorporating other phases dispersed in the matrix so that under stress the resultant inhomogeneities interact so as to interfere with the deformation process. These are the bases of alloying, dispersion-hardening, and precipitation-hardening processes in metals, and account for some compositions of available ceramic tools wherein attempts have been made to increase durability.

B. Chemical Reactivity

Aluminum oxide is a very stable compound and does not readily react with other materials even at elevated temperatures. The specific reactions of concern to ceramic tools are those between the tool material and the atmosphere, and those between the tool material and the metal.

Most ceramic tools are fully oxidized, and therefore do not react with air at high temperatures. This is not true of the G.E. O-30 tool which contains TiO and can be further oxidized to TiO_2. General Electric's data sheet (68) on O-30 indicates that a thin layer of oxidized material will form on the surface after prolonged heating at 1000°C, and that oxidation is rapid at 1500°C. Microstructural studies on G.E. O-30 indicate that the alumina is the continuous phase and surrounds the TiO particles. For the TiO to oxidize internally it is necessary to diffuse oxygen through the alumina grains or along grain boundaries, and this is a slow process. The TiO at the surface would oxidize more rapidly. A satisfactory tool life is a much shorter interval than that required for appreciable oxidation, and the G.E. O-30 tool is capable of cutting operations at very high speeds without difficulty.

If chemical reactions occur between the tool material and the work piece, tool life will suffer accordingly by an accelerated-wear process. Whether or not these reactions occur is dependent first on the chemistry, and second on the temperature. Metcalfe has listed the welding-on temperatures of various actual and possible tool materials to iron, as shown in Table VII.

TABLE VII

WELDING ON TEMPERATURES BETWEEN STEEL AND HARD PARTICLES[a]

Particle	Welding-on temperature (°F)
Chromium boride	2250
Titanium boride	2250
Zirconium boride	2250
Tungsten carbide	2400
Titanium carbide	2500
Aluminum boride	2600
Alumina	over 2800

[a] From Metcalfe (67).

These temperatures were determined by heating the tool material with iron and observing the lowest temperature at which a melt formed. Tungsten carbide and iron form a melt at 2400°F, which upon solidification, forms a strong weld. Metcalfe points out that these welds that occur at high machining temperatures would cause pieces of the tool to be pulled out resulting in accelerated wear. This argument is reasonable on the basis of wear theory (see Chapter 5), where local temperatures between two sliding objects approach the melting point of the lower-melting phase. The actual temperatures at which welding occurs during machining will be different from those shown in Table VII for two reasons.

First, the two surfaces in machining are pressed together with very high-unit pressures which promote bonding, and second, the process of cutting generates a fresh, clean surface without absorbed films, which could either interfere with, or enhance the bonding process. The alumina test indicated that no bonding occurred at the melting point of iron. This result is validated by machining experiments where under severe conditions the iron chips contained a large percentage of molten droplets which solidified into small spheres, without observable evidence of bonding with the tool.

Ryshkewitch states that alumina is inert to manganese and metals of the iron group (iron, cobalt, nickel); therefore, alumina can be used for crucibles for the melting of these metals in nonoxidizing atmospheres. These metals do not wet the crucible and the metals are not contaminated by the alumina container. Economos and Kingery (69) have investigated the reactions between various metals and oxides to 1800°C by heating them in contact in an inert atmosphere. The system $Ni \cdot Al_2O_3$ did not react at temperatures up to 1800°C. Metals of the second periodic group (Be, Mg) can react with aluminum oxide. The system:

$$3\ Be + Al_2O_3 \rightarrow 2\ Al + 3\ BeO$$

has a free energy of reaction calculated to be —54 kcal. Beryllium can be melted in aluminum oxide crucibles with only a gray discoloration forming in the crucible. Ryshkewitch points out that chrysoberyl ($BeO \cdot Al_2O_3$), which forms on the crucible, could inhibit further reaction. Economos and Kingery found a well-defined reaction layer of chrysoberyl at 1800°C. In the case of machining beryllium, this layer would continuously be removed by abrasion and rapid tool-wear rates would be expected. Magnesium metal reduces alumina at about 900°C and tool wear could be rapid if temperatures in this range are achieved during machining.

The only element in the third group likely to be encountered in machining is aluminum. Ryshkewitch lists the reaction:

$$4\ Al + Al_2O_3 = 3\ Al_2O$$

which occurs at temperatures between 1100°C and 1500°C.

The oxide film which forms on aluminum metal is very tenacious and indicates that Al_2O_3 and Al can form a strong bond. Because of the reactivity and bonding between Al and Al_2O_3, ceramic tools might not be as efficient as other materials in the machining of aluminum alloys. One manufacturer does not recommend ceramics for machining aluminum bronze.

In the fourth periodic group appear the elements C, Ti, and Zr. Carbon and alumina have a eutectic-melting point at about 1840°C. The two phases Al_2O_3 and Al_4O_4C are stable below this eutectic. Ceramic tools have been used successfully for machining carbon and graphite with excellent tool life. This would seem to indicate that temperatures high enough for this reaction do not occur. The carbon content of ferrous alloys would, on this basis, not be expected to cause rapid wear. Molten titanium metal attacks alumina at 1725°C. There are very few oxides that can resist the reactivity of titanium metal. Titanium paper weights, resting on glass desk tops, bond to the glass and produce scratches when moved. Titanium hydride is used for metallizing alumina ceramics prior to brazing. Economos and Kingery list a slight reaction between titanium and zirconium and alumina at 1400°C with corrosion developing at 1600°C. It is not surprising that ceramic tools are not recommended for machining titanium metal.

The fifth group of elements (V, Nb, Ta), according to Ryshkewitch, do not react with alumina in the temperature range 1650–1700°C. Economos and Kingery's experiments showed that no reaction between Nb and Al_2O_3 occurs up to 1800°C. Similarly the sixth group (Cr, Mo, W) does not react and, on the basis of chemical compatibility, should be satisfactorily machined by ceramic tools. Successes in machining tungsten have been reported. Chromium in a mildly oxidizing atmosphere will bond to alumina through the solid solution of Cr_2O_3 and Al_2O_3. The formation of $Cr \cdot Al_2O_3$ cermets is promoted by small amounts of oxidation.

TABLE VIII

CERAMIC TOOL COMPATIBILITY CHART[a]

Nickel[b]	Silver
Cobalt	Copper
Gray cast irons	Aluminum
Steels and inoculated cast irons	Beryllium
Lead	Titanium

[a] From Shaw and Smith (70).

[b] Arranged in order of excellence—from excellent to poor, starting from top of first column.

Shaw and Smith (70) have prepared a ceramic-tool compatibility chart on a variety of metals.

This listing roughly parallels the expected results on the basis of metal·Al_2O_3 reactions, and roughly parallels machining experience. The chart is not meant to imply that a metal toward the bottom of the list cannot be machined by ceramics, but rather that the relative efficiency is less. For example, ceramic tools have excellent tool life machining copper up to 2000 fpm, as determined by actual use.

Duwell and McDonald (71) list various hard materials and their rate of wear on mild steel and gray cast iron. Their data are produced in Table IX.

These data were collected on abrasive grits but are pertinent to machining with the same materials fabricated into more massive shapes. It can be seen from the table that alumina is more wear resistant on steel than any of the other hard materials, excluding diamond. This resistance to wear is attributed to its hardness and

TABLE IX

RATE OF WEAR OF VARIOUS MATERIALS[a]

Mineral	Metal	Hardness (Knoop)	Wear rate (mm^3/kg km)
1. Al_2O_3	Steel	2100	0.002–0.01
2. SiC	Steel	2480	0.01–0.05
3. $Al_2O_3 \cdot {}_3FeO \cdot {}_3SiO_2$ garnet	Steel	1360	0.054–0.066
4. SiO_2 (flint)	Steel	820	0.12–0.13
5. $Al_2O_3 \cdot Fe_3O_4$ (emery)	Steel	1400	0.055–0.075
6. ZrO_2	Steel	1160	0.01–0.085
7. B (crystalline)	Steel	2900	0.06–0.105
8. WC	Steel	1880	0.017–0.084
9. C (diamond)	Steel	7000	0.0010–0.002
10. TiC	Steel	2470	0.1
11. ZrC	Steel	2100	0.1
12. AlB_{12}	Steel	3500	0.12
13. B_4C	Steel	2750	0.08–0.14
14. BP	Steel	—	0.14–0.18
15. ZrB_x	Steel	—	0.04–0.08
16. TiB_x	Steel	—	0.02–0.05
17. Al_2O_3	Gray cast iron	2100	0.0017–0.0039
18. SiC	Gray cast iron	2480	0.0006
19. B (crystalline)	Gray cast iron	2900	0.26
20. C (diamond)	Gray cast iron	7000	0.00013

[a] From Duwell and McDonald (71).

to its lack of chemical reactions with either the steel or the atmosphere. The latter reactions would cause rapid breakdown of alumina.

C. Friction

In orthogonal cutting, two main forces act on the chip—the frictional force of the chip sliding over the tool, and the normal force pressing the chip against the tool. These two forces will be counterbalanced by forces within the tool tip. The coefficient of friction between the tool and metal being cut will be determined by the ratio of these two forces. Or to phrase it differently, the frictional force will be determined by the product of the normal force and the coefficient of friction.

The frictional force produced by an object sliding over another will in part be determined by the materials from which these objects are made. The most important case for this discussion is the sliding of steel on alumina. Duwell (72) studied the effect of crystallographic orientation of sapphire on wear rates calculated from sliding on steel. In the course of this study, a relationship was discovered between the coefficient of friction and the rate of wear, which was in turn determined by the orientation of the sapphire. His data are shown in Fig. 73.

Duwell attributes this correlation to formations of greater areas of contact between the sapphire and steel at higher wear rates. These formations result in increased frictional forces. In a randomly oriented polycrystalline aggregate the coefficient of friction should assume an intermediate value.

Our measurements of the coefficient of friction of ceramic tools (VR97) on soft steel were taken under conditions similar to those produced in metal cutting at Watertown Arsenal. A ⅛-inch-diameter rod of tool-bit material was pressed against a revolving steel disk. The two forces were measured with a tool-post dynamometer calibrated specifically for this configuration.

Sliding speeds of 1500 fpm and loading pressures up to 72,400 psi were used in the test. Under these conditions the tool specimen became red hot. At 72,400 psi the coefficient of friction was 0.17, and at 47,000 psi the coefficient was 0.24. These values are intermediate between the extremes of Duwell's data (72).

Coffin (73) has measured the coefficient of friction of sapphire on nickel in a variety of atmospheres. His values range from 3.0 to

0.55 depending on the atmosphere with the higher values occurring in strongly oxidizing environments. He also measured friction on Au, Ag, Pt, and Rh with values averaging about 0.5.

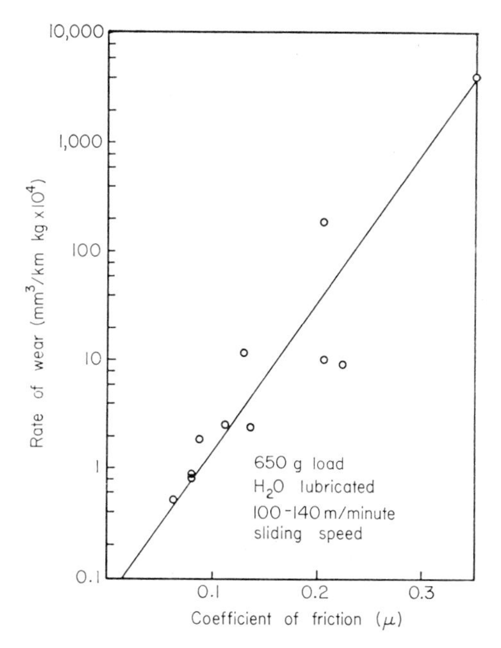

FIG. 73. Rate of wear of sapphire versus coefficient of friction sliding on steel (Duwell, 72).

Machlin and Yankee (74) measured the coefficient of friction of titanium and copper against alumina with values of 0.4 to 0.6 for titanium and 0.35 to 0.55 on copper.

D. Thermal Shock

A cutting tool as it enters or leaves the work is subjected to mechanical and thermal shock. The resistance to mechanical shock is determined by the strength of the tool. The resistance of the tool to thermal shock is determined by a number of physical properties and according to Schwartz (75) the expression:

$$K^1 = \frac{2S\,(1 - \nu)}{EX}\ (^\circ\text{C})$$

determines the resistance to thermal shock of a given material, where

K^1 = physical property factor
S = tensile strength
ν = Poisson's ratio
E = modulus of elasticity
X = linear coefficient of thermal expansion

In addition to the physical property factor K^1, a shape factor is involved in determining the thermal-stress resistance of a particular object. This will be constant, of course, for a particular shape.

As we saw in an earlier section, the strength S and the modulus E vary with temperature and the variation of thermal-stress resistance correspondingly will be expected to vary with temperature. Figure 74 shows Schwartz's data on thermal-stress behavior of alumina with temperature, where Q is the heat flow per unit mean area per length (75). The curves in the Fig. 74 represent values calculated from physical properties and the points represent the conditions where thermal-stress fracture occurred on actual tests.

The thermal stress resistance for alumina drops with temperature to about 1300°C and then rises with higher temperatures. The points in Fig. 74 were determined experimentally and the curve predicted

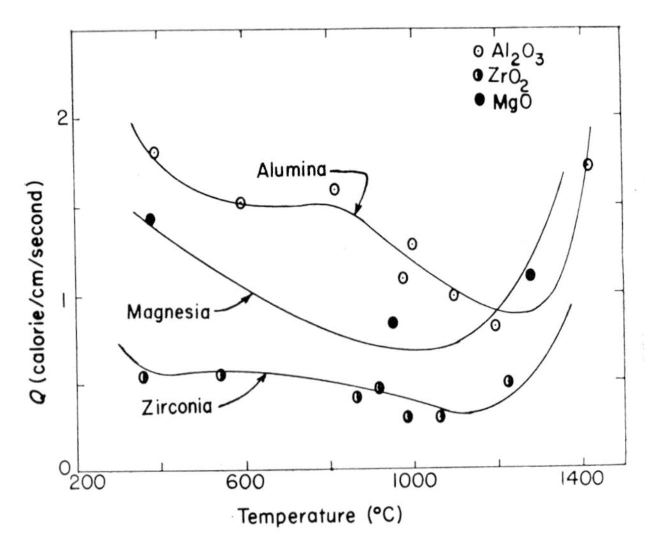

FIG. 74. Thermal-stress fracture resistance at steady state of refractory materials (Schwartz, 75).

from measured physical properties. The agreement is excellent. Schwartz attributes the rise in thermal-stress resistance to plasticity developed at the higher temperatures. Table X compares the pertinent physical properties of Carboloy ceramic and carbide tools.

TABLE X

THERMAL SHOCK RESISTANCE OF CERAMIC AND CEMENTED CARBIDE TOOLS

	Physical properties (25°C)				
	S(psi)	V	E	X	K^1
Ceramic tools (0–30)	90,000	0.25	58	3.40	685
Cemented carbide (883)	215,000	0.212	88	2.78	1420
Ratio					
$\frac{K^1 \text{ ceramic}}{K^1 \text{ carbide}} = 0.48$					

By this method of computation the thermal-shock resistance of the O-30 ceramic tool is about half the value of Carboloy-cemented carbide, grade 883. In a machining application where entry or exit failures are encountered, the relatively poor thermal-shock resistance of the ceramic may well be a contributing factor. Since a shape factor also enters into the equations defining thermal-stress resistance, a change of tool geometry or angle of approach may alter tool performance under these conditions.

The thermal-stress resistance of ceramics can best be improved by increasing the tensile strength. Further strength increases should increase ceramic tool utility in intermittent cuts where thermal shock is extreme. The tool engineer can best minimize thermal-shock failure of the tool tip by altering the tool geometry.

Coble and Kingery (76) measured the thermal-stress resistance of alumina by Schwartz's method as a function of porosity. Figure 75 summarizes their conclusions.

As can be seen from Fig. 75, the thermal-stress resistance increases rapidly with the denser specimens and again points out the justification for high-density ceramic tools.

E. Effects of Temperature on Microstructure

If a ceramic tool is reheated to a high temperature, changes in microstructure can occur. These changes will have an effect on the

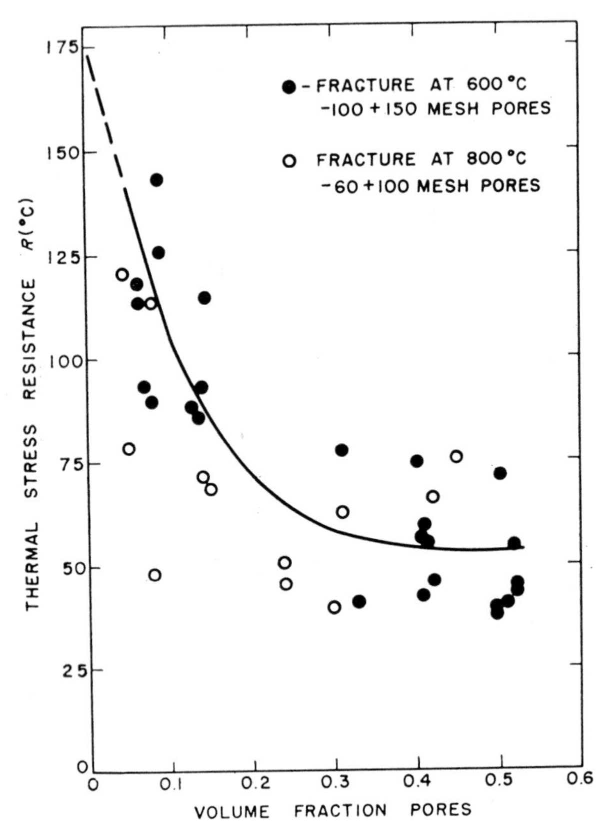

FIG. 75. The thermal-shock resistance of alumina with porosity (Coble and Kingery, 76).

physical properties of the tool material. Fortunately, the temperatures encountered during normal high-speed machining are not high enough to effect these changes. Some experiments of interest were made by us to study some of these phenomena. They are not so directly pertinent to machining practices today as they are to possible machining practices in the future.

Grain growth in VR97 did not occur when the tools were reheated to 1500°C. Figure 76 shows the microstructures before and after annealing and it is evident that grain growth has not occurred.

Experimental tools with a 1-micron grain size did show extensive grain growth upon annealing at 1500°C. These microstructures are shown in Fig. 77.

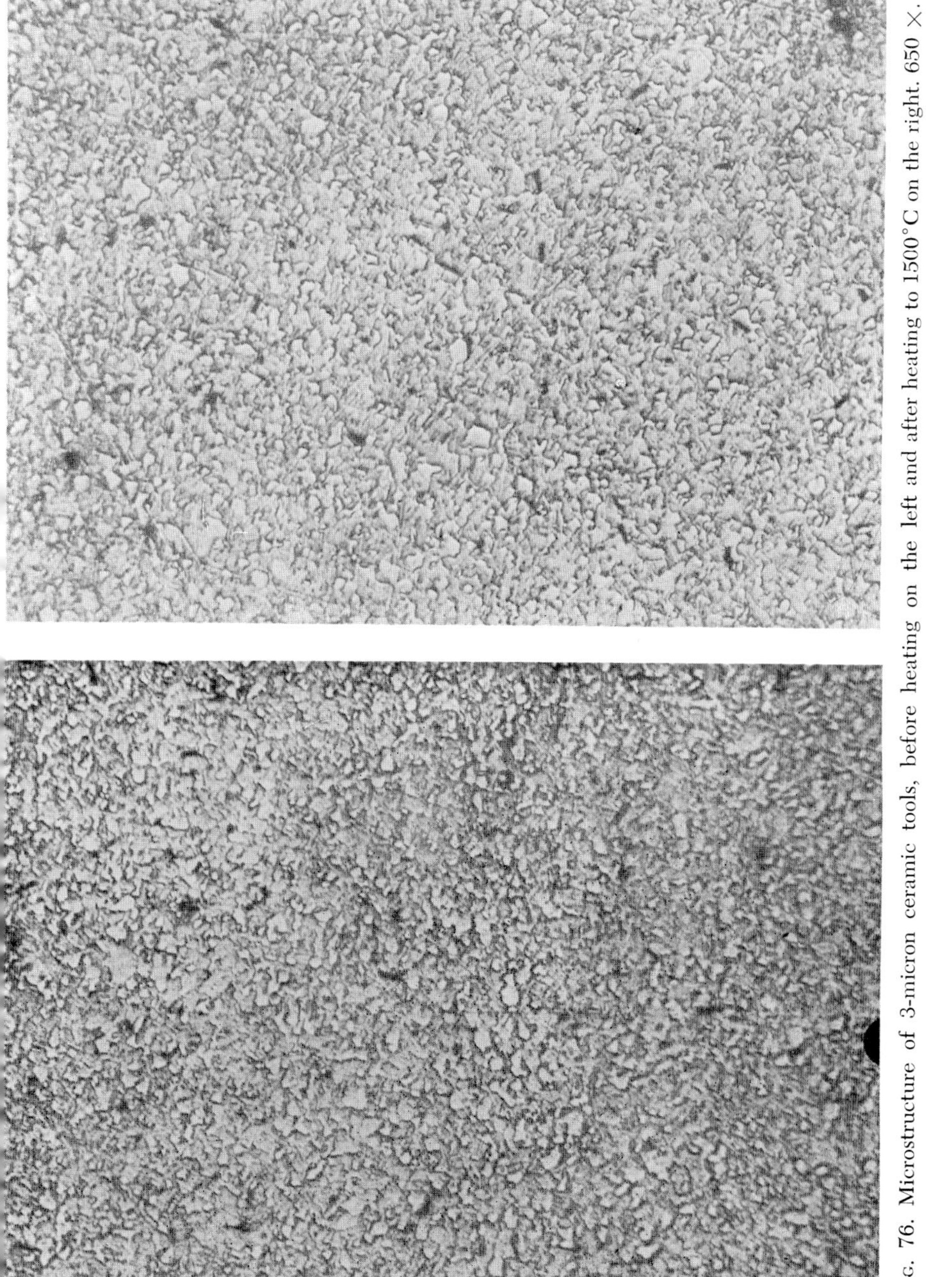

Fig. 76. Microstructure of 3-micron ceramic tools, before heating on the left and after heating to 1500°C on the right. 650 ×.

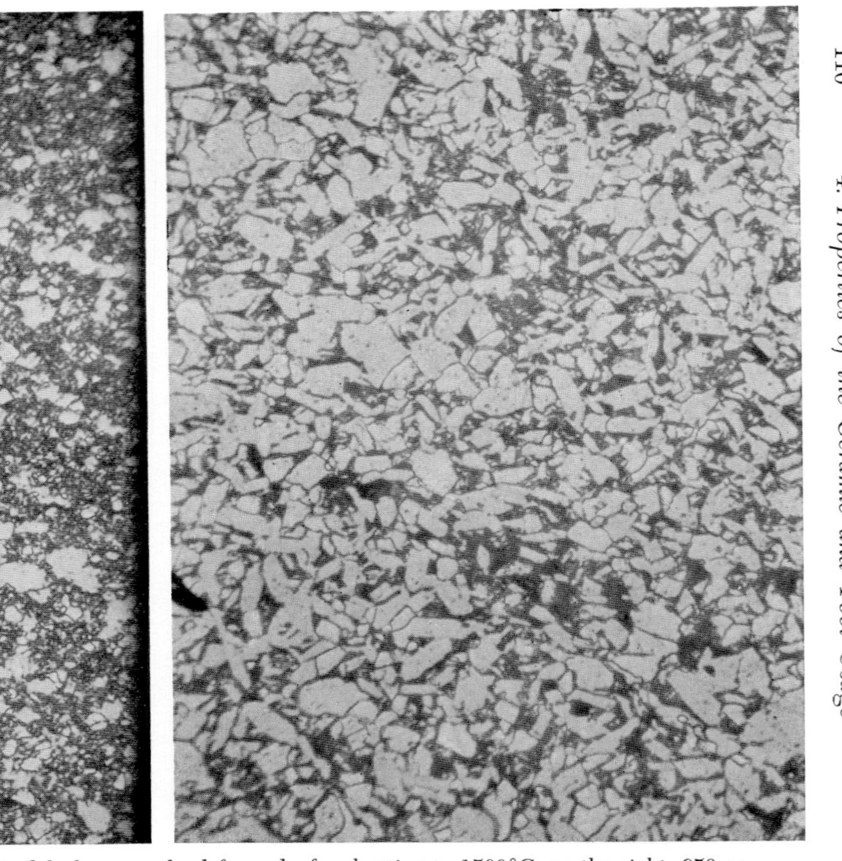

FIG. 77. Microstructure of 1-micron ceramic tool before, on the left, and after heating to 1500°C, on the right. 650 ×.

The resultant microstructure of this material is coarser than that of the 3-micron material even though the total severity of heat treatment is less. Grain growth was reinitiated in the fine material because of residual strain energy left from the hot-pressing process. Whether or not grain growth occurs, is dependent upon processing variables, and it is evident that the recrystallization temperature is lowered if residual strains are present in the material.

Changes in microstructure of this sort would be very deleterious to tool performance. Microstructural changes in the tool-cutting edge have been looked for on used tools, and not observed. The assumption is made on this basis that microstructural changes do not occur during machining. This is consistent with the lack of changes in the 3-micron material after annealing at 1500°C.

When VR97-type materials are heated above 1200°C, pores are nucleated within the object and the specific gravity decreases. Figure 78 shows this behavior on materials which were originally hot pressed at 1500°, 1600°, and 1700°C.

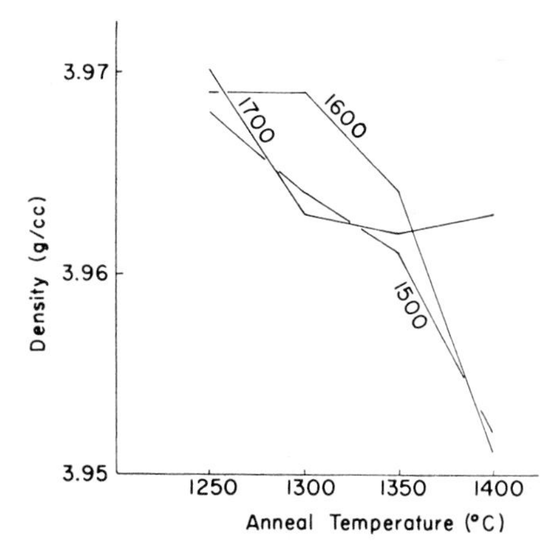

Fig. 78. The increase in porosity upon annealing hot-pressed ceramics which were fabricated at various temperatures.

It is evident from the Fig. 78 that the 1500° and 1600°C materials act similarly to each other but different from the 1700°C tool material. Further heating of the 1700°C ceramic does not result in additional losses in density beyond those obtained at the 1300°C anneal. The materials fabricated at the lower temperatures continue to swell as the annealing temperature is raised. This process of swelling during annealing treatment is thought to arise from dissolved gases nucleating as pores, when the temperature is raised high enough to promote diffusional processes and plastic deformation due to gas pressure within the pores. The materials fabricated at the lower temperatures have larger amounts of gas available for pore formation.

As substantiation of this conclusion, experimental results on vacuum calcination show that absorbed films are not removed from alumina until temperatures of about 1400°C are reached. The experiment was conducted by placing permeable, lightly sintered compacts of alumina in a vacuum furnace and then heating the compacts, sequentially, to higher temperatures. The pressure rise in the vacuum chamber was recorded as a function of time for each temperature increment. The system was repumped at the end of each curve and the normal leak rate of the system subtracted from the data obtained. Figure 79 presents the data.

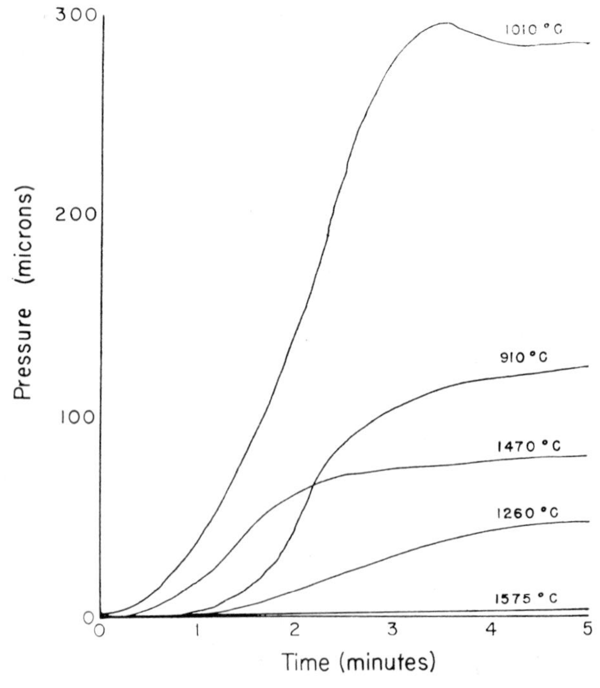

FIG. 79. The increase of pressure in a closed vacuum furnace with time. A vacuum was repumped between each curve.

The first curve at 910°C shows a burst of gas resulting in an increase of pressure and an end pressure of about 110 microns after 5 minutes of heating. This gas was pumped out and with the pumping system reclosed, the temperature was raised to 1010°C with a large burst of gas being evolved.

The amount of gas evolved at 1260°C was smaller than that evolved at 1470°C. At 1575°C no more gas was given off by the alumina. At some temperature between 1260° and 1470°C the last monolayer of absorbed gas was driven from the alumina surface. The amount of gas present in the system from the 1470°C calcine was calculated to be approximately equal to the amount that would be produced from the last monolayer. In the hot-pressing process, densification starts at approximately 1200°C and proceeds rapidly at temperatures above 1300°C. If pore interconnections are obliterated before 1400°C, this monolayer of absorbed gas will be trapped in the structure. From the degree of densification produced prior to 1400°C, in our experimental procedures, it is probable that this does occur. When the sample is subsequently reheated without a confining pressure, this gas nucleates into pores resulting in a decreased density. The materials which are hot pressed to higher temperatures do not contain as much gas because the enhanced diffusivity at the higher temperature probably permits much of it to escape by diffusion along grain boundaries or by solution into the grain interiors.

If the assumption is made that the gas which forms the pores is originally present along grain boundaries, then the higher fired materials, being coarser, would have much less boundary available, and consequently, less gas that can participate in pore formation.

Chapter 5

Tool Life and the Mechanism of Tool Failure

The subjects included in this chapter are thought to be the most related to tool life. Any discussion of tool life must, by necessity, center around tool-failure mechanisms. An understanding of failure mechanisms directs new research into the development of more durable materials and, qualitatively at least, helps the tool engineer in establishing metal-cutting parameters and tool design. There are three main processes by which ceramic tools fail in service: wear, fatigue, and shock fracture. Tool wear and fracture are processes which limit ceramic metal-cutting utility. Quite a bit is known about fatigue and shock in ceramic systems. Other properties including strength are pertinent to tool life in a less direct way.

A. Wear

When two surfaces in contact are moved relative to each other, wear occurs. No two surfaces match with such perfection that actual contact between them comprises more than a small percentage of the total surface area. These small projections or asperities must bear the total load pressing the surfaces together; unit pressures at these points become very high. As Bowden and Tabor (77) point out, plastic and elastic deformation of these contact areas will occur until a sufficient bearing surface is established to sustain the load. When the surface is sheared, these high-pressure contact points are subjected to intense deformation. This results in the local development of a high temperature. Temperatures often reach the melting point of the material at the points of contact. When two clean metal surfaces are sheared under load, actual welding can occur; and material will be transferred from one surface to the other. This process requires energy and results in the property of friction. Wear occurs by the subsequent fracture and removal of the deformed material. There can be several consequences of this wear process—depending on chemical or mechanical conditions under which the process occurs.

1. Plastic Deformation

Duwell (72) studied the effects of the orientation of sapphire crystal, when sliding on steel, on the rate of wear. He found that wear rates of sapphire can vary over three orders of magnitude depending on the crystallographic orientation. Highest wear rates were obtained in those orientations where the crystal offered the least resistance to shear. Figure 80 is Duwell's data of wear rate on the basal plane (0001) of alumina plotted against the direction of sliding on that plane.

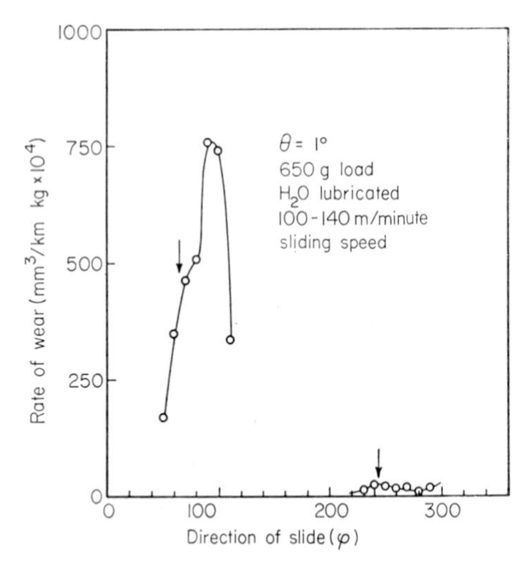

Fig. 80. Wear rate on sapphire basal plane as a function of slide directions (Duwell, 72).

The orientations at 90° and 270° have vastly different wear rates depending on which direction the sliding occurs. Figure 81 shows periodic wear rates on a great circle, perpendicular to the c-axis, with the sixfold symmetry that would be expected from a hexagonal crystal.

The conclusion was made that accelerated wear occurs when the sliding surface is parallel to a slip system in the alumina. Figure 81 indicates that the $(1\bar{2}10)$ planes in the $(10\bar{1}0)$ direction which are not normally active, can be made to slip under the high pressure and high temperature conditions that occur locally during the sliding process. As was pointed out previously, friction was maximum for those directions with the largest wear rates. Scheuplein and Gibbs (78) illustrated these two-slip systems in sapphire as shown in Fig. 82.

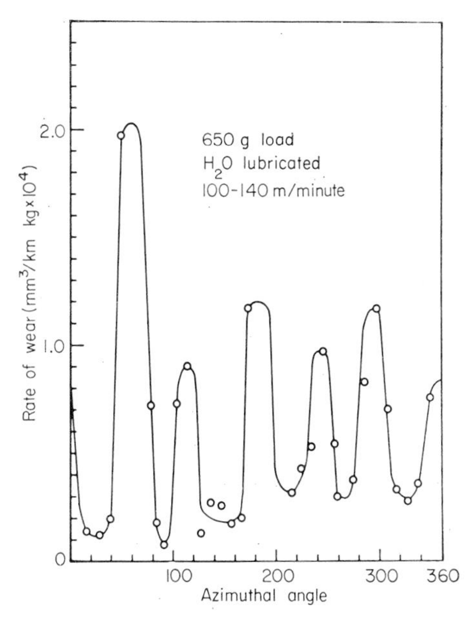

FIG. 81. Wear rate on sapphire around great circle perpendicular to c axis (Duwell, 72).

Steijn's (79) photographic evidence of etched structures on wear scars, paralleling these directions, further substantiates plastic deformation as an active wear mechanism. Figure 83 shows the texture which Steijn interpreted as slip traces on the sapphire crystal.

When the fact that the wear rate of alumina can vary over three orders of magnitude depending on crystal orientation is taken together with photographic evidence of slip traces on wear surfaces, a strong case is made for the occurrence of the deformational process of wear.

A ceramic tool-cutting steel operates under more severe conditions than those employed by Duwell (72), and the plastic deformation process of wear should be expected. Figure 84 shows an obliquely lighted photograph of a used ceramic tool. The tool has been acid washed to remove metallic or metallic-oxide films.

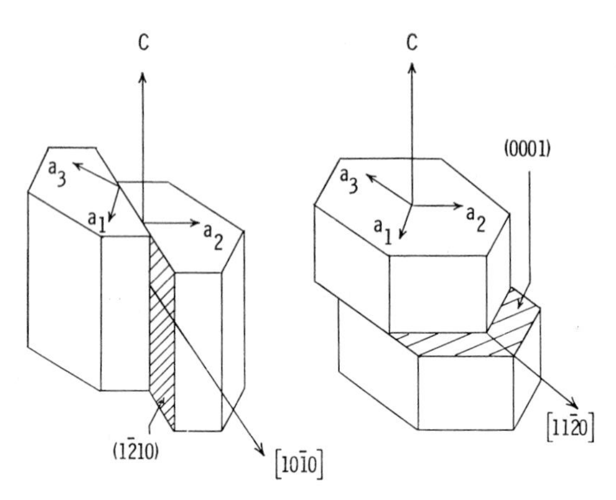

FIG. 82. Slip systems in alumina. Prismatic slip on the left. Basal slip on the right (Scheuplein and Gibbs, 78).

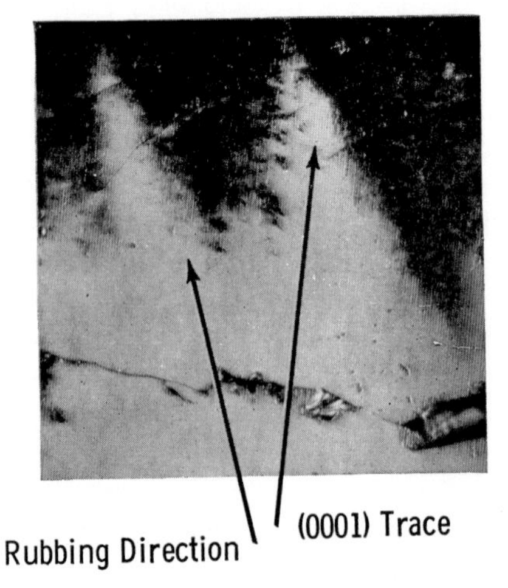

FIG. 83. Slip traces paralleling the 0001 direction in sapphire after sliding against cemented carbide. 500 × (Steijn, 79).

Fig. 84. Cutting-tool edge deformed during machining. Oblique lighting from below illuminates lower edge of deformed surface indicating that it projects above the tool flank. 57 ×.

The tool was used to cut Rc 50 AISI Type A-6 tool steel at 1200 fpm. The wear land that developed can be seen to project above the original ground surface. No evidence of fracture is visually observed and the conclusion is that the edge deformed plastically.

On a number of occasions, teardrop projections were observed on wear lands when they were microscopically examined. These projections sometimes occurred in rows parallel to the top face of the tool and near the bottom of the wear land. Figure 85 is an electron photomicrograph of such a projection reproduced as a stereo pair. The replication technique reversed the relief and it appears as a depression.

A structure of this type could have been formed in one of two ways: a wear-resistant hard spot left by differential attrition, or the projection built up from alumina being transported across the surface. A polished section was cut through one of these projections and a photograph of it appears in Fig. 86 (80).

Metallic inclusions, that are not present in the bulk material, occur in the projecting area. These inclusions could only have been produced as a result of the metal-cutting process, and the alumina, which forms a continuous phase around them, was built up on the surface by a mass-transport process.

The maximum temperatures encountered locally are probably not much greater than the melting point of iron (1535°C). This is much lower than the melting point of alumina (2050°C) and melting of surface films is probably not involved in alumina transport. The difficult point to reconcile here, is that the tool is polycrystalline with all possible orientations, and it is hard to visualize continuous deformation across many grain boundaries. Since the alumina in the teardrops is a continuous phase, a process is suggested involving a continuous film of alumina in transport rather than a rewelding of comminuted detritus.

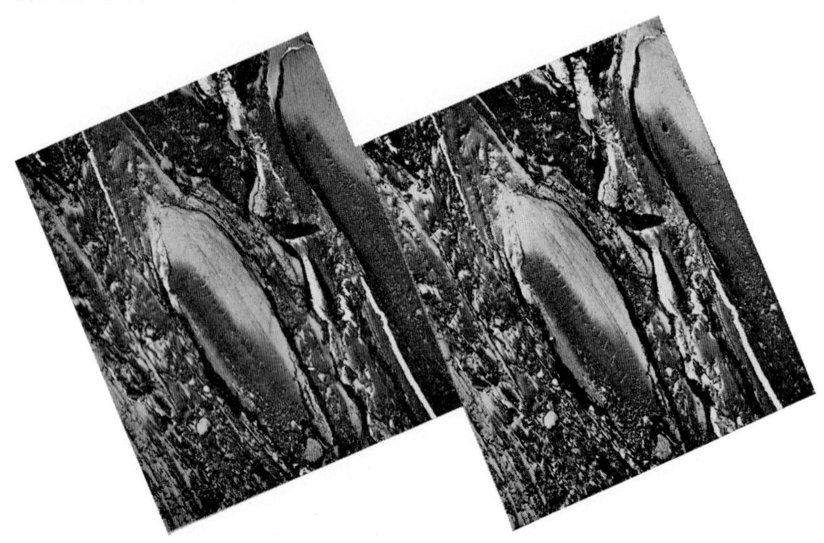

FIG. 85. Ceramic tool-wear texture which formed on the wear land after machining Rc 52 A-6 tool steel. 2000 ×.

If a surface film formed with basal sheets properly oriented on the surface, it could be sheared by plastic deformation of the sheets over long distances.

The presence of reoriented and deformed material in wear scars is commonly observed with metals. Scott and Wilman (81) studied the surface reorientation of the hexagonal metals beryllium and magnesium by electron diffraction. The surfaces developed a main-fiber orientation of the (001) type with the basal sheets inclined about 20° toward the direction from which the abrasion came. This direction was coincident with the resultant of the normal load and the

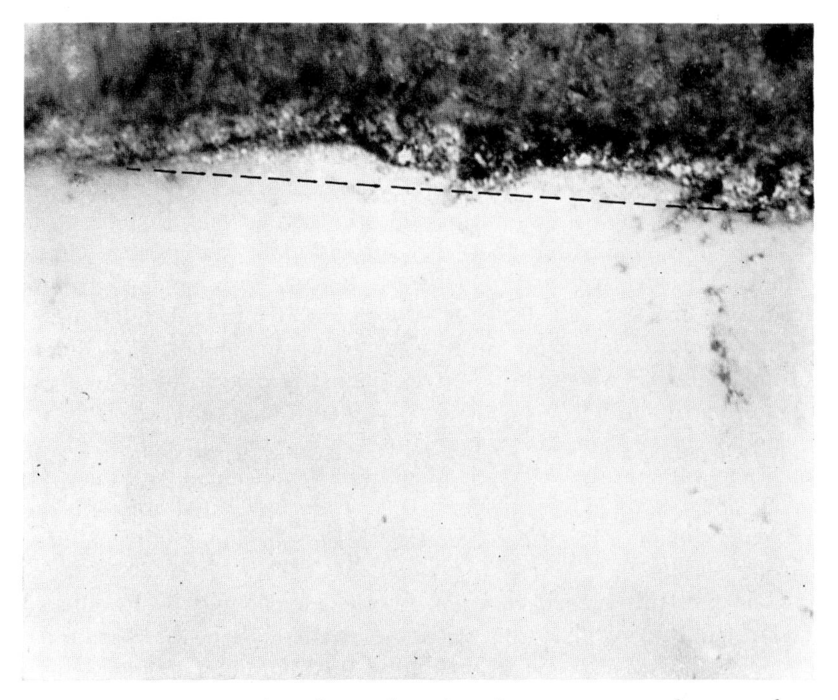

FIG. 86. Cross section through tear-drop-shaped projection on tool-wear surface. 1000 ×.

friction force. These metals reoriented on the surface in a direction which allowed a principal slip system to be coincident with the resultant force tending to produce slip. The angle of this fiber orientation was largely independent of load, abrasion velocity, particle size of the abrasive, or type of abrasive. Under conditions of heavier loading, an additional texture was developed with the basal slip planes of the beryllium parallel to the surface. The amount of this normal texture was much less than the texture which was inclined at 20°. Easy shear of this orientation could remove this layer almost as fast as it formed and accumulations of basal sheets parallel to the surface might not be expected. The analogy between the wear behavior of hexagonal metals and alumina is reasonable since the deformational processes in each case are largely controlled by crystal structure.

Since, as Duwell showed, aluminum oxide will wear about 800 times faster if properly oriented, this reoriented material will be removed as fast as it forms and little residual material will remain on the wear surface. The rate-limiting process will then be the reorientation and not the actual transportation process of the sheets over long distances.

Whatever the details of the process, it seems clear that plastic deformation does occur and that material is transported away from the cutting edge by this process. With this degree of deformation occurring, it is possible that the nucleation of the surface cracks, which subsequently lead to fracture failure, is related to the deformation process. The role of dislocation pile-ups at interfaces to produce crack nuclei is well established in metals and ductile ceramics. Under a machining environment, alumina exhibits a degree of surface ductility.

Under certain conditions, tools develop a reticulated crack pattern on the wear surface which is similar to that shown by Sibley and Allen (82) in their wear experiments. They attributed this cracking, which is shown in Fig. 87 to thermal stresses developed in the alumina during sliding.

Cracks of this type have been observed by us and by Pekelharing (83). He proved that this cracking occurs when the product of speed and feed exceeds a certain value and the frictional energy which results exceeds 1 kw. The cracking is due to nonuniform heating and plastic deformation in preferred directions during the cutting cycle.

In our tool evaluation studies, a specific and predictable crack pattern was observed. Whether or not these regular patterns nucleate from deformation processes cannot be stated with certainty.

It is possible under certain manufacturing conditions, to make work-hardened alumina ceramics. These work-hardened materials would be expected to show an increased resistance to plastic deformation and, hence, a reduced wear rate. These ceramics are of different grain size, with the 1-micron ceramic being more work hardened than the recrystallized 3- and 7-micron materials. Figure 88 plots Moore and Kibbey's data (84) of the flank wear obtained on these ceramics against cutting time on Rc 47 AISI Type A-6 tool steel.

These data show that the work-hardened tools are more wear resistant in metal cutting; this would be expected if plastic deformation is a process responsible for the tool wear.

FIG. 87. Cracking of alumina surface produced by sliding wear (Sibley and Allen, 82).

Figure 89 is an electron photomicrograph of the bottom of the wear land where it intersects the original tool surface.

The alumina undergoing transport by deformation is being removed by a fracture process as evidenced by the rough-surface texture and configuration at the bottom of the wear surface. The material above this interface is smooth without much evidence of fracture processes occurring. There is adequate evidence supporting the belief that fatigue processes occur in ceramic materials during either cyclic or static loading. In machining of metals, these processes can occur in the deformed layer of alumina, and might be respon-

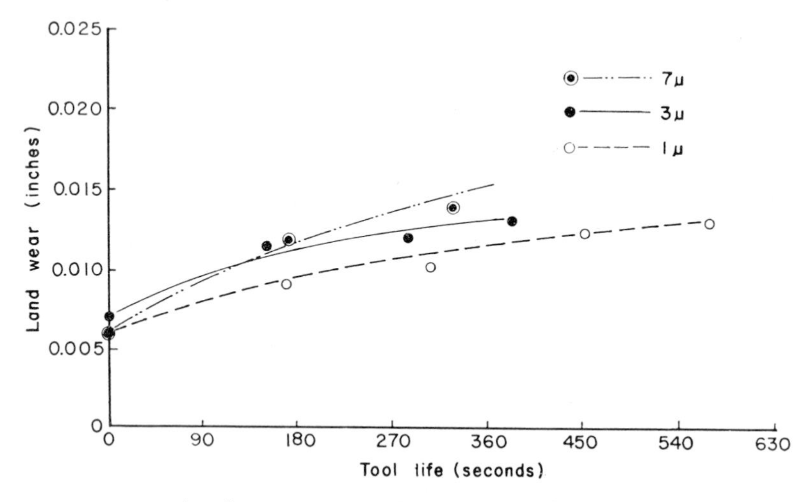

FIG. 88. Rate of tool wear cutting AISI Type A-6 tool steel at Rc 47 1000 fpm, 0.015 inch/rev feed, 0.080-inch depth of cut. The three tools averaged 1-, 3-, and 7-micron grain diameters (Moore and Kibbey, 84).

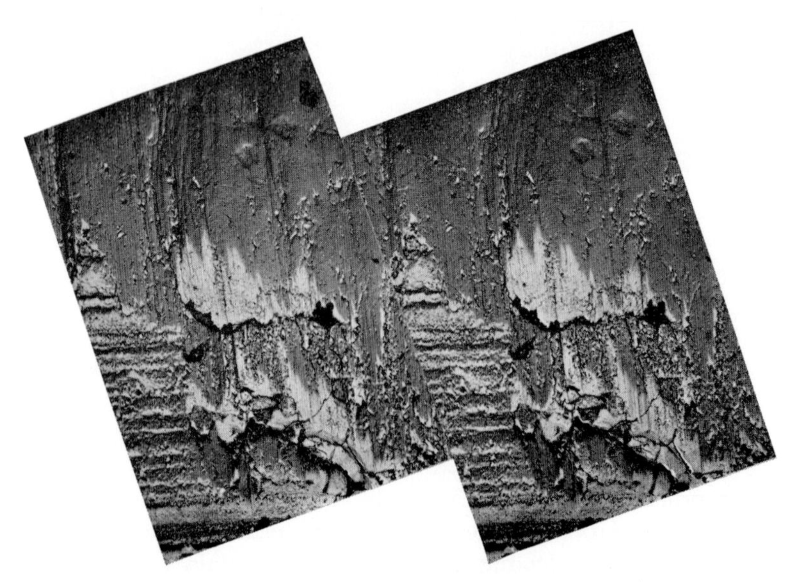

FIG. 89. Stereo-electron photo of tool-wear surface at the intersection with the tool flank, showing the generation of wear ditritus. 3000 ×.

sible for nucleating the crack patterns which are developed. These processes could also be responsible for nucleating the fractures which produce the wear detritus which is formed at the bottom of the flank wear surface.

2. Wear Promoted by Chemical Reaction

Aluminum oxide is a very inert material and this lack of chemical affinity is a contributing factor that permits alumina to be used as a cutting-tool material. One contributing reason for the successful use of aluminum oxide as a cutting tool was its chemical inertness. In realiy, alumina will react slightly with metal oxides and these reactions do contribute materially to the wear processes. Characteristically, the amount of reaction and the amount of wear are small compared to other tooling materials.

In the case where alumina and iron are heated in contact in an oxidizing atmosphere, the iron oxide film can and does react with the alumina to form a thin layer of the spinel $FeO \cdot Al_2O_3$. This spinel has been identified by x-ray diffraction in grinding swarf, by Coes (85) and by Brown *et al.* (86), in wear tracks of sapphire sliding on steel; therefore, there is little doubt that this reaction does occur when machining ferrous metals with alumina. It is also evident that wear on the alumina occurs by the removal of this reacted surface. The amount of wear that occurs depends on the particular chemical species involved in the reaction, the physical environment, and the mass-transport process. The wear rate can be varied within limits by the introduction of other reactants which can inhibit or catalyze the reaction, modify shearing forces and temperature; or effect deformational processes which are responsible for the shearing mechanism.

Coes (87) has shown that the wear of alumina on hardened steel increases by about threefold if the steel was wet with water as compared with the same test in a dry system. Wear, for steel with an oil film, was only about $2/3$ of the wear calculated for dry steel. Duwell and McDonald (71) have shown that aluminum oxide has twice the wear rate in the nitrogen atmosphere as compared with an air atmosphere. Numerous examples (such as the work of M. C. Shaw) appear in the machining literature pertaining to the effects of different atmospheres and cutting fluids on machining behavior (88). Shaw has studied extensively the action of CCl_4; he shows that even though the cutting forces and energy are reduced, the high-speed steel cutter has a shorter tool life because of chemical reactions occurring (89). Coffin (73) has shown that the metal damage produced by sapphire sliding on nickel depends strongly on the atmosphere. Figure 90 shows the wear tracks on the metal for different atmospheres.

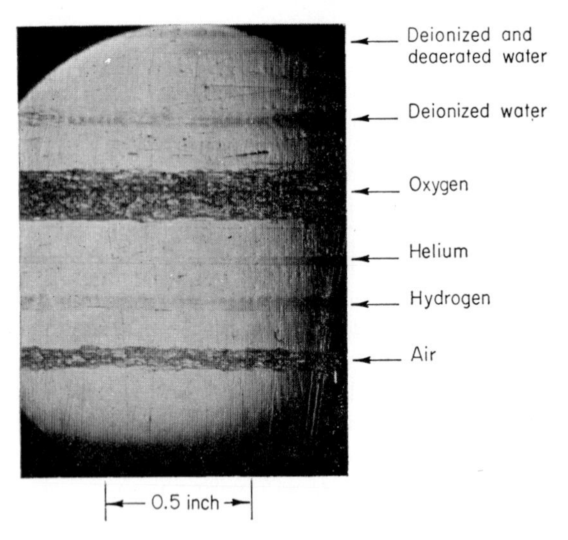

FIG. 90. Wear tracks on nickel by sapphire rider in different atmospheres (Coffin, 73).

This experiment by Coffin clearly shows that the oxidizing atmospheres alter the shearing mechanism so that the tearing occurs within the metal. This tearing generates a very rough wear track. Table XI shows his data for the coefficient of friction for five metals in different atmospheres.

The coefficient of friction in oxygen is as high as 3.0, where in an inert atmosphere the coefficient of friction is typically around 0.6. Since metal-atmosphere-sapphire reactions involve the inert metals, an increase in friction when tested in the various environments does not occur for these reactions because the inert metals do not oxidize. We would expect from these results, and also from Duwell's, that oxygen plays an important role in ceramic-tool wear.

The interface between the chip and the ceramic tool crater can have a number of possible solid chemical species present under oxidizing conditions. These are shown in Fig. 91.

TABLE XI

COEFFICIENT OF FRICTION OF ALUMINA ON VARIOUS METALS IN DIFFERENT ATMOSPHERES[a]

Atmosphere	Coefficient of friction				
	Nickel disk	Gold disk	Silver disk	Platinum disk	Rodium disk
Air	0.95	—	—	—	—
Oxygen	0.6–3.0	0.38	0.55	0.62	0.63–1.9
Helium	0.55	0.36	0.43	0.5	0.63
Hydrogen	0.70	0.37	—	—	—
Water	0.73	—	—	—	—
Water (deaerated)	0.58	0.47	0.55	0.72	—

[a] From Coffin (73)

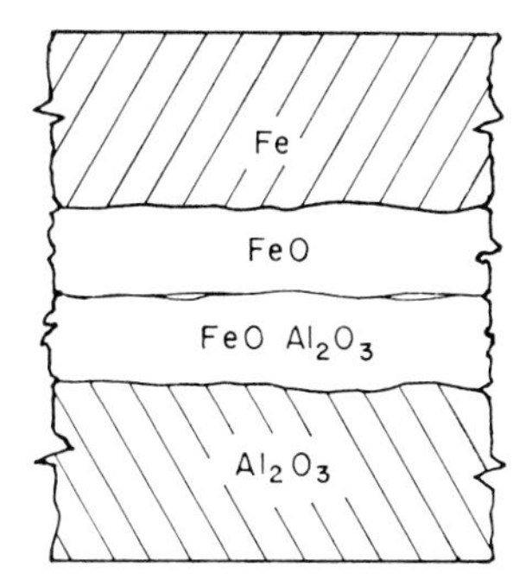

FIG. 91. Possible species present at the tool-metal interface during machining.

Shear can occur at any one of seven possible locations:

1. In the iron
2. At the iron-iron oxide interface
3. In the iron oxide
4. At the iron oxide-spinel interface
5. In the spinel
6. At the spinel-alumina interface
7. In the alumina

Only the last three of these choices will produce tool wear. Shear in the spinel or at the spinel-alumina interface is wear of the chemically reacted tool surface. Shear within the alumina is deformational wear and was discussed in the previous section. Since spinel is not observed on the tool-wear surface, the rate controlling process must be the rate at which the iron oxide reacts with the alumina rather than the rate of the mass-transport mechanism. This reaction involves solid-state diffusion of iron and aluminum in an oxygen lattice; here, diffusional kinetics would be expected to apply. The mechanical strength of the reaction layer and the bond strength to the tool and metal will control the magnitude of the shearing stresses developed locally. If these stresses are materially altered by the addition of a suitable atmosphere, the primary shear can change from one locus to another, thereby changing the rate of tool wear or producing a change in finish on the metal being cut. This type of reaction is suggested in Shaw's experiments with CCl_4 where marked improvements of surface finish are produced at low cutting speeds. The presence of oxygen would be expected to change the forces necessary to shear along the iron-alumina interface. In the manufacture of chromium-alumina cermets, a small amount of oxygen facilitates the formation of strong bonds between the metal and ceramic phases through the formation of a chromium-oxide film which is mutually soluble in both phases. This is used primarily to illustrate that this bonding can occur. In machining, the case is not the same and the forces may be less in oxygen as Duwell (71) suggests in his experiments on alumina abrasives. Unfortunately, these data are also associated with the chip-cutting process and cannot be directly applied to the case of sliding wear. Coffin's (73) data on sliding of nickel and sapphire in oxygen suggests that the bond that is formed exceeds the shear strength of the nickel itself. In this way shear is produced within the metal. What occurs in a specific case will depend on the particulars, not on the generality.

During cutting a ceramic tool has its nose buried within the work piece and continuously generates a virgin-metal surface which slides across the tool. Under these conditions, wear cannot occur by reaction because the thermodynamics do not favor the iron$\cdot Al_2O_3$ reactions. Oxygen can only reach this surface by diffusing along the chip-tool interface toward the nose. The virgin-metal surface is highly reactive and will chemically combine with oxygen during cutting. The maximum rate at which oxygen is reacted will depend upon the rate at which the virgin-metal surface is created; or in terms of machining, it will depend upon the cutting speed. The reaction will tend to sweep the tool-chip interface clear of oxygen while diffusion will tend to distribute oxygen along this surface. These two processes are opposed. Wear by reaction will only occur at the locus on the tool where the diffusion rate exceeds the reaction rate. This will normally be at the chip-atmosphere-tool interface, the depth of cut mark, and on the wear land. The width of the wear marks due to reaction will be dependent on the cutting speed. At low cutting speeds, the reaction rate is low and the atmosphere can diffuse greater distances before complete reaction. This produces a wide mark. At high speeds, oxygen is largely excluded from the surface and a narrow wear mark is produced.

An experiment was conducted at Watertown Arsenal to see if this actually occurred by machining two work materials at four speeds and in three atmospheres. Results are shown in Table XII.

TABLE XII

CUTTING CONDITIONS FOR WEAR MARK EXPERIMENT

Work pieces	4140 annealed, 205 bhn, A-6 Tool steel, Rc 50
Speeds (fpm)	100, 200, 400, 800
Atmospheres	Air, oxygen, argon
Geometry	15° lead angle, −5° side rake, −5° back rake
Feed	0.011 inch/rev.
Depth	0.080 inch
Cutting time	80, 160, 320, 640 seconds

The atmosphere was provided by blowing a jet of either argon or oxygen onto the chip-tool interface. This crude method was not expected to completely exclude air from the system, which would have been a much more difficult task.

Figure 92 shows the wear surfaces produced by cutting 4140 steel at the four speeds in the argon atmosphere.

It can be clearly seen from the photograph that the wear mark is wider at the lower speeds and systematically decreases in width as the cutting speed increases. The severity of wear was also greater at the lower speed. The results in air and oxygen were almost identical with those produced in argon.

Figure 93 shows the width of the wear mark plotted against cutting speed for the three atmospheres cutting 4140 steel.

The width of the wear marks cannot be explained by variations

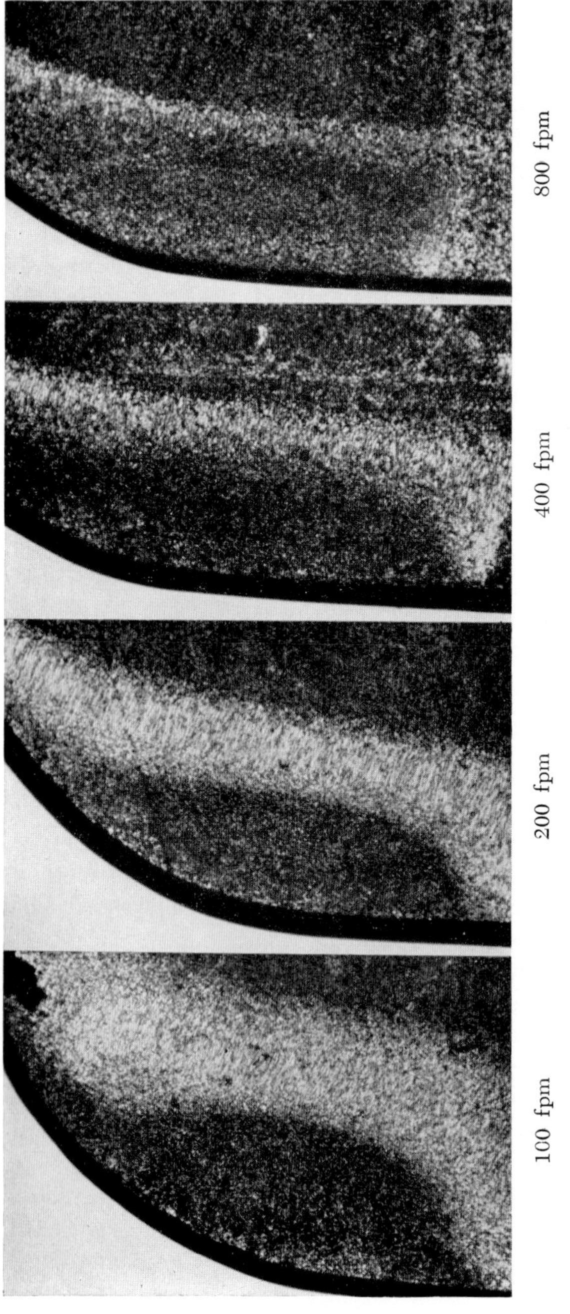

FIG. 92. Crater-wear surfaces, 4340 steel in argon atmosphere at four cutting speeds. View looking down onto crater at tool nose. 57 ×.

in chip curl because curl was tighter at the lower speeds, and this would produce the opposite effect from that which was observed.

The results from the hardened AISI type A-6 steel were more difficult to interpret. The trend was present toward wider wear surfaces at lower speeds, but in some cases the wear surface extended up to the cutting edge making the width measurement meaningless. It may possibly be that the deformational-wear process is predominant with these cutting conditions and as a result the "reaction-diffusion" process is obscured. In those cases where the width could meaningfully be measured, the trend toward wider marks at lower speeds was observed. When cutting at higher speeds in oxygen, the

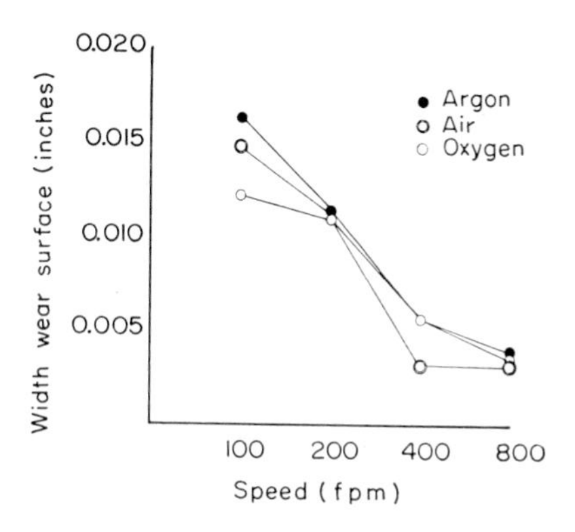

FIG. 93. Crater width with speed; 4340 steel in three atmospheres.

tool tip operated at a much hotter temperature level than that of a normal tool. These tools developed a much more severe wear crater than that normally observed. The chips produced from Type A-6 steel are very small in size, and the large-chip surface area readily reacted with the oxygen atmosphere to release large quantities of heat. This did not occur with 4140 because of the larger chip which was produced. The higher temperatures would favor accelerated wear either by the deformational or the reactive-wear processes. Cutting Type A-6 steel in air showed the same chip-burning effect but to a much lesser extent. Figure 94 shows the wear surfaces produced in oxygen at the four cutting speeds.

In argon, and in air up to 400 fpm, the wear surfaces generally appeared similar to that produced at 200 fpm in oxygen. In all atmospheres at 100 fpm the wear surface was identical with the double-

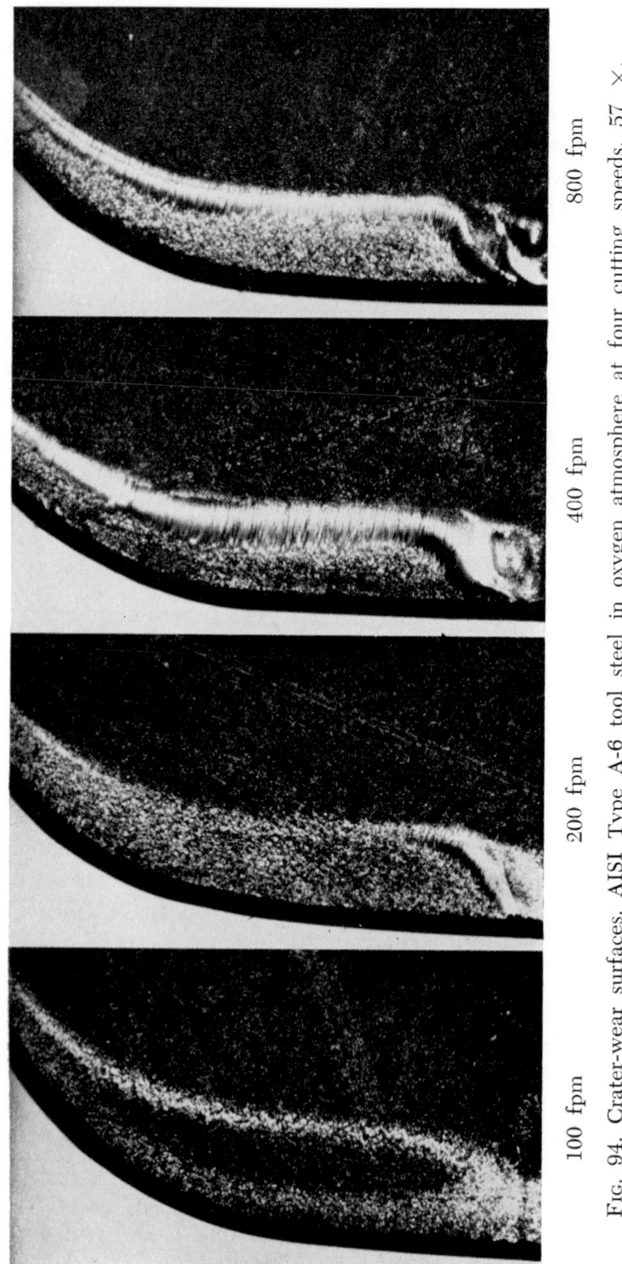

FIG. 94. Crater-wear surfaces. AISI Type A-6 tool steel in oxygen atmosphere at four cutting speeds. 57 ×.

wear mark as shown in Fig. 88. The wear mark at the cutting edge is thought to be due to oxygen counter diffusion up the wear land and spilling-over on the top of the tool. At low cutting speeds, this could well be expected. This wear mark makes any explanation based on tool protection by a built up edge difficult. Normally the built-up edge will extend up to the cutting edge and not appear, as this wear pattern suggests, back from this edge on the top surface. Furthermore, a built-up edge would not be expected on ceramic tools cutting these materials at (at least) the higher speeds used. In the oxidizing atmospheres the gouge that is produced at the depth of the cut mark progressively becomes deeper as the cutting speed increases. The gouge characteristically occurs at an angle to the tool edge. This configuration suggests that oxygen diffusion in from the side is gettered by the chip which is moving at right angles to the diffusion. The locus of oxygen penetration would then be a curve which makes an angle to the tool edge, as was actually observed. The chip tapers to a sharp edge at this locus, and this edge would be more subject to oxidation thereby causing localized heating and rapid wear at the depth of cut mark. The severity of the wear by either the deformational or the reactive process was shown to be essentially speed insensitive (see Fig. 92). The fact that wear severity at the depth of cut mark was speed sensitive, certainly suggests that chip oxidation is a likely cause of the deep wear at this locus.

Oxide films on the work-piece OD could also contribute to wear at the depth of cut mark, if these films are turned under at the edge during the chip formation process. This would cause the direct contact between iron oxide and alumina in much greater proportions than that which occurs by diffusion. The amount of depth of cut wear is anomalous in these samples, and even more so in others not shown here. At present it is not known just how much these factors contribute and just how much the work hardening of the work-piece OD contributes to tool wear. Certainly when machining metals that work harden easily, the retarded deformation of this layer does produce deeper wear gouges at the depth of cut mark than metals which do not work harden as readily.

The effort to exclude air with the argon jet was abortive. Actually very little oxygen is needed to produce the films of oxide or spinel, and atmosphere control would have to be much more refined for this effect to be noticed.

The processes of wear by deformation and reaction are undoubtedly related in that the bonds which form between the metal and ceramic can alter the surface stresses in the tool. A strong bond would tend to produce higher shearing stresses in the alumina and consequently a greater amount of deformation would be expected.

Brewer's data (48) on tool life versus cutting speed show a maximum life at speed slightly over 200 fpm for cutting steel. Tool life was determined by the appearance of a certain width-wear land, presumably 0.016 inch or 0.018 inch wide, Fig. 95.

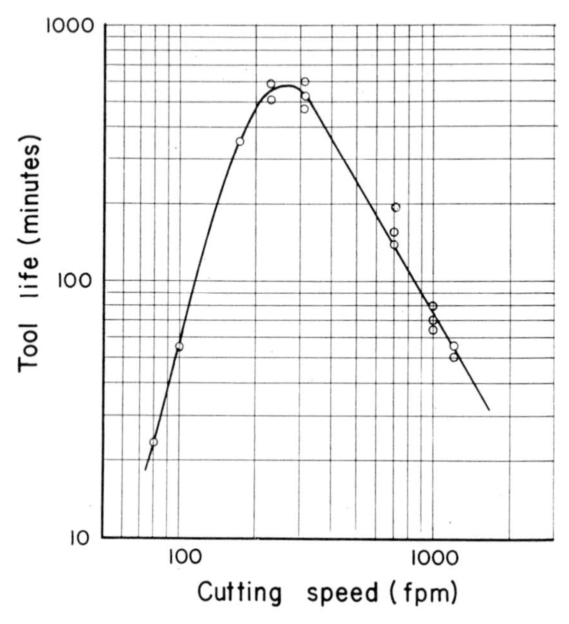

FIG. 95. Relationship of cutting speed with tool life. Ceramic tools cutting 50-ton carbon steel (Brewer, 48).

The increased wear at slow speeds can be attributed both to the increased cutting forces and oxygen diffusion to the cutting edge under these conditions.

The topological character of the developed wear surfaces seems to be partially dependent upon location in regard to oxygen availability. Figure 96 is an electron photomicrograph of the negative land which was ground on the tool. This tool was used for machining SAE 6150 steel.

Comparing this wear surface with that of Fig. 97, which is the

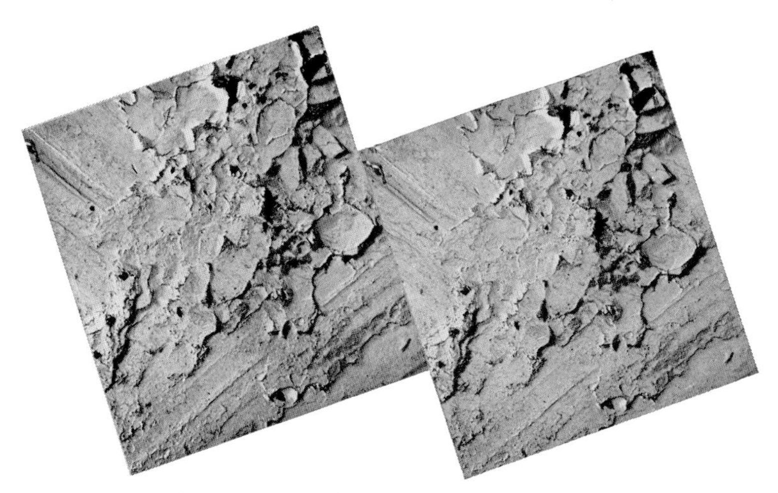

FIG. 96. Stereo-electron photo of wear surface at the top of the tool-cutting edge. 3000 ×.

same tool but taken on the wear land, it is evident that very little wear occurs on the actual cutting edge with these particular machining conditions (1500 fpm, SAE 6150 steel, 200 bhn, 0.011-inch feed/rev, 0.100-inch depth of cut.)

Figure 97 shows an electron photomicrograph of a wear land; the photograph was taken at a position adjacent to the depth of cut mark.

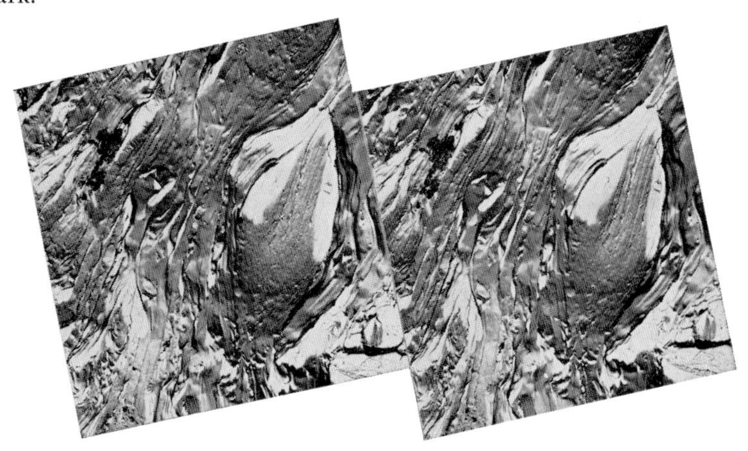

FIG. 97. Stereo-electron photo of tool-wear surface showing smooth wear at a locus of easy oxygen availability. 3000 ×.

The surface is characterized as a striated smooth surface with much visual evidence of flow.

Figure 98 shows the same wear land but at a position toward the tool nose where oxygen is less available.

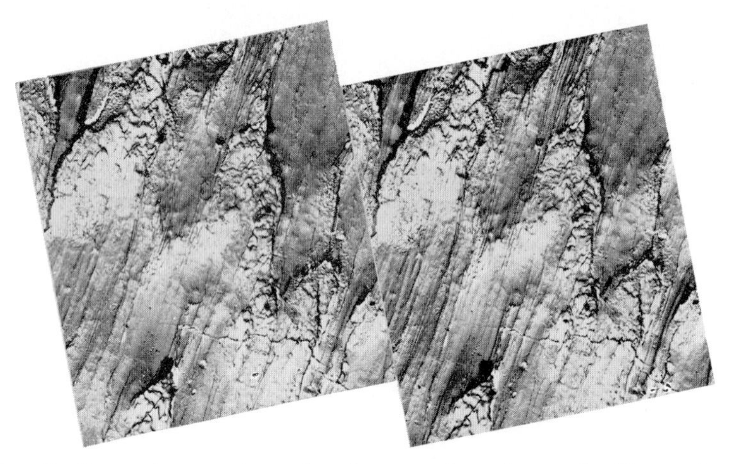

FIG. 98. Stereo-electron photo of tool-wear surface showing hackley surface at a position on the tool near the nose where oxygen availability is reduced. 3000 ×.

Less evidence of flow appears in this photograph than in Fig. 97. The surface is rougher textured with evidence of small fragments that pulled loose during cutting. Examination of many such photographs leads one to the conclusion that the difference in wear process across the surface depends upon the availability of oxygen. Since oxygen can change the shearing forces by chemical bonding, it follows that the deformational wear process would also be altered. It appears that oxygen forms a better bond and that the shearing forces are increased.

Figure 99 shows a wear-land produced machining A-6 tool steel at 1200 fpm. The wear mark at the depth of cut mark is so highly polished that it is difficult to focus the microscope on the surface.

Any process producing such a surface must, by its nature, be a continuous smooth process such as a chemical reaction or deformation. The most severe wear occurs at the depth of cut mark where oxygen is available from two directions by diffusion and as absorbed films on the OD of the work piece. This coupled with the effects of the work-hardened surface and higher temperatures due to chip

FIG. 99. Highly polished wear surface on a ceramic tool at the depth of cut mark. 57 ×.

oxidation could result in a local increase of forces and rapidly accelerated wear at this position.

The composition of the work piece would be expected to have a major effect on the reaction-wear process. The oxygen-avid metals would have the tendency to bond more strongly to the alumina and produce accelerated wear. This is, in general, exactly what Shaw and Smith (70) found as was shown in Chapter 4.

Shaw and Smith have pointed out that the metals least efficiently machined with ceramics (Ti, Be) are oxygen-avid elements. The obvious speculation is that these metals bond so strongly to alumina that wear processes and tool-loading forces are greatly exaggerated with resultant premature tool failure. Other factors are undoubtedly involved, however, such as remachining of the work-hardened surface.

3. MICROSPALLING

Wear by plastic deformation or by chemical reaction is a continuous processs. With some tool materials, wear occurs in a discontinuous fashion with the sudden removal of whole alumina grains or small aggregates of grains, a process we call microspalling. If this process occurs more or less continuously, greatly accelerated wear results. Some early ceramic tools did wear in this manner and their quality left something to be desired.

Figure 100 is a stereo-electron photomicrograph of a microspalled tool surface.

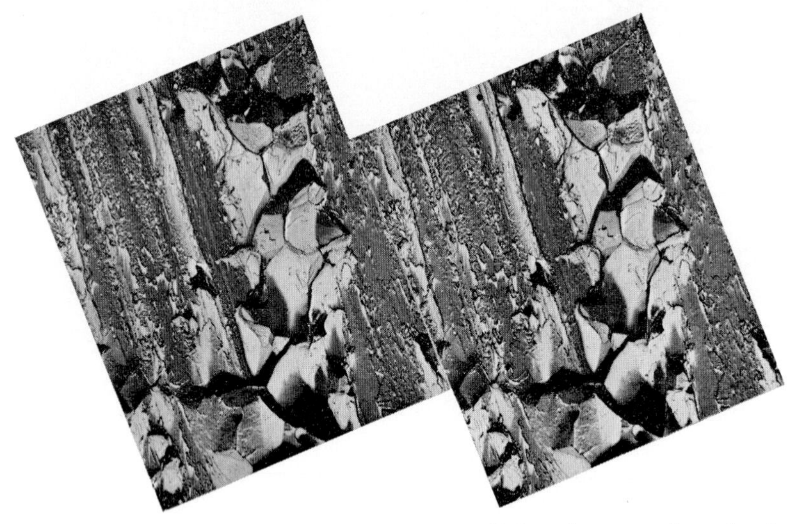

FIG. 100. Stereo-electron photo of a microspalled tool-wear surface showing the internal grain structure. 3000 ×.

It is evident that whole grains have been plucked from the surface during metal cutting. The normal striated wear surface can be seen to the sides of the grain texture. The strength of the grain boundaries in a material such as this are not strong enough to withstand the tensile forces developed normal to the surface. Figure 101 shows another microspalled surface of a rather coarse-grained tool where the process has repeatedly occurred during tool wear.

The texture formed by microspalling has been altered by subsequent deformational wear on this tool. Neither of these tools was particularly good in service.

Various tool materials were made having different grain sizes from one micron to about seven microns. It was noted that the character and texture of the wear surface after machining was systematically varied with grain size. Figure 102 is an electron photomicrograph of the 10-micron size.

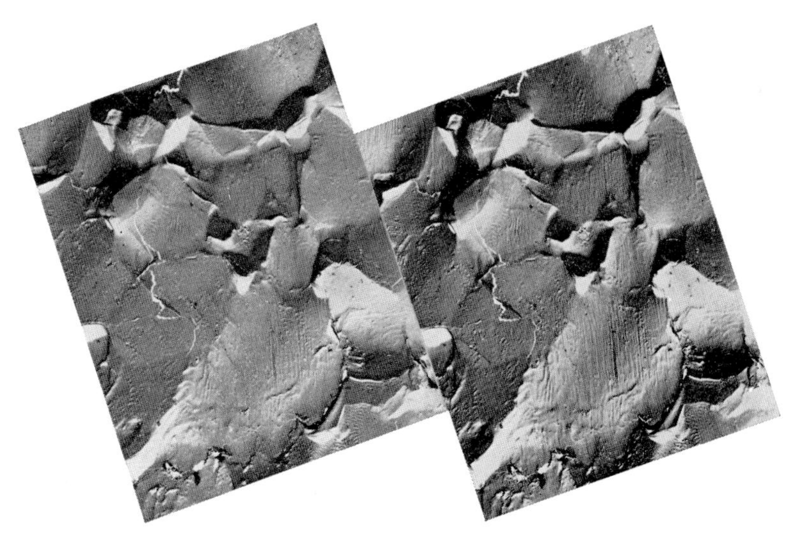

FIG. 101. Stereo-electron photo of a coarse tool which had rapid wear by an intermittent microspalling process. 3000 ×.

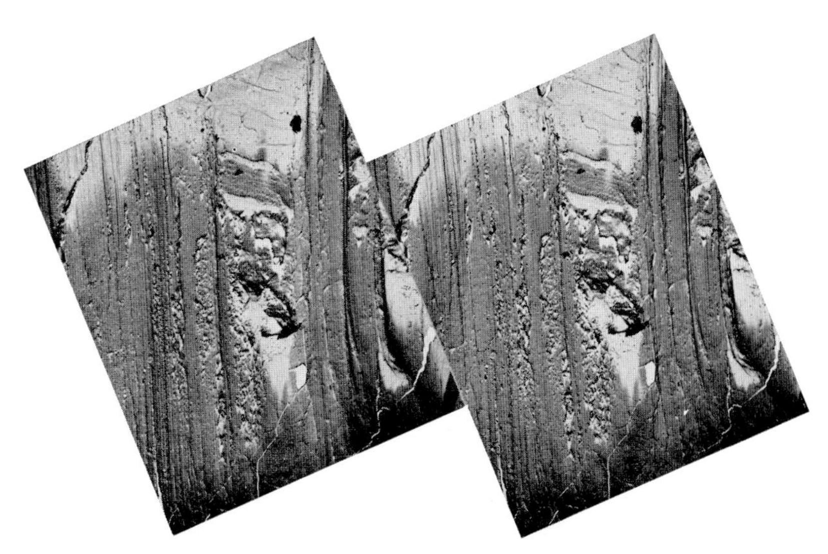

FIG. 102. Stereo-electron photo of a 10-micron ceramic tool-wear surface with coarse-wear striations. 3000 ×.

The texture is coarsely striated with the width of the striations approximately equal to the grain size. The deep groove (actually a ridge on the original sample because of the replication technique) running vertically through the center is just 10-microns wide.

Figure 103 shows the wear surface of a 7-micron tool.

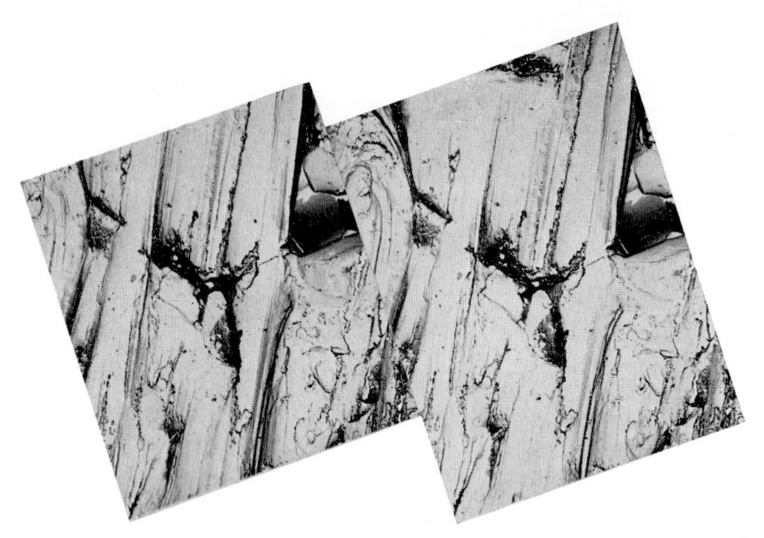

FIG. 103. Stereo-electron photo of a 7-micron ceramic tool-wear surface. 3000 ×.

The deep groove running diagonally through the lower right is 7-microns wide. A grain has been plucked from the material at the top of this groove. Figure 104 shows the wear surface on a 3-micron tool.

The diagonal grooves are above 2- or 3-microns wide. Again, the grain texture is revealed where microspalling has occurred in the groove. This tool is a good one that performed well cutting steel.

Figure 105 is the wear surface on a 1-micron grain-size tool.

The striations running vertically are about 1-micron wide, again showing a good correlation between wear, texture, and grain size of the tool.

A plot of the width of the prominent-wear striations and tool grain size is given in Fig. 106.

Actually, the correlation between grain size and wear texture is not as perfect as this correlation implies. The texture varies depend-

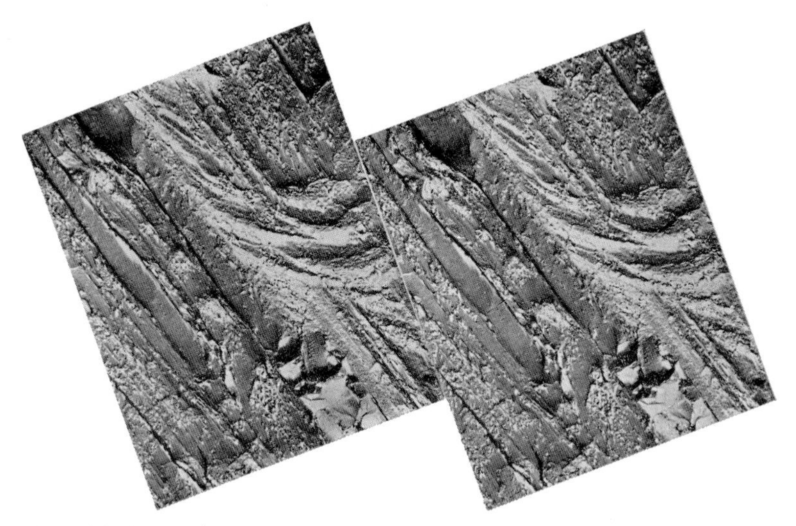

Fig. 104. Stereo-electron photo of a 3-micron ceramic tool-wear surface. 3000 ×.

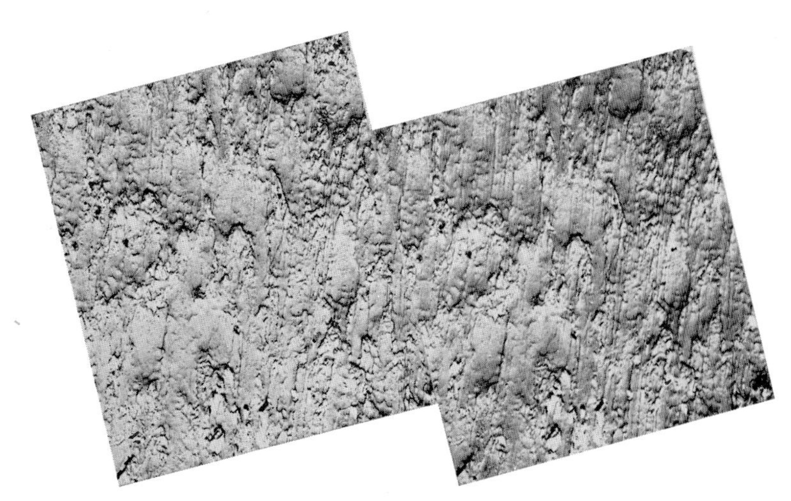

Fig. 105. Stereo-electron photo of a 1-micron ceramic tool-wear surface showing the finely striated smooth texture. 3000 ×.

ing on the location on the wear land. The qualitative correlation does exist, however, as this plot suggests. This was verified in our own minds by examination of many more photographs than could be shown here. In almost every case, the wear texture is accompanied by microspalling. The texture-control process probably starts with the microspalling of an alumina grain creating a depression one-grain-width wide in the wear surface. The grains that are removed are those that are so truncated by the tool surface that they are not mechanically locked by adjacent grains. The boundaries could be

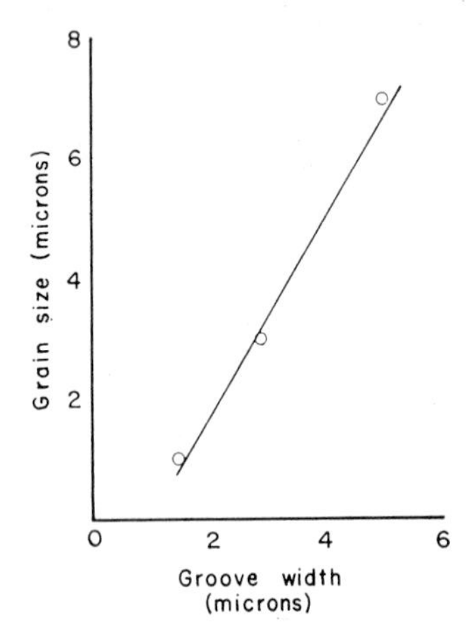

FIG. 106. Correlation between the wear-groove width and average-grain size of the ceramic tools.

weakened by grain-boundary deterioration from a fatigue process associated with repeated grain-boundary sliding and accumulation of structural defects. Figure 107 is an electron photograph of a used tool surface where extensive microspalling has occurred.

The stereo pair clearly shows that the plastic replica material penetrated into the grain boundaries indicating that actual separation occurred during machining. The black filigree on the grains in Fig. 107 indicates this penetration.

A grain, which pulls loose from the surface, creates a depression which will act as a stress riser on its edges which are normal to the flow of metal; and these edges will wear preferentially. The effect will be to elongate the depression only in the direction of flow. The grain that was removed will be dragged down across the tool face

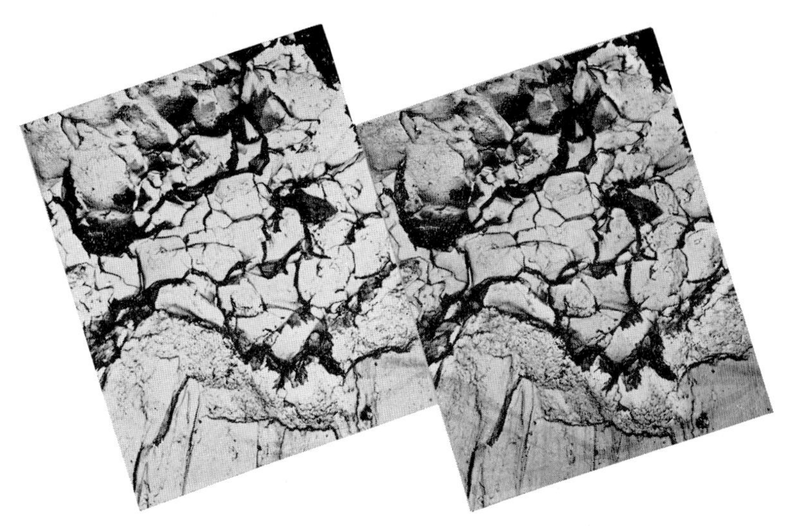

FIG. 107. Stereo-electron photo of a microspalled tool surface showing the black filagrees of plastic replica which penetrated into open-grain boundary cracks. 3000 ×.

in this direction and may produce a scratch which can serve as the nucleus for more rapid and continued degradation of the surface down stream from the original depression. The correlation suggests that microspalling primarily occurs with the removal of a single grain rather than aggregates of grains. The latter case is, however, observed to occur in other surfaces examined.

4. Variation of Wear Rate with Microstructure

The tool materials which were hot pressed at different temperatures and showed a systematic variation of microhardness (Fig. 69) were also tested for wear resistance. The obvious expectation was that the harder tool would be the more wear resistant. Figure 108 shows the Graton-Vanderwilt polishing machine on which these tests were performed.

The tool-bit samples were cemented to the Bakelite holders as shown. The tools revolved against a cast-iron plate in the machine which was charged with 1g of 600-grit green silicon carbide in 1 cm^3 of kerosene. The charge and samples were systematically controlled to insure even abrasion on all samples. This technique is quite similar to one reported by Van der Beck *et al.* (34) in their studies on the CCT-707 (then Stupalox) ceramic tool. The weight loss for our data after a given time was plotted against the temperature of fabrication as is shown in Fig. 109.

FIG. 108. Graton-Vanderwilt polishing machine.

The amount of alumina removed varies fivefold depending on the hot-pressing temperature. The materials which were fabricated at the lowest temperature were extremely wear resistant. As was expected, this material was also the hardest, with the 1600°C material being intermediate.

The primary physical difference between these materials is the average grain size. The alumina hot pressed at 1700°C had an average size of 3 microns; the 1500°C averaged 1 micron; grain growth has occurred with the higher hot-pressing temperatures. Referring back to Fig. 45, the tool specimens with the fine microstructures were brittle in impact fracture; and as we have just seen, harder and very wear resistant. They act like a work-hardened material by analogy with the behavior of metals. This point of view is not at all unreasonable. We saw earlier that here these fine-grained materials do indeed contain an excess of strain energy as evidenced by anomalous grain growth when they are reheated. This energy is stored in the alumina as a result of the deformational aspects of the hot-pressing process. If extensive recrystallization does not occur, as with the material in Figs. 52 or 77, this energy will be retained

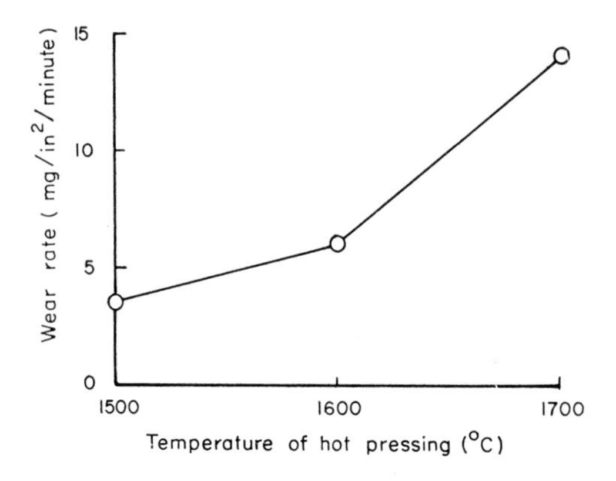

FIG. 109. Wear resistance of ceramic-tool materials versus temperature of fabrication.

in the specimen producing a work-hardened material. If grain growth occurs, by fabricating the tool material at a higher temperature, then these stresses are relieved due to the recrystallization which occurs across the moving grain boundaries. This is by no means a new concept. Figure 110 shows the recrystallization of high-purity aluminum.

This work by Beck and Sperry (90) indicates that the recrystallized zone is essentially strain-free. They attribute the motion of the grain boundary to the strain energy stored in the deformed grains, which is analogous to the extensive recrystallization in the work-hardened ceramic as was discussed on page 111.

The properties of impact strength, wear resistance, and microhardness, as they vary with grain size, can be explained on the basis of work-hardening and recrystallization phenomena.

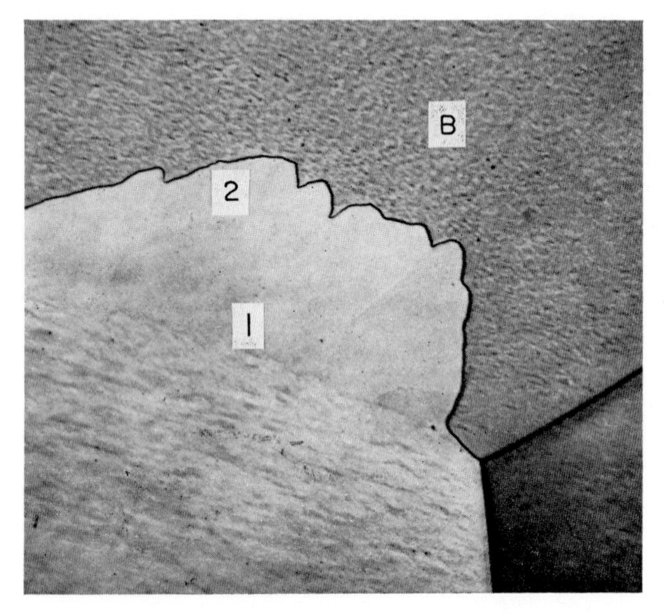

FIG. 110. Recrystallization of strained aluminum results in strain-free metal (Beck and Sperry, 90).

5. WEAR DURING MACHINING

The size of the wear land on a tool increases with time as the tool is being used. This is, of course, a commonly used measure of tool life. Schmidt *et al.* (91) measured flank wear with cutting time at various cutting speeds on AISI 4150 steel. Some of their data appear in Fig. 111.

The increase in slope of the curves with higher cutting speeds is evident. If only the steady-state wear is considered after initial fluctuations and adjustments have settled down, the wear rates calculate as follows in Table XIII.

Conventional plots of cutting speed versus tool life, as determined by a wear criterion, form a straight line on a log-log plot as is shown in Fig. 95. The pertinent half of Fig. 95 is that part on the right, beyond speeds, where the other wear process is active.

The plastic deformation mechanism of ceramic-tool wear is also compatible with the observation of increased-wear rates with increased fee. Brewer's (48) data on wear versus cutting time for three-feed rates are shown in Fig. 112.

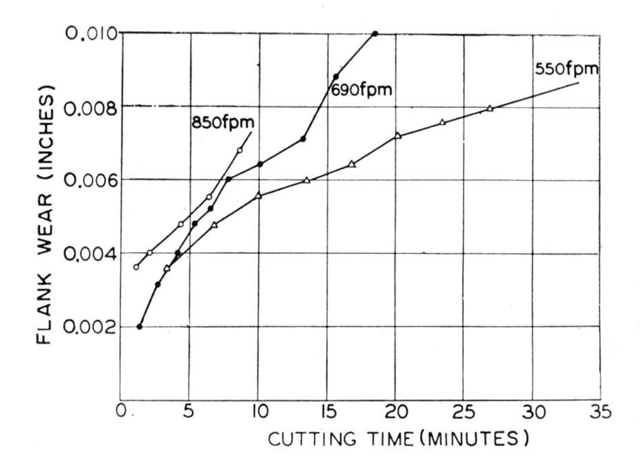

Fig. 111. Flank wear of ceramic tools with cutting speed (Schmidt *et al.*, 91).

TABLE XIII

Flank Wear Rate of Ceramic Tools[a]

Speed	Wear rate $\times 10^{-4}$ inches/minute
550	1.5
690	3.6
850	5.7

[a] Schmidt *et al.*, 91.

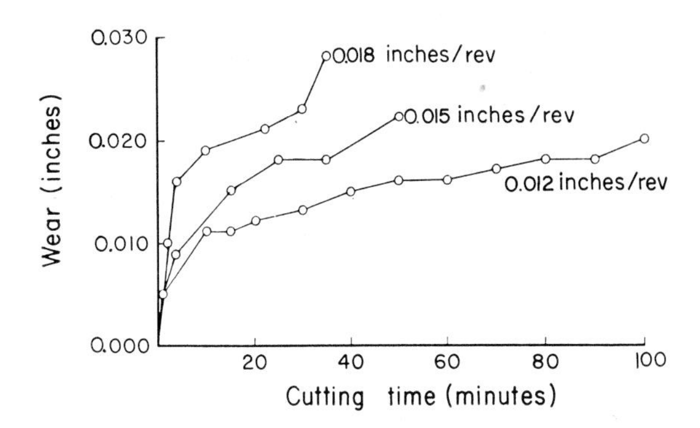

Fig. 112. Wear of ceramic tools with feed rate (Brewer, 48).

The higher feed rates will increase the interfacial pressure and thereby increase the shearing forces which cause the plastic deformation. The increased slopes of the curves with increased feed rates is an expected phenomena. Some earlier tests of our own, performed at Watertown Arsenal, indicated a correlation between grain size and the amount of metal removed. The tests were performed on AISI 6150 steel, mill annealed, 200 bhn, 1500 fpm, 0.011-inch feed/rev, and 0.100-inch depth of cut.

The data which appear in Fig. 113 also show the effects of three raw materials on tool performance.

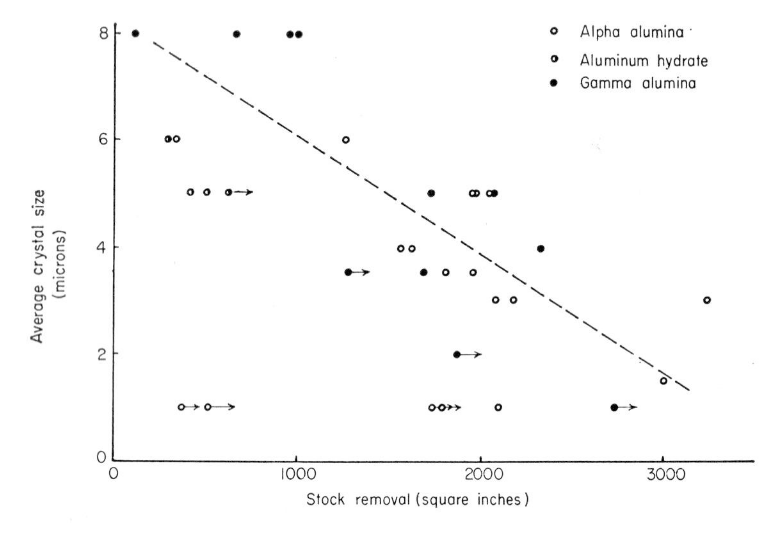

Fig. 113. Machining characteristics of ceramic tools of various grain size. Stock removal expressed as the area of the new generated surface. Points with arrows fractured prematurely should be displaced to the left for an equivalent comparison.

The tool-life criterion used in this test was the appearance of a 25% increase in feed load as measured with a tool-post dynamometer. If the assumption is made that the feed load increases uniformly with wear, then a wear scale could be superimposed on the metal removed axis. While we doubt the complete applicability of this assumption, it is probably a workable first approximation. The dashed curve shows a marked increase in tool performance as the average-grain size of the tool decreases. The tests, marked with an arrow pointing to the right, fractured prior to the 25% increase in feed load. The arrow implies that the points should be displaced toward the curve if the full amount of wear was achieved. Please note that almost all of the tools showing premature fracture had grain sizes of 2 microns or less. The inferior tools made with aluminum hydrate and the associated fracture is discounted. The incidence of fracture failures associated with fine-grain sizes is consistent with our impact fracture test data and our general concept of strain-hardened and embrittled ceramics. The slope of the curve reflects the increased wear resistance of the work-hardened alumina and is again consistent with this concept.

The increased wear resistance of finer microstructures suggest a possible criterion for ceramic tool grades. In cutting low-shear-strength but abrasive materials, like cast iron, a finer microstructure may well have increased utility. Because these materials do not generate high-loading forces on the tool tip, the brittleness of the finer microstructures may not prove to be troublesome. One difficulty is associated with the lack of hot-pressing equipment that can densify the alumina at the low temperatures necessary to preserve this microstructure. Conventional equipment does not operate at high enough pressures or with sufficient economic efficiency to produce this tool. This problem can be overcome in equipment design. Another difficulty is that these materials are very difficult to grind. They are hard and have a severe tendency to chip during grinding. This problem can probably be overcome but increased grinding costs are to be expected.

Another reasonable approach is to modify the physical properties of the ceramic by such metallurgical processes as alloying, precipitation hardening, or dispersion hardening. Examples of these already exist in the chromium-alumina tools or in the attempts to increase wear resistance with the addition of SiC or other hard carbides. The trick is to modify the material to increase wear resistance without effecting deleterious changes in other properties. Attempts in the Norton Company Research Laboratory to accomplish this usually resulted in strength reduction. The currently available ceramic tools with hard-metal additions do not seem to exhibit any particularly unique properties. Since the yield point of materials in general, and alumina in particular, is temperature sensitive, higher wear rates are expected to be associated with higher cutting speeds. This naturally follows since an active tool-wear mechanism is plastic deformation.

6. The Influence of Wear on Tool Failure

In many tool applications, tool life is limited not so much by the wear as it is by fracture failure. A typical feed-force curve measured with a tool-post dyamometer in our standard test shows very little increase in tool-loading forces when cutting steel for long periods of time. Failure starts by a discontinuity in the curve with the forces rapidly increasing at an accelerated rate. Fracture follows immediately. Obviously, there is a change in the tool tip when the force curve swings upward, that is different from the wear processes described previously. This failure process is probably related to fatigue phenomena that will be described in the next section. The initiation of these fatigue phenomena may, in some respects, be related to the wear process.

As the tool wears, there is usually an increase in the forces on the tool tip due to a dulling of the cutting edge. The stress necessary to fracture ceramics shows a statistical distribution, with definite probabilities of fracture existing well below the mean-fracture stress. During wear of a ceramic tool, the probability of fracture will increase as the forces increase. Sudden unexpected fractures within a cut may occur just because the strength of the ceramic was exceeded on a statistical basis. The increase in stresses due to wear can also accelerate other processes which are occurring, such as deformation and fatigue.

With higher stresses, the temperatures developed at the interface between the tool; the work will also increase which will again accelerate these failure processes.

Wear also produces changes in the shape of the cutting surface which in turn brings about a redistribution of the forces acting on the tool. Referring back to Fig. 99, the deep-notch cut into the tool at the depth of cut mark will undoubtedly change the stress distribution locally. For example, the resultant normal forces acting on a cylindrical notch will produce tensile stress in the notch in much the same way a hollow cylinder is placed under tension by an internal pressure. These forces will tend to produce a tensile fracture along the axis of the evacuated notch. The same reasoning holds true for the more subtle curvatures produced more generally on certain wear surfaces, such as the crater shown in Fig. 61 in Chapter 3. The shape of the wear surface is partially controlled by machining parameters such as work-piece material and feed per revolution.

Changes in work piece or feed could have secondary effects on tool life as a result of the configuration developed on the wear surfaces. We do not know whether or not this is a significantly important parameter.

Potentially, the most important consequence of wear might be related to crack nucleation on the wear surfaces. Cottrell (92) has summarized the various processes in a review paper by which cracks can be initiated in solids. Our particular concern here are those processes by which cracks can be formed as the result of deformational processes. Basically, most theories depend upon the pile-up and coalescence of dislocations at a boundary to form a void, which then acts as a stress riser and is propagated as a crack. For example, dislocations running along a slip band can pile up at a grain boundary to produce the necessary crack nucleus. This process had been observed in MgO crystals by Stokes *et al.* (93). Cottrell points out that in layered structures, a crack can form at the intersection of a slip plane and a tilt boundary. The theory of the process was worked out by Friedel (94) and Stroh (95). Aluminum oxide is, in a sense, a layered structure with slip predominately occurring only in the basel planes. Figure 114 is an electron photomicrograph of a fracture

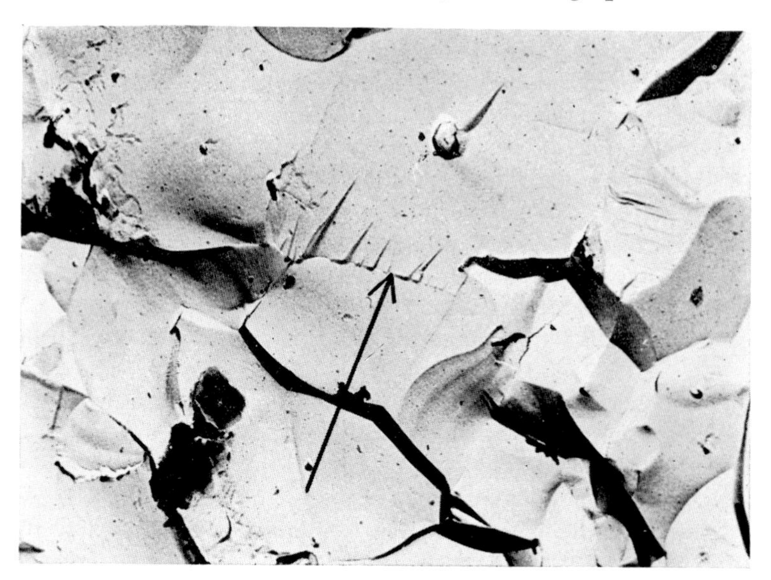

FIG. 114. Electron photomicrograph of a tool-fracture surface showing a boundary between two grains. Approximately 17,000 ×.

surface showing what is probably a tilt boundary in an alumina tool.

In his discussion, Cottrell says that structures of this type which slip only in the basel plane cannot relieve the elastic energy brought to the dislocation pile-up by plastic flow. This conclusion results from the lack of other slip systems available for deformation. In this case, the stress will increase at the pile-up, ultimately resulting in crack formation. Cottrell thinks that the brittleness of some hexagonal metals may be due to this effect. This is also a possible crack nucleation mechanism in aluminum oxide.

Biggs and Pratt (96) have shown the surface films can act as barriers for dislocation motion. If our speculation on the occurrence of a basal surface film on the wear surface has any merit, this film could act as the barrier against which the dislocations pile up. These pile-ups would occur in the top layer of crystallites and produce cracks extending down into the body of the material. Certainly, other interfaces could also act to stop dislocation motion, such as grain boundaries or subgrain boundaries. Figure 115 is a transmission electron photomicrograph of a tool bit showing extensive subgrain structures.

Films of tool-bit material, such as this one, develop patterns of holes through them when heated in the electron beam. These holes might result from screw dislocations which cause preferential sublimation of the alumina in the vicinity of the dislocation. A film in which this has occurred is shown in Fig. 116.

The application of shear stress at high temperatures will cause dislocations already present to move if they are not too strongly pinned; or it can cause new dislocations to form. In any event, it is plausable to expect dislocations moving and piling up against boundaries during the wear process. The plastic deformation which occurs during the wear process has not been demonstrated to cause crack nucleation, and the foregoing discussion is correspondently speculative.

The evidence presented in Chapter 1, Fig. 16, indicates that of the ceramic tools tested, all tools fell into one of two categories. The tools which exhibited the higher wear rate at 1500 fpm were also those tools (except Revolox which is not a true ceramic) which were able to survive the most stringent machining conditions and those (except Degussit) which have received wide acceptance by U.S. industry due to their superior performance. The higher wear rate could be an advantage in the particular case in which the wear,

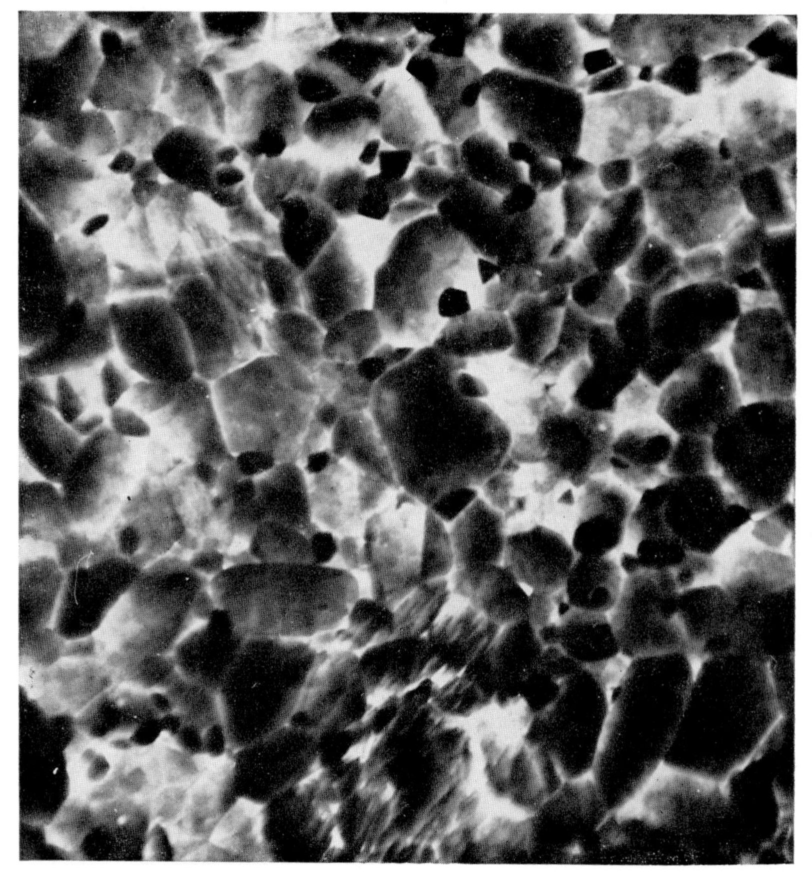

Fig. 115. Transmission-electron photomicrograph of a ceramic tool showing subgrain structure. 15,000 ×.

normal to the tool surface, occurs at a rate equal to or slightly greater than the propagation of crack nuclei. When this occurs, the tool should be durable in terms of fracture failure—and perhaps the higher wear rate is advantageous with particular machining conditions.

B. Fatigue

Our present knowledge about fatigue processes in ceramics is very sketchy. In this section, we cannot hope to present authoritative and irrefutable evidence, either from the literature or from our own

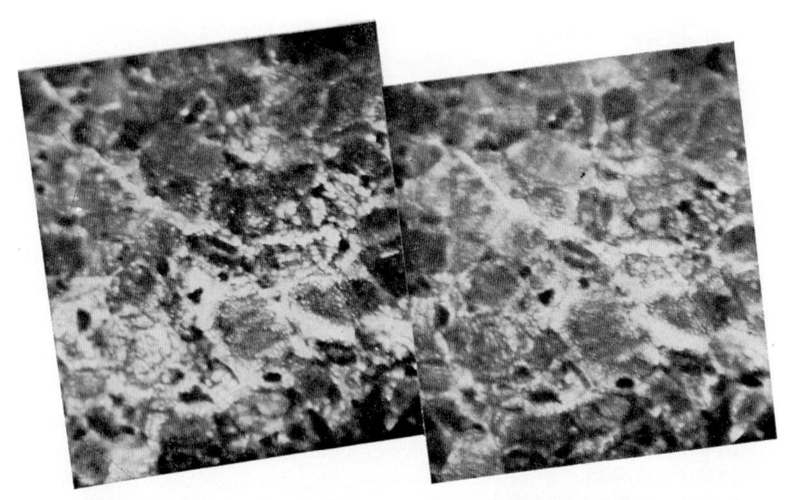

FIG. 116. Transmission-electron photomicrograph of a tool-bit section heated in the electron beam. The small holes are thought to arise from higher vapor pressure in the disturbed region around screw dislocations. 3000 ×.

experience, for fatigue being indisputably responsible for ceramic-tool failure. Nor, can we hope to define the exact atomistic mechanisms which are functioning to produce this failure. We are reluctant to write on a subject about which we know so little. But, we are even more reluctant not to write on a subject which we consider central to the tool-life problem. What we hope to do is present evidence and reasoning which indicate that fatigue is most probably a subject that must be further considered in regard to tool-material problems. Furthermore, we can discuss fatigue mechanisms taken from the literature which should be considered as potential causes of ceramic-tool behavior.

Essentially, there are two stress conditions that must be considered in fatigue: cyclic stress and static stresses. In both cases, the stress levels are below the macroscopic yield point or rupture strength and are applied for extended periods of time. In both cases and under appropriate conditions, there may or may not be macroscopic deformation accompanying the development of fractures. One primary distinction between fatigue and short-time stress applications, is that in fatigue sufficient time is provided for slow processes to contribute to the materials degradation.

For example, processes requiring diffusion of vacancies or impurities can, if given enough time, assume a greater importance. No doubt, fatigue processes are related to failure processes that occur at shorter durations, and must ultimately be explained by such defects as dislocations, vacancies, impurities, boundaries, and interactions between these.

1. Evidence for Fatigue Failure

In the common case where a ceramic tool is cutting metal and a sudden unexplained failure occurs without any observable changes in cutting conditions, this is a fatigue failure—almost by definition. The tool tip is subjected to stress, both static and cyclic, for a period of extended duration before failure occurs. This behavior by itself suggests that internal-structural degradation is occurring prior to the ultimate failure. This is also substantiated by the performance of reground CCT-707 ceramic tools cutting brake drums by industry, where tool life of the refinished bits is substantially lower than that of the original tools (97). If tool failure was related exclusively to the configuration changes accompanying wear, this reduction of performance would not be expected. This is cited as a priori evidence that fatigue mechanisms are operating. This sort of reasoning leads us to take a close look at used ceramic tools to see if this degenerative damage could be observed. Figure 117 is a photomicrograph of a polished section of a VR97 ceramic tool which was used to cut A-6, Rc 50 steel.

The rounded portion on the right is a section through the wear land with the black lines representing the original configuration of the surface. The small original land ground on the tool was about 0.006-inch wide. A number of cracks can be seen in the wear land and in the crater area at the top. This particular crack pattern, while by no means universal, was found to be typical under a variety of test conditions. It should be pointed out that this tool was still functioning at the time the test was stopped. This damage then is cumulative damage in the tool at some stage of development prior to failure. These are fatigue cracks.

Figure 118 is a similar section through the wear surface of a VR97 tool after extensive use machining A-6 tool steel at about Rc 50.

The section was photographed using polarized light (crossed nicols) so that the structural damage in the crater area was revealed. The light areas and bright spots under these lighting conditions are indicative of strain and microcracks occurring in this area.

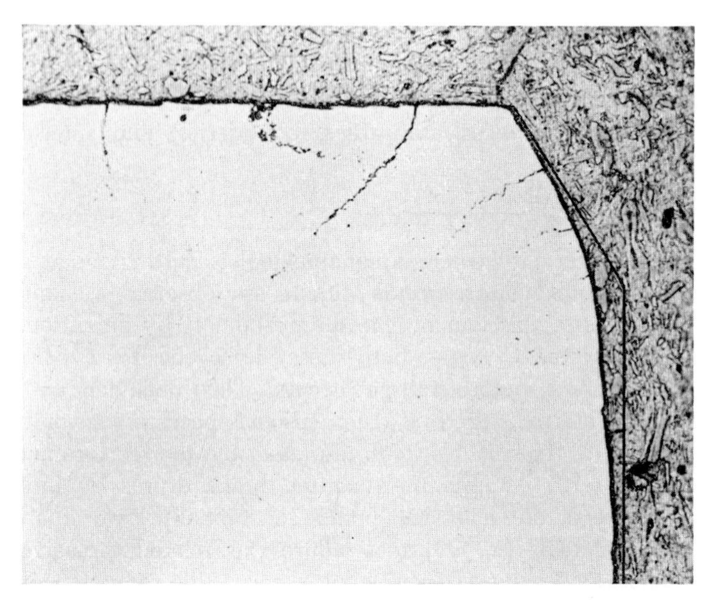

FIG. 117. Polished section through a used ceramic tool showing wear and fatigue cracks. 200 ×.

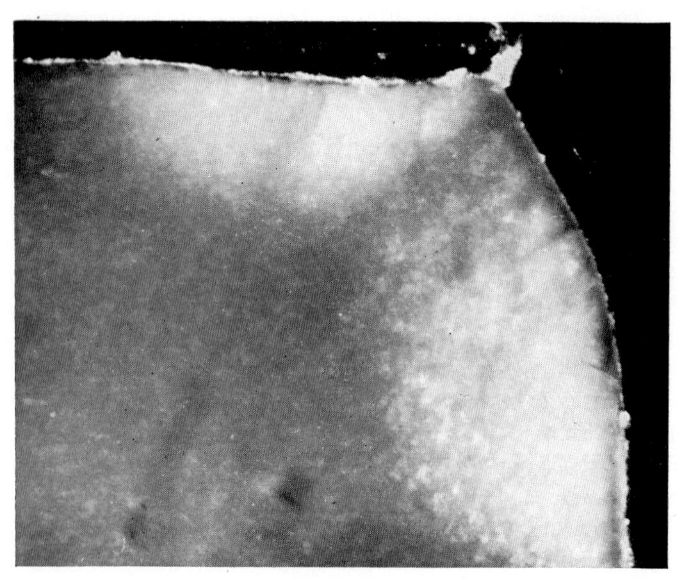

FIG. 118. Polished section through a used ceramic tool which was photographed using polarized light to show internal damage. 200 ×.

Fatigue cracks are seen in approximately the same positions as before. The predominate mass of fatigue damage is in the crater area and extends about 0.007 inch below the crater surface. This tool had not failed in service and was functioning satisfactorily at the time the test was discontinued.

A series of machining experiments was initiated at Ohio State University by Moore and Kibbey (98) in the effort to study the effects of machining vibrations on ceramic-tool life. In general, the effects of cyclic stresses on materials is to cause fatigue failures at stresses lower than static loading, and much lower than the stresses in short-duration strength tests.

These tests are, properly considered, cyclic endurance fatigue tests in an actual machining operation. The vibrations were self induced during cutting by the use of a specially designed tool holder with a reduced cross section which allowed the tool to chatter in a controlled manner.

Figure 119 is a drawing of the tool holder which was used.

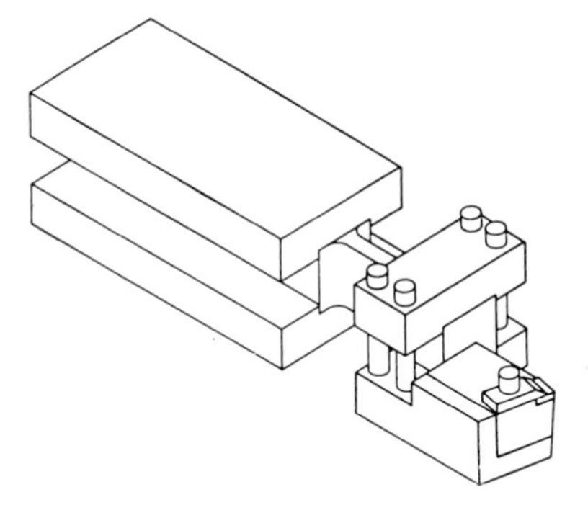

FIG. 119. Replaceable reduced area-shank tool holder for self-induced vibrations (Moore and Kibbey, 98).

The length of the reduced section controlled the frequency of the vibration. The orientation of the cross section controlled the direction of vibration. For the configuration shown, it is evident that the tool will have the tendency to vibrate predominately in the feed direction. The amplitude of the vibration could be controlled by the cutting speed. It was found that as the tool wore, the vibration damped. This prohibited tool-life measurements.

The sizes and configurations of the reduced section are shown in Table XIV.

TABLE XIV

Configuration of Reduced Section in Tool Holder

Curve[a]	Reduced section	Orientation of predominate vibration
1	3/8 × 1 1/2 × 1/2 inch[b]	Feed
2	3/8 × 1 1/2 × 1/2 inch	Tangential
3	5/8 × 5/8 × 1/2 inch	Symmetrical
4	3/8 × 1 1/2 × 2 inches	Feed
5	3/8 × 1 1/2 × 2 inches	Tangential
6	5/8 × 5/8 × 2 inches	Symmetrical

[a] Curve numbers refer to Fig. 120 (Moore and Kibbey, 98).
[b] Length of reduced section.

The data for the wear rate of the tool with cutting speed for the six holders are shown in Fig. 120.

Higher wear rates were obtained at high-vibration amplitudes (high speeds) and at higher frequencies (shorted reduced sections). The preliminary experiment was qualitative in nature and the actual amplitudes and frequencies were not measured. The most interesting

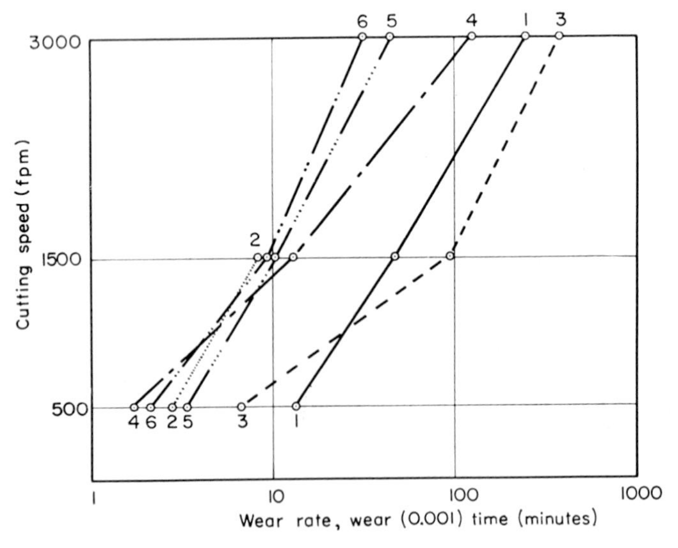

Fig. 120. Wear rate of ceramic tools with speed for different vibration conditions. Curve numbers refer to tool-holder configurations given in Table XIV (Moore and Kibbey, 98).

conclusions drawn from the experiment are that the direction of vibration is of great importance on wear rate and that higher frequencies are much more detrimental than lower frequencies. Vibrations in the tangential direction would have the effect of varying the cutting speed and tool-loading forces are insensitive to changes in cutting speed in this range of high speeds. Vibrations in the feed direction would have the effect of changing the feed, and the forces are very sensitive to these changes. Vibrating in the feed direction would be expected to be detrimental if these vibrations produce forces exceeding the fatigue limit of the tool material or produced momentary higher cutting temperatures. The energy contained in a vibration is proportional in the cube of the frequency and when the vibrating object is working against a restraining force, much of this energy is absorbed. It is expected then that under machining conditions, the tool wear might well be sensitive to vibrational frequency because of the larger amounts of energy involved (assuming an equivalent amplitude). Also, with the more rapid accelerations that occur at higher frequencies, the conditions can approach shock loading, and the brittle character of the ceramic becomes more important in the failure mechanism.

Williams (99) has published an extensive review on fatigue processes in ceramics and shows that fatigue processes are common with these materials. Shand (100) taking Williams' data showed that the cyclic endurance limit of sintered alumina was only 0.56 of the single-stroke strength, and the static-endurance limit 0.77 of the single-stroke strength. Williams develops a reasonable basis for comparison of fatigue failure in alumina with hexagonal metals under appropriate temperature conditions. In machining, an additional "simplification" occurs in that the restraining high pressures permit plastic deformation, and Williams' analogy with metal behavior can be extended to a more general case. While we do not know what to expect in particular with alumina, we can reasonably expect certain processes to occur in general. It would be as bad a mistake to disregard this analogy as it would be to take it too literally, or to attempt to draw from it detailed conclusions. Two different fatigue conditions exist on the cutting tool depending upon its position in relation to the surface. The material undergoing deformation, right at the surface, is exposed to processes of degradation that are different from these acting on the material which comprises the body of the tool tip. In the first case, deformational process can become predominate;

and deterioration plays a greater role in the bulk of the material-grain boundary. Fatigue processes in the surface layer will affect the wear rate. Fatigue processes in the underlying mass of material will affect massive-fracture processes and microspalling. Fatigue behavior has to be considered in both ductile materials and brittle materials.

2. Fatigue Processing

Any fatigue process has to be explained ultimately on the basis of crystal imperfections acting under stress so as to alter the physical properties and eventually nucleate and propagate cracks. A variety of mechanisms has been proposed for different cases which offer explanations of the observed phenomena. The two separate cases of fatigue behavior in ductile materials as well as fatigue behavior in brittle materials will be considered.

a. Ductile Fatigue

In general, a ductile metal undergoing cyclic stresses will follow one of two mechanisms of failure, depending upon the stress level employed according to Wood (101). The curves plotting amplitude of the cyclic stress (S) against the number of cycles necessary to produce failure (N) show a change in fatigue mechanism below a particular stress level, as shown schematically in Fig. 121.

Wood refers to the mechanism operating in the steep portion of the curve on the left as the "H" mechanism. The mechanism operating on the flat curve to the right he calls the "F" mechanism. Both of

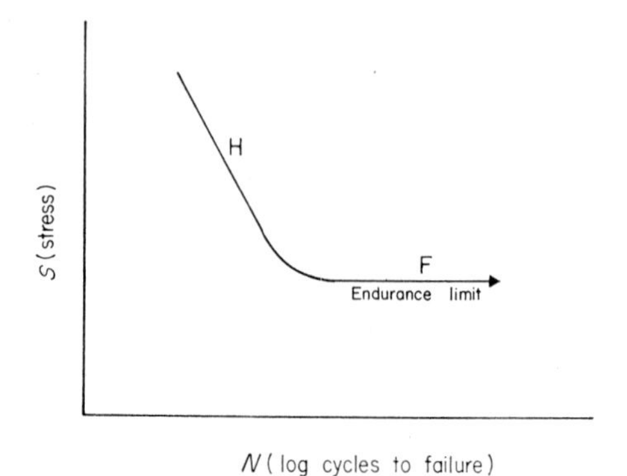

Fig. 121. Fatigue of materials for stress amplitudes S and number of cycles to failure N (Wood, 101).

these mechanisms depend upon plastic deformation and the development of slip bands in the crystals. The "H" mechanism is similar to that which occurs in unidirectional stressing, and due to dislocation pile-ups the material work hardens. These pile-ups can concentrate stresses and nucleate microcracks in the specimen. The "F" mechanism proceeds by fine slip without appreciable work hardening occurring. Coffin and Tavernelli (102) have shown that over a wide variety of conditions and for a wide variety of metals the number of cycles to failure is inversely proportional to the square of the plastic-strain amplitude. Gilman (103) has pointed out that the coalescence of debris formed by dislocation motion would be expected to result in this relationship. Gilman considers that this process is more important at the beginning of the strain-hardening process and, therefore, might account for the fatigue mechanism operating in Woods "F" portion of the S-*N* curve where only limited strain hardening occurs. Extensive strain hardening occurs in the "H" portion of the S-*N* curve and direct elastic interactions between dislocations which occur at high concentrations in the slip bands may account for the change in hardness. The crack nucleation mechanism in the "H" portion could be dislocation pile-ups and subsequent coalescence against obstacles such as those shown by Stroh. The crack nucleation mechanism in the "F" portion at lower stress levels could be the coalescence of dislocation debris, as suggested by Gilman.

In any case, the fatigue process is most certainly associated with dislocation formation, motion, and reactions which occur between dislocations and between dislocations and other structural or interstitial discontinuities. The deformation layer of metals (or ceramics) in wear scars must be subjected to fatigue processes such as those described above. Fatigue in this sense would cause work hardening of this surface layer (the bearing "running in" process?) and ultimately become effective in providing the conditions necessary to fracture asperities to produce wear debris. The fatigue behavior of a material subjected to sliding wear would be an important factor governing the rate at which material is removed from the surface.

Figure 122 is an electron photomicrograph of a wear land on a ceramic tool at the intersection with the original ground-tool surface.

The irregular rough texture of the wear surface at the bottom is indicative of alumina-wear debris which formed on the wear surface and was removed. The texture of the wear surface further up the land is much smoother and suggests that wear debris was not forming

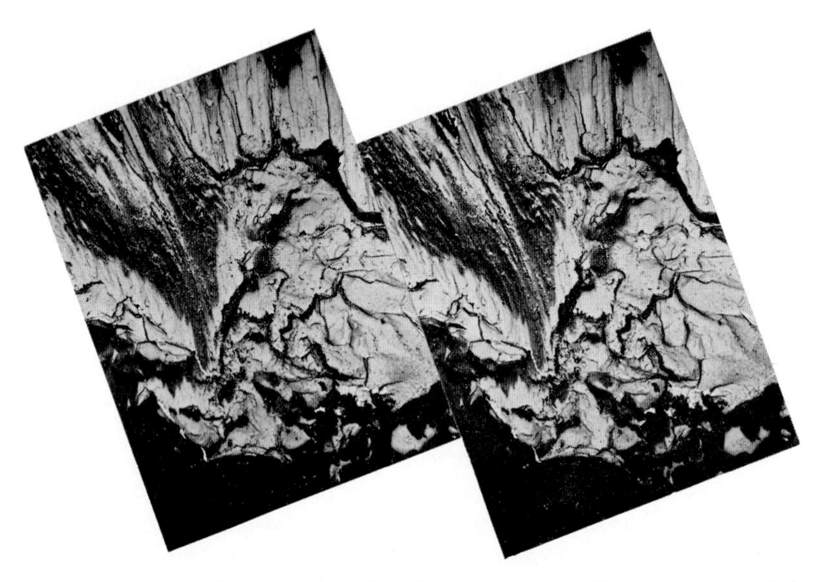

Fig. 122. Stereo-electron photo of tool-wear surface at the intersection of the tool flank. 3000 ×.

at this location. Excluding the microspalling mechanism of wear debris, the actual removal of alumina from the tool on the wear land seems to occur predominately at the bottom of the land. This material evidently has undergone extensive deformation strain and is most probably work hardened.

b. Brittle Fatigue

Materials that are normally brittle, such as ceramics, often do not show macroscopic evidence of deformation prior to failure. Still, in a fatigue test, these materials often fail at stress levels below the normal breaking strength, indicating that some damage must accumulate at these lower stress levels. This damage is often associated with grain-boundary deterioration. Most proposed mechanisms that attempt to explain fatigue behavior of brittle materials also depend upon lattice defects. One primary difference associated with these materials, from the ductile case, is that mechanisms are not present for the internal release of stress concentrations, such as by cross slip. It appears that under these conditions very high internal stresses can accumulate very rapidly with a minimum of lattice defects contributing to them, thereby, making macroscopic defection of plastic flow difficult. Williams has considered that the elastic strain associated with cyclic loading can cause motion of defects or flaws already present in the material and lead to fatigue failure without the necessity of generating new defects. Since flaws are universally present in structural materials, each cycle of elastic strain could, for example, cause a minute propagation of an existing Griffith crack. Forty (104) has shown that cleavage cracks in NaCl and LiF will partially reheal if the stress tending to produce them is removed. In a cyclic stress condition, he visualized a process of cracking and partial rehealing that would advance the crack a small increment for each cycle. As the crack becomes longer, the stress needed to propagate it becomes less, and degenerative failure could occur. Deformational processes are probably associated with the material at the crack tip, but the detailed explanation of crack propagation is still obscure.

Pearson (105) has shown that the delayed fracture (static loading) of alumina can be largely eliminated if the sintered-alumina specimens are heat treated and tested in a vacuum. The implications of these measurements are that the atmosphere reacts with the stressed material, in such a way, to promote fracture. Stress corrosion of metals, or the effects of atmospheres and protective coatings on metal-fatigue specimens, are well known, of course, and atmosphere effects are not completely unexpected. Perhaps, it is somewhat surprising that similar processes occur with very inert materials like aluminum oxide.

In a polycrystalline aggregate, which is cyclic stressed at high temperatures, it is not uncommon to find cracking along grain boundaries. Internal friction studies indicate that grain-boundary sliding adsorbs energy and the cracking that occurs in fatigue tests suggests that part of this energy is used in forming additional defects at the boundaries which contribute to cumulative deterioration. Stavrolakis and Norton (106) have shown that alumina subjected to torsion at high temperatures develops cracks along grain boundaries. The propagation of these grain-boundary cracks leads to ultimate failure. Figure 123 is an area on the wear land of a ceramic tool showing extensive grain-boundary cracking in the underlying material.

The thin black wisps of material projecting from the visible boundaries are remnants of the plastic replica material which soaked into grain-boundary cracks. When the replica was stripped from the specimen, some of this plastic pulled out, leaving the films on the surface. Some of the extensive damage shown earlier in Fig. 118 is probably of this type.

Systematic and quantitative data on the fatigue properties of ceramics are rare. Some of the best data which exist are from the work of Parker *et al.* (107) on the breakdown of alumina bearings. Carter and Zaretsky (108) developed the method for the evaluation of ceramic bearings, utilizing intermittent loading at high-loading pressures. The sample being tested is a precision-ground sphere of

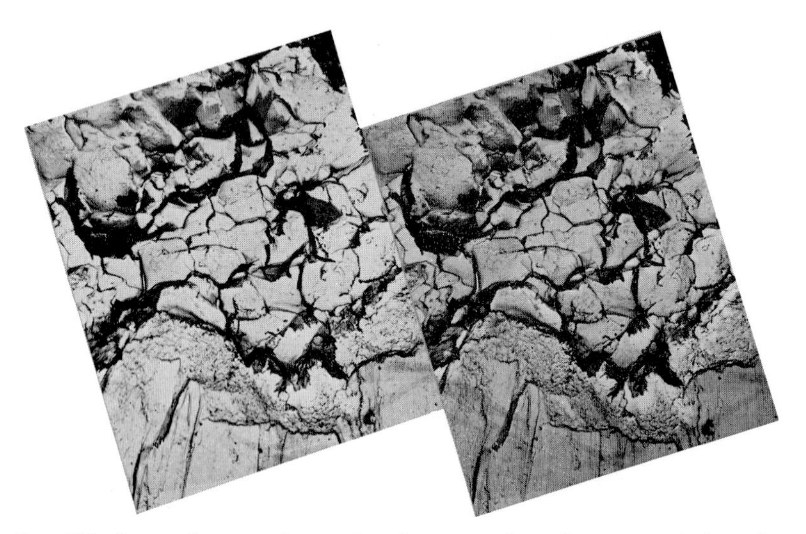

Fig. 123. Stereo-electron photo of tool-wear surface showing grain-boundary cracking in the underlying material. 3000 ×.

either hot-pressed or sintered alumina, which is supported by four other balls which rest on a race and are held in place by a separator as shown in Fig. 124.

The load and rotary motion are transmitted to the test ball through a drive spindle which is notched to match the tongue cut into the test specimen. As the sample rotates, the surface which contacts the four support balls is stressed four cycles per revolution. Failure of the test specimen is recorded when the pitting which develops reaches the full width of the running track. Their data appear in Fig. 125.

Figure 125 shows that an increase of loading stress of about 30 or 40% decreases the fatigue life by a factor of 10. The authors concluded that the load-carrying capacity of hot-pressed alumina was seven times greater than that of cold-pressed and sintered alumina.

Figure 126 shows their data plotted as the cycles to failure against the maximum stress, with the curves depicting the expected behavior for failure of 10% and 50% of the samples tested.

It will be helpful to our tool-failure hypothesis if a correlation can be made between tool life and this fatigue data, at least within an order of magnitude. A precise comparison is not possible since the stresses on the cutting edge can only be approximated, and at present

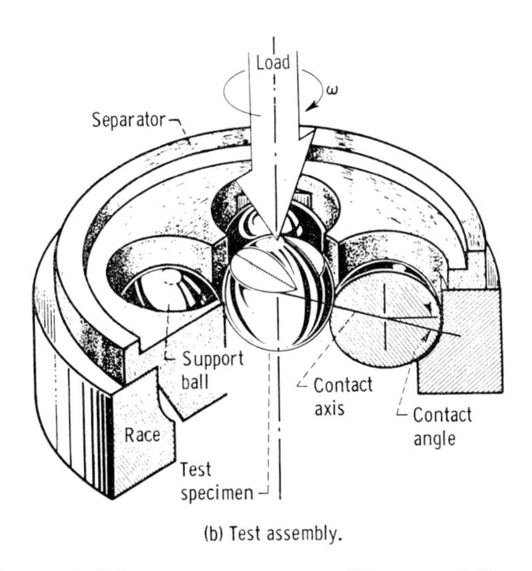

(b) Test assembly.

FIG. 124. Five-ball fatigue-test apparatus (Carter and Zaretsky, 108).

we have no measure of the degree to which these stresses are relaxed during a vibration cycle. The vibration frequency in the feed direction can be determined by measuring the peroidicity of the marks on the shoulder of the work piece which were left after the tool was extracted from the cut. Knowing the fpm and the tool life, the cycles to failure can be computed. The edge pressures have been estimated to be of the same order as the compressive strength of the tool material, as was shown in Chapters 1 and 3. Briefly, the argument is that the discontinuity in the wear curves as shown by their intercepts in Table III, Chapter 1, indicates that a discontinuous wear process occurs. The correlation between compressive strength and tool quality as shown in Fig. 18 suggests that the initial wear is due to the crushing of the cutting edge. It follows then, that the original pressures on

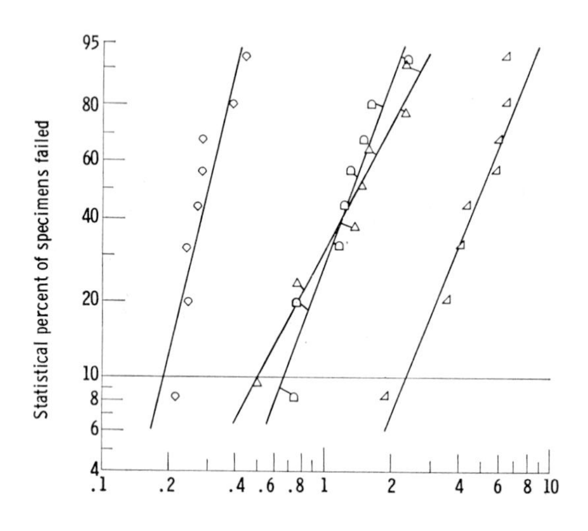

(a) Hot-pressed alumina.

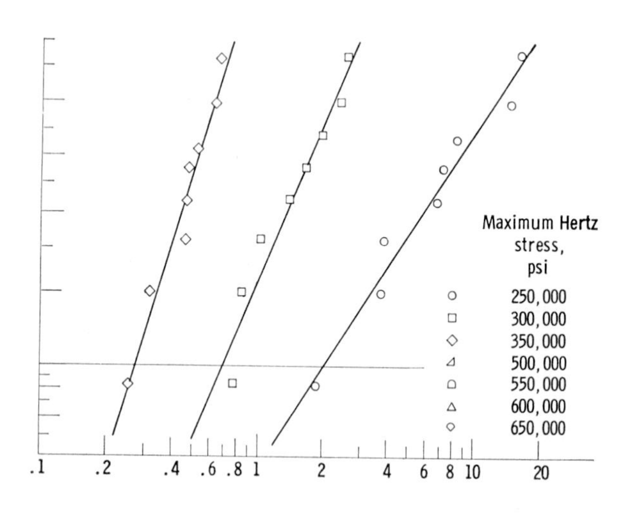

(b) Cold-pressed alumina.

Specimen life, millions of stress cycles

FIG. 125. Rolling-contact life of alumina-ball specimens, shaft speed, 950 rpm; contact angle, 20°; race temperature, 80°F; lubricant, mineral oil (Parker *et al.*, 107).

the tool edge are of the same order as the compressive strength of the ceramic material. Obviously, this is only an approximation, which becomes even less certain as there is no way at present to estimate to what degree this stress is relaxed during the vibration cycle.

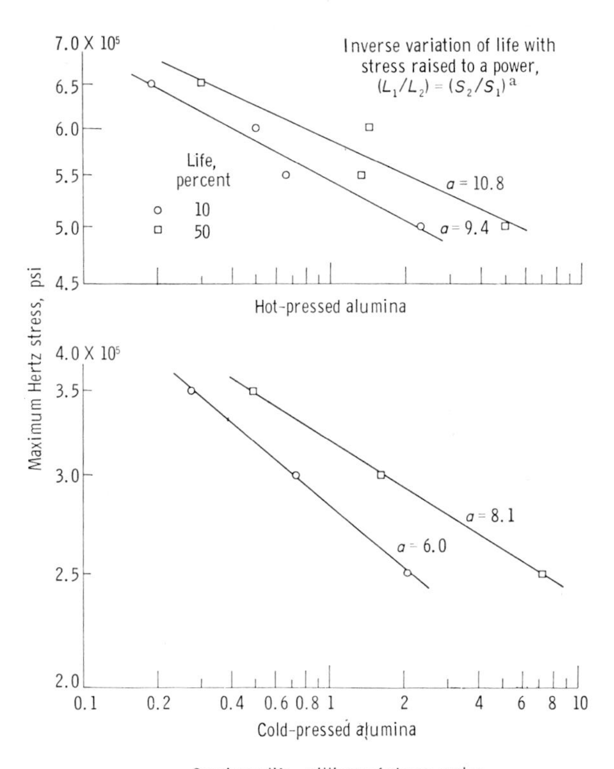

FIG. 126. Stress-life relation of hot- and cold-pressed alumina-ball specimens. Shaft speed, 950 rpm; contact angle, 20°; race temperature, 80°F; lubricant, highly-refined naphthanic mineral oil (Parker *et al.*, 107).

The data listed for the six samples in Table V, Chapter 3, for the ground chamfer tools indicate that at 1200 fpm, the 50% tool failure will occur at about 80 seconds using smoothed data. The vibration marks on the machined shoulder are about 0.010 inch apart, and therefore, about 2×10^6 cycles to failure occurred at 50%-sample survival. The average strength of this material is 5.7×10^5 psi as is shown in Table II, Chapter 1. The fact that this data—2×10^6 cycles and

5.7×10^5 psi—fall on the 50%-life curve shown in Fig. 126 is no doubt fortuitous. While we do not claim quantitative agreement to this degree of exactitude, we do feel that within the limits of the estimates there is at least a qualitative agreement between fatigue data and tool life, for this case. The testing conditions are obviously not identical, but a degree of similarity does occur in that in each case the material under stress is supported by surrounding matter which tends to inhibit catastrophic fracture. The sliding speeds varied by a factor of 10 in the two cases, with the tool-life data being collected at 1200 fpm and the bearing operating at about 125 fpm. The bearing was lubricated with a napthenic mineral oil, while the ceramic tools cut without the use of any coolant or lubricant. Other notable differences were the residual porosity in the bearing alumina as contrasted to the void-free ceramic tool and the higher temperature at which the ceramic tool operated. While all of these considerations temper our confidence in the conclusions, it should be pointed out that in essence the two cases are similar in that the interfacial pressures, cycles to failure, and materials are all essentially similar. Certainly at least the hypothesis that the delayed fracture failure of ceramic tools is related to a fatigue mechanism is consistent with the available fatigue data on alumina ceramics.

Most certainly, fatigue processes play an important role in tool life, both in wear and fracture failure. In general, stronger materials also show advantages in fatigue behavior and the development of stronger ceramics should increase ceramic-tool life beyond that now attainable. A more sophisticated approach in materials research directed towards the fatigue process itself could further increase tool life. This is a challenging problem of the future in ceramic-tool research.

Chapter 6

Tool Design

A. Tool Geometry

Research has established the feasibility of using ceramic tools for machining metals and for production processes.

Although ceramic tools have been developed with lower bending strengths than metallic tools, the use of ceramic tools has not been extended to the degree that some would like. Also, we are just recognizing that the variation in properties for the same tools produced by different manufacturers is a valid criterion in tool selection.

Acceptable aluminum oxide ceramic-tool materials have a compressive strength of 400,000 to 500,000 psi, a transverse rupture strength of 50,000 to 100,000 psi, and a tensile strength somewhat less than the latter. It thus becomes obvious that tool geometries should minimize opportunities for fracture failure and, in fact, this can be done to a remarkably satisfying degree.

The strongest cutting edge is obviously the one that is developed with the greatest included angle, 90° or more between adjacent surfaces. This principle is used to advantage in the employment of negative rakes, cutting-edge lands, and lead angles.

The actual tool geometries, however, are invariably selected according to the cutting operation to be performed, the type of machine to be used, and the type of tool holder to be used.

Table XV gives the general range of cutting angles and geometries that have been employed successfully on a variety of work materials. See Fig. 127 for a key to angle and geometry nomenclature (8). Angle combinations within these ranges may, of course, be varied to meet the specific job requirement.

1. Rake Angles

Positive- and negative-rake angles have been widely investigated. The majority of experiments with steels have indicated that in order

TABLE XV

General Range of Cutting Angles and Geometrics

Material to be machined	Side rake[a]	Back rake[a]	End relief[a]	Side relief[a]	Side cutting edge angle[a]	End cutting edge angle[a]	Nose radius (inch)
Soft steel to 200 bhn	0 to −15	0 to −15	2 to 10	2 to 10	0 to 60	5 to 20	1/32 to 1/8
Medium soft steel to 275 bhn	0 to −15	0 to −15	2 to 10	2 to 10	0 to 60	5 to 20	1/32 to 1/8
Medium steel to 350 bhn	0 to −15	0 to −15	2 to 10	2 to 10	0 to 60	5 to 20	1/32 to 1/8
Medium hard steel to 450 bhn	5 to −10	5 to −10	2 to 5	2 to 5	0 to 60	5 to 15	1/32 to 1/16
Hard steel to 600 bhn	0 to −7	0 to −7	2 to 5	2 to 5	0 to 60	5 to 15	1/32 to 1/16
Cast iron	0 to −7	0 to −7	2 to 10	2 to 10	0 to 60	5 to 20	1/32 to 1/16
Nonmetallic	0 to +10	0 to +10	6 to 18	6 to 18	0 to 60	5 to 20	1/32 to 1/8

[a] Measured in degrees.

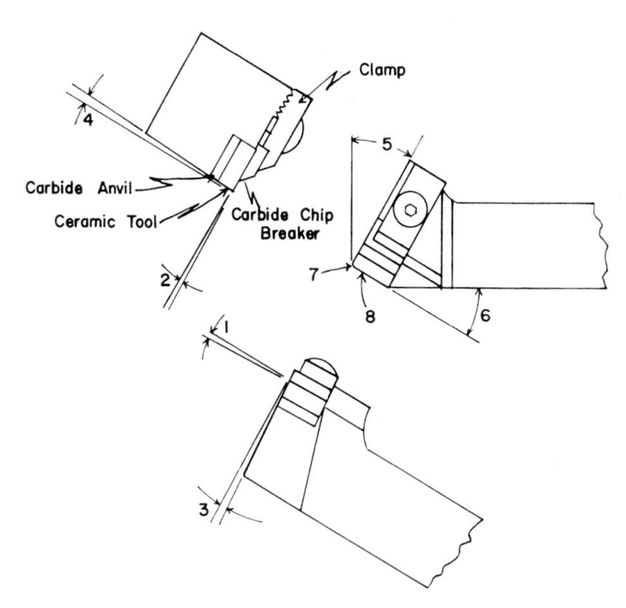

FIG. 127. Ceramic tool holder. Key to tool angle nomenclature: 1, back rake angle 2, side rake angle; 3, end relief angle; 4, side relief angle; 5, end cutting edge and angle; 6, side cutting edge angle; 7, nose radius; 8, cutting edge.

to optimize tool life it is desirable to have a negative-rake angle at the cutting edge for a distance at least equivalent to the feed per revolution. From there on the tool top may be raked positive or negative depending on the desired chip control.

The most common form of ceramic tool is the disposable or "throwaway" insert which is supplied by manufacturers in square, triangular, and circular shapes and a wide variety of dimensions (Fig. 128). The rake angle is usually built into the holder so that the insert may use all of the cutting edges. Selection of the rake angle is usually a compromise between the design for maximum strength and the desired surface finish. Strength decreases with negative-angle decrease while finish increases or improves. Greater advantages, however, can be taken of the strength of negative rakes on ceramic tools than on carbide without fear of detriment to surface finish because of the lower affinity of ceramics for metals and the small inclination to a loaded or built-up cutting edge. Consequently, the resultant force of cutting can be directed into the tool so as to utilize the ceramics' high-compressive strength.

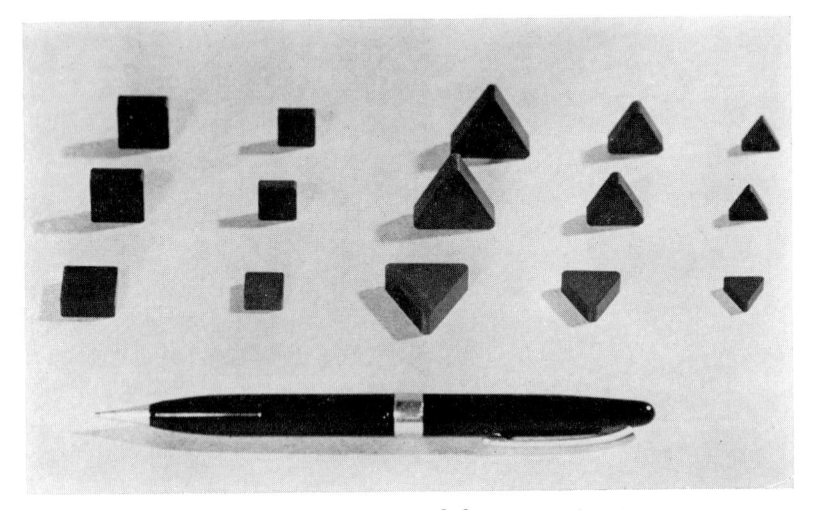

Fig. 128. Precision-ground throw-away inserts.

Prior experience with throwaway cemented-carbide tooling has been most helpful in developing optimum practice for ceramics. However, the limiting geometries for carbides differ from those for ceramic tooling. High negative-rake angles subject cemented carbide tools to rapid failure, probably by increasing temperature beyond a certain critical range and promoting welding of the chip, followed by subsequent shear failure. This effect does not appear to exist with oxide tools. Rake angles up to $-20°$ have showed advantage according to one investigator (109).

2. Relief Angles

The function of the relief or clearance angles is to prevent the tool surface, directly below the cutting edge, from rubbing against the unmachined surface of the work piece. Theoretically, these angles can be very small (less than $10°$) and would be most desirable insofar as maximum strength of cutting edge is concerned. To determine angle to eliminate tool flank-rub, a number of variables must be taken into consideration. These include work-piece characteristics, tool and holder rigidity, machine condition, and tool wear. Thus $2°$ becomes a practical minimum in most cases and the maximum is dictated by retaining sufficient strength (support) to prevent breaking off of the cutting edge.

The analysis of numerous experiments of steel turning in Russia (110) indicates that clearance strongly affects radial wear of the tool. Tools with small clearance have improved dimensional stability but frequently they have a poorer overall life than larger clearances. Thus the choice of a larger clearance may be influenced by desired tool life between regrinds. In any case the maximum value of the clearance angle is determined by the mechanical strength requirement of the cutting edge.

3. Cutting-Edge Angles

Cutting edge or lead angles greater than 0° are desirable when work-piece configurations permit their use. A number of benefits accrue from the use of lead angles; three of the more important ones are as follows.

1. Impact loading on the cutting tip is reduced as it enters the work piece. At the start of a cut, the first contact with work is well back from the radius and up along leading edge where the tool is strong.

2. Compressive loading on the cutting edge is gradually reduced as it breaks through and leaves cut. On break-out at the end of the cut, the tool does not cut off a ring, but takes a chip that is even decreasing in size until just a light chip is being removed as the cut finally ends. Thus the change of a reaction tensile failure is considerably reduced.

3. The unit cutting pressure is reduced as the lead angle is increased by distributing total load over a greater length. With a fixed-feed rate, the chip becomes longer and thinner as the lead angle is increased. The stock removal remains the same volumewise, but the cutting load is distributed over a longer cutting edge.

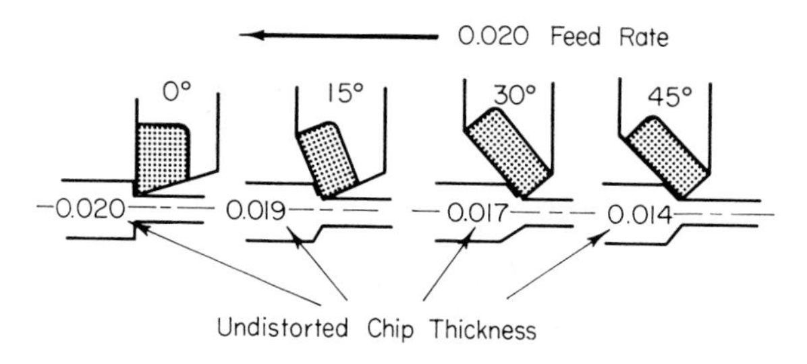

Fig. 129. Side cutting-edge angle versus undistorted chip thickness.

The first and second benefits of a lead angle are obvious and easy to understand. By orienting the tool around, so that the nose trails the leading edge, the tool does not suddenly get a full-chip load the moment the work is entered or go from a full chip to a no chip the moment the tool starts breaking out of the cut.

The third benefit, a thinning of the chip is less obvious but follows similar straight forward reasoning. Consider the three conditions illustrated in Fig. 129, the first a 0° lead angle; the second a 45° lead, and the third a 70° lead. In each case the depth of cut is 0.25 inch and the feed 0.010 inch per revolution. As the tool is turned so that the lead angle is increased, the chip is spread out over a wider area of the edge of the tool. At a 0° lead, the 0.25-inch depth gives a chip 0.25-inch wide by 0.010-inch thick. At 45° lead, the chip width increases to 0.350 inch along the cutting edge of the tool and chip thickness reduces to 0.007 inch. At 70° lead, the chip width spreads out to 1.45 inch along the leading edge of the tool and chip thickness is further reduced to 0.0017 inch.

Because edge pressure on ceramic tools is more critical than cemented carbides, a thin chip, which greatly extends the edge length carrying the load, is a substantial advantage. Therefore, as much lead angle as the rigidity of the machine and part will allow is usually used. It is wise to remember that a large lead angle has a tendency to push the work away from the tool and for this reason, large lead angles are not usually used on long slender work pieces.

Another reason for the use of lead angle may be the control of chip direction and flow. This point will be covered more fully under machining conditions.

Some lead angle can be used in the majority of cases and the actual amount for optimum results will be determined by test.

4. Nose Radius

The nose radius is often dictated by the design of the work piece. If the radius is not so established, it is desirable to make it as large as practical within the limits imposed by operating conditions. A minimum nose radius on the tool eliminates or reduces chatter (vibration). However, a nose radius that is too small can result in either chipping or fracture near the nose.

A large radius is further beneficial to the extent that it functions like an increased lead angle and allows for more gradual entrance and exit from the work piece.

However, with larger nose radii, a greater radial wear is created at the tip of the tool because it is at this point that chip thickness is at a minimum and abrasive rubbing is at a maximum. Furthermore, the larger nose radii produce greater chip distortion and require more power which may produce chatter.

Thus it is obvious that the nose radius should be as large as possible without producing dangerous chatter (vibrations) which would shorten tool life and result in poor finish.

Extensive work by Moore and Kibbey (111), where nose radii were varied between $\frac{1}{64}$ inch and $\frac{1}{8}$ inch, indicated in all cases that an increase in nose radius resulted in a decrease in tool chipping. A doubling of the radius decreased the tendency for chipping by approximately 50% under test conditions using rigid equipment and a heavy work piece.

The work of Makarov (110) in Russia with steel turning indicated an optimum nose radius of 1–1.5 mm (0.040 inch–0.060 inch) for minimum radial tool wear and best surface finish. Further increase of nose radius increased radial tool wear.

Similarly, the work of Okushima and Yoshiya (42) in Japan showed that tool life is improved substantially with increase in nose radius from 0.1 to 1.0 mm. But when a nose radius is over 1.0 mm, reduction of tool life is caused by chattering. The larger radius tends to present a favorable flank wear and improve surface finish.

Tests by Gion and Perrin (112) in France indicate a nose-radius-speed relationship of importance. At surface speeds below 400 meters/minute, nose radii from 1 mm (0.040 inch) to 2 mm (0.080 inch) performed no differently; but at higher speeds, a 1-mm radius was found to be vulnerable to cracking and consequently the tool was weakened.

Extensive tests by Siekman and Sowinski (109) have shown that nose radius and angles of use of ceramic tools are important and differ from the optimum for carbide tools. The graphical representation of the results of their studies of machining of normalized AISI 1045 steel billets are presented in Fig. 130–136.

5. The Cutting Edge

A narrow negative land honed onto the cutting edge of a tool (Fig. 137) substantially decreases the tendency for tool tip to fracture.

The use of edge lands, first proposed by Moore and Kibbey (111) of Ohio State University in 1957, is today generally accepted for use

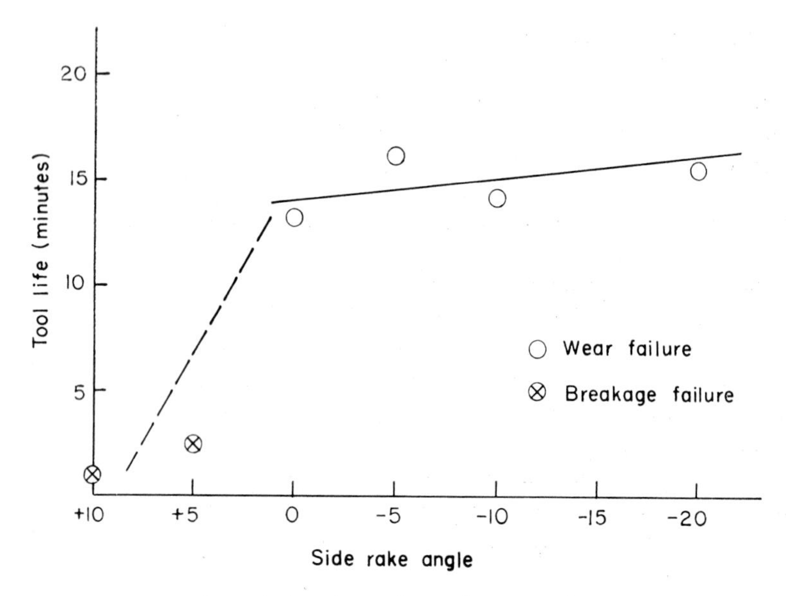

FIG. 130. Effect of side-rake angle (Siekmann and Sowinski, 109).

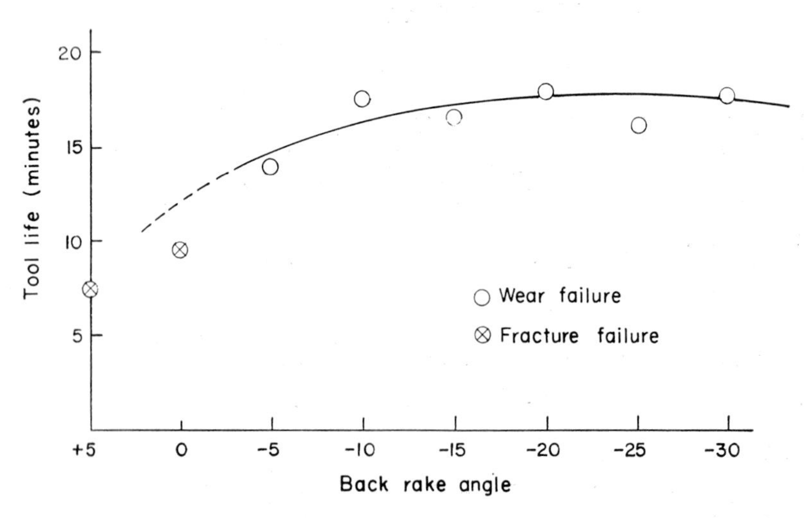

FIG. 131. Effect of back-rake angle (Siekmann and Sowinski, 109).

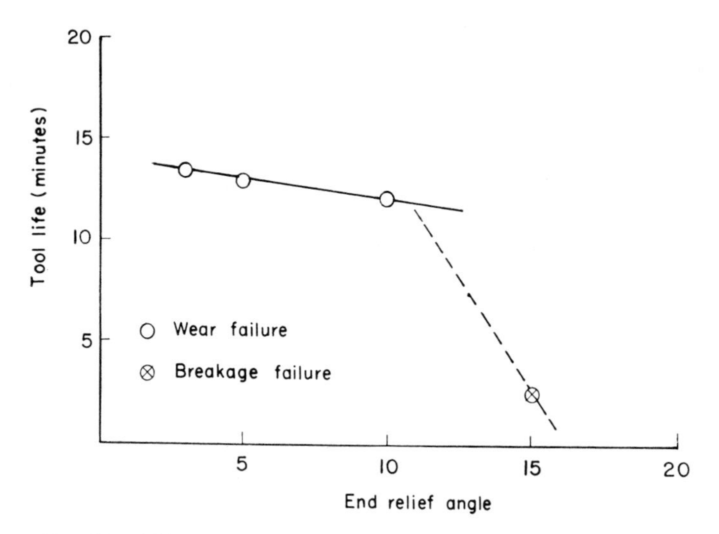

FIG. 132. Effect of end-relief angle (Siekmann and Sowinski, 109).

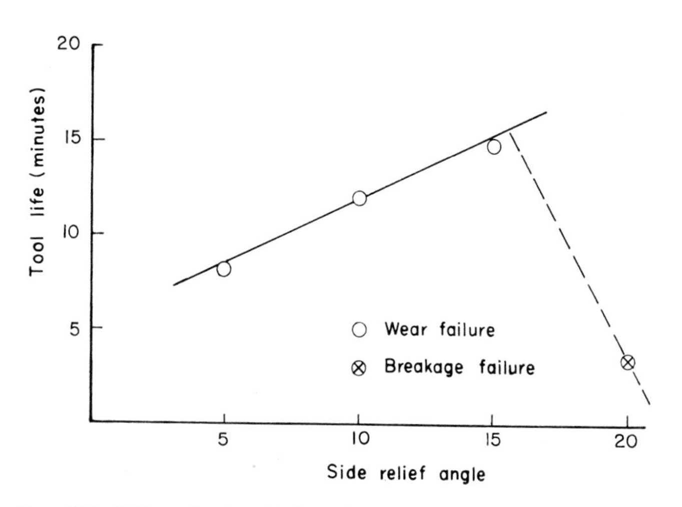

FIG. 133. Effect of side-relief angle (Siekmann and Sowinski, 109).

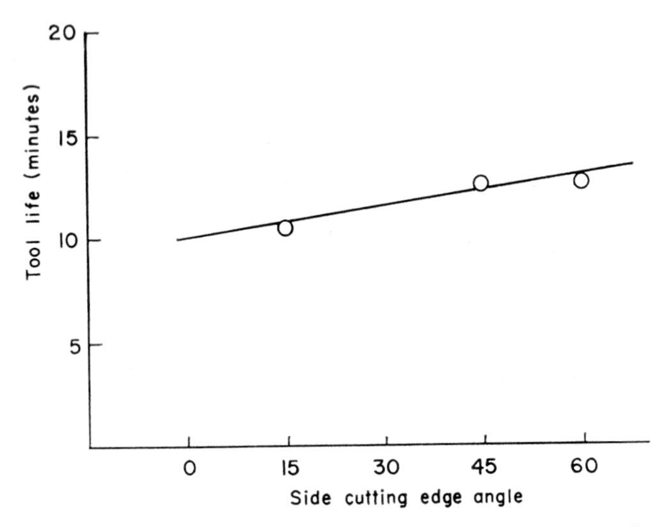

FIG. 134. Effect of side cutting-edge angle (Siekmann and Sowinski, 109).

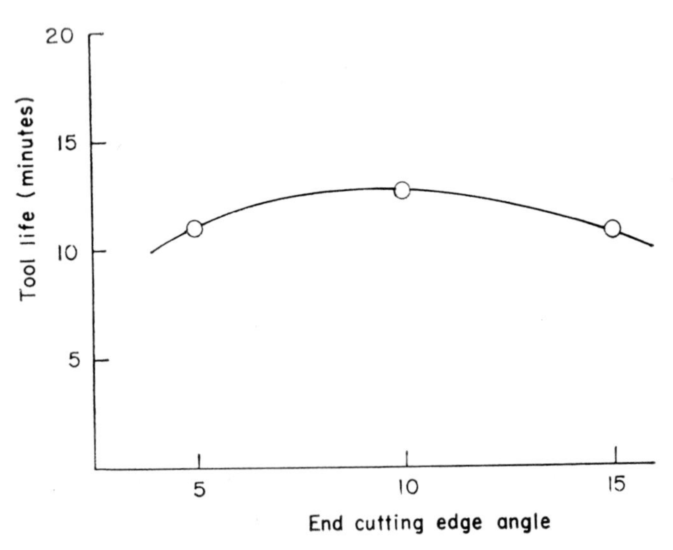

FIG. 135. Effect of end cutting-edge angle (Siekmann and Sowinski, 109).

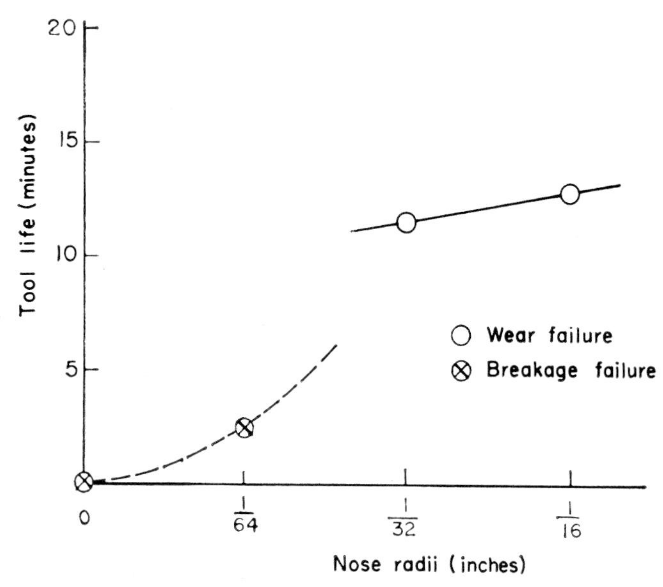

FIG. 136. Effect of nose radii (Siekmann and Sowinski, 109).

on steel and for heavier feeds on cast iron. Lands are recommended as follows:

1. On steel where feed is above 0.010 inch
2. On steel if the depth of cut is above 1/16 inch
3. On all heat-treated steel cuts harder than Rc 40
4. On all cast-iron stock-removal cuts

Edge lands can be hand honed or prehoned mechanically. A flat land width of 50–80% of the feed at 45°–60° to the top-tool surface or a convex land of 0.005 inch radius have been generally found to be satisfactory.

Moore and Kibbey advanced several reasons for consideration of edge lands as a means of controlling early tool failure. Frequently in early tests, sharp tools developed a small cutting-edge chip which appeared to correct the geometry in such a way that the tool had an extended performance life. It was reasoned, if the small chip was in fact a correction in geometry, then it should be possible to duplicate the correction by grinding the tool before use. Also, consideration of stresses in a cutting tool indicates that the reorientation of loads by

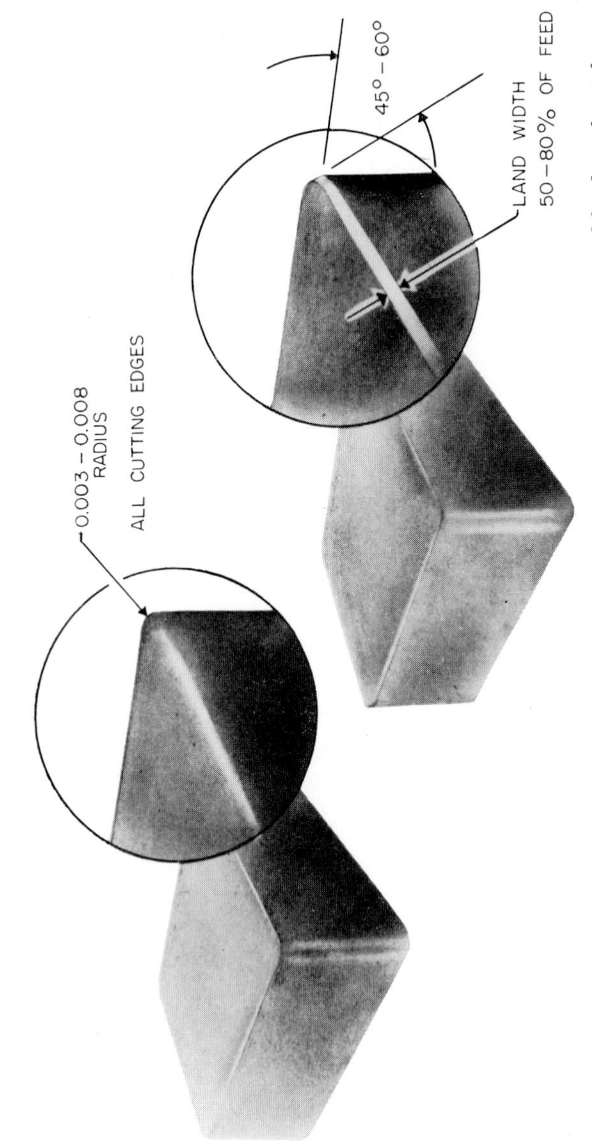

FIG. 137. Ceramic tool-edge preparation. Tumbled and rounded edge on left, ground land on the right.

the angular land would result in lower tensile stresses in the tool, even though tool loads might be higher and compressive stresses in the material would be higher. This would be advantageous as we have shown ceramic tools to be relatively weak in tension but quite strong in compression.

The authors' examination of a cross section through the cutting edge of an experimental tool that gave an extraordinarily long tool life, appears to show a wear pattern that simulates a convex land and has led to the technique of Wheildon and Barnes (113) for producing rounded-edge lands by tumbling or barrel finishing with an abrasive media.

A study at OSU of various edge lands, widths, angles, and shapes, shows, definitely, that the presence of a land of any size, angle, and shape will produce improvement in resistance to failure by flaking or fracture. It appears that there is an optimum size and shape of lands. Probably, this optimum shape has yet to be determined. However, data have been assembled and analyzed to select very beneficial configurations and dimensions.

Moore and Kibbey (98) developed a unique tool-life test utilizing interrupted feed conditions. Machining both hardened and annealed steels, they used this test to study the effects of edge-land angle and width. Their data are summarized in Table XVI.

TABLE XVI

THE EFFECT OF EDGE-LAND CONFIGURATION TOOL LIFE[a]

	0.002-inch land width Angle to cutting direction			0.008-inch land width Angle to cutting direction		
Work material	60°	40°	20°	60°	40°	20°
1045 Steel	43	45	36	34	35	17
A-6 Tool steel, Rc 51	75	37	20	156	45	18

[a] Measured in average number of cuts.

The 1045 steel was machined at 2500 fpm and the AISI A-6 tool steel at 1000 fpm, so a direct comparison between the number of cuts on these two materials is not valid. In general, the wider land at the higher angle to the cutting direction is advantageous with the A-6 steel. The narrow land is advantageous when machining soft steel and is relatively insensitive to land angle. At this time no broad generality can be derived which will define the best conditions for a particular application. It is readily evident, however, that tool life can be greatly extended for a particular application through the proper selection of an edge configuration. The uncertainties that exist are most likely due to the lack of a sophisticated analysis of stress distribution on the cutting edge which is influenced by the geometry of the edge and the physical properties of the work piece. In light of these data it would seem that while some advantages will be received from hand-honing tools, the inherent tool utility is almost certainly not optimized.

Moore and Kibbey further studied the effects of convex- or rounded-cutting edges which were prepared by tumbling the tools in an abrasive medium. Their data are summarized in Table XVII for three different edge radii on two steels, and compared with a tool with a 60°-ground land about 0.006-inch wide.

TABLE XVII

THE EFFECT OF EDGE RADIUS DIMENSION ON TOOL LIFE[a]

Edge radius:	0.002 inch	0.005 inch	0.0075 inch	Ground land
1045 Steel:	82.6	59.2	29.6	57.4
A-6 Steel, Rc 51:	43.6	22.5	5.6	2.5

[a] Average number of cuts (0.011-inch feed).

It is again evident that the details of edge configuration have profound effects on tool life. The tumbled radii were better than ground lands on the hardened steel in all cases. The 0.002-inch tumbled radii was significantly better than the ground land on 1045 steel but the largest radii gave a poorer performance. The cutting speed for the A-6 steel in this case was 1100 fpm and the results are not directly comparable with those in Table XVI.

These two sets of data indicate that by proper tool design the relatively low-tensile strength of ceramic tools can be circumvented in machining practice, at least for certain applications. The reasons for this are similar to those for using an overall negative geometry, but in this case they extend down to the next-smallest scale. A small-negative land, or tumbled land, causes a net compressive load on the tool-cutting edge which retards the development of fractures. This small land also increases tool-loading forces. The net benefits from dulling the cutting edge depend upon which increases the most: the increased effective strength due to compressive loading, or the tool-loading forces tending to produce fracture. The data in Tables XVI and XVII suggest that steels with different mechanical properties interact with the tool edge in such a way to produce different stress distributions. In tooling practice this would suggest separate edge configurations for different applications so as to optimize the cutting edge stress level and distribution for each generic case.

6. Special Geometries

Several investigators have developed special geometries for specific jobs that have shown definite advantage or superior performance.

Siekmann (114) disclosed in 1959 that oxide inserts of cylindrical configuration with a large negative cutting-edge land as shown in Fig. 138 were suitable for machining hardened steel in the Rc 60 to Rc 63 range. He recommends for turning, a feed of 0.005 ipr, a speed of 600 fpm, and a depth of cutting range from 0.015 to 0.030 inch. Under these conditions, with cutting edge set $\frac{1}{32}$ to $\frac{1}{16}$ inch below the centerline, work finished on WO 52 steel of 30 to 80 microinches was generated.

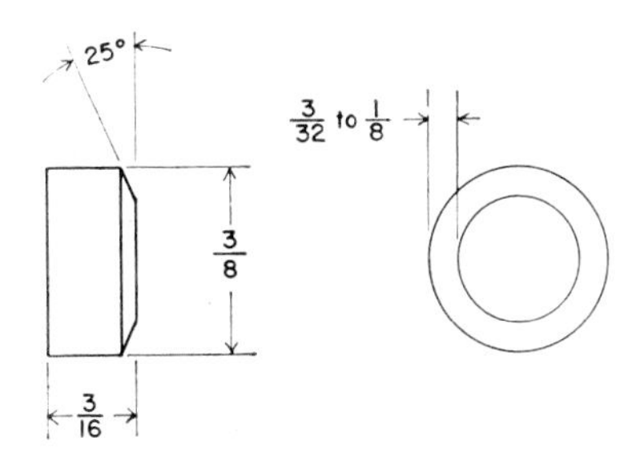

Fig. 138. Turning and boring insert (Siekmann, 114).

Later Bagley (115) of Watertown Arsenal, working with the authors of this book, discovered the special geometry shown in Fig. 139 and pursued its merits for rapid stock removal of high-strength, high-hardness steel.

Using this tool in a standard-type double-negative 5° and 5° holder, some excellent performances were achieved machining Type 5 manganese, air-hardened tool steel at Rc 62. One tool with this high-negative nose rake was still producing a good surface finish after 52 minutes of continuous cutting at 400 fpm with a 0.005-ipr feed and 0.030-inch depth of cut. Other successful cuts were achieved up to 0.080-inch depth, 0.005-inch ipr feed, and 1000 fpm. Chips produced under these conditions are small, fragile, or molten due to the high pressure and temperatures generated at the tool-chip interface. The spray of molten particles makes it necessary for the machine operators to have protection. Such a high-strength geometry allowed the developing of feed and radial forces during the tests in excess of 1000 pounds, without causing tool failure. These high forces preclude the use of this geometry when turning thin-wall tubing and small diameters.

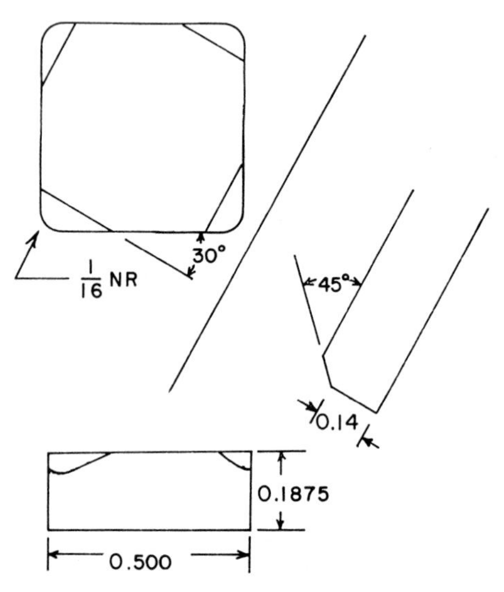

FIG. 139. Specially shaped insert developed to machine tool steel hardened to Rc 60 (Bagley, 115).

Neither one of these special geometry illustrations are compared with metallic tools because the metallic tools will not perform at all under the same range of conditions.

Another special geometry has been created by the authors and associates involving chemical-polishing procedures described earlier. Tools with 60° ground lands 0.006-inch wide were chemically polished for a minimum time so as not to greatly alter the edge configuration. This edge preparation was developed by John C. Logan and therefore we call this the Logan land (116). Tools with the Logan land have shown reproducible tool-life increases of three and four times that obtained with tools from the same lot and with the same edge configuration. However, these latter ones were not polished when machining heat-treated steel in the Rc 48 hardness range.

These few illustrations show that it is possible to improve and broaden tool performance by design of special geometries that are under control of the tool engineer. It is, therefore, likely that further substantial improvements of cutting characteristics for individual applications can be made with existing ceramic tools.

7. Size

The size of the ceramic tool is important; it must be large enough to do the job. In general, the tool cannot be too large but it can easily be too small. The size usually is regulated at least in part by the type of holder available and the material to be machined. The thickness should be consistent with the bending stress applied, generally between $\frac{3}{16}$ inch and $\frac{3}{8}$ inch. For heavier cuts or rough surfaces, $\frac{1}{4}$-inch-thick inserts are a minimum, $\frac{5}{16}$ inch is usually employed, and $\frac{3}{8}$ inch thickness should be used on more difficult cuts. See Table XVIII for a general guide to insert thicknesses (117).

TABLE XVIII

General Guide to Insert Thickness

Shape of insert	Depth of cut (inches)	Thickness of insert
Square or rectangular	To 1/8	3/16
	1/8–1/4	1/4
	3/16–3/8	5/16
	Over 3/8	3/8 or more
Triangles	To 3/32	3/16
	3/32–3/16	1/4
	1/8–1/4	5/16
	Over 1/4	Use square or rectangle

B. Machining Conditions

1. Effects of Speed

The effect of speed or velocity of machining on tool forces and coefficient of friction with ceramic tools shows a very similar pattern to that created by carbide and cermet tools.

Figures 140 and 141 from the work of Krabacher and Haggerty (9) show a direct comparison on soft steel between a commercial aluminum oxide ceramic tool, a commercial cermet (a nickel-bonded titanium carbide), and a C-8 cemented carbide.

At the slower cutting speeds, tool loads are higher and the ceramic tools are more apt to chip or fracture because of their lower relative tensile strength. Thus it is desirable to operate ceramic tools at the higher speeds and employ the strongest geometries.

The main difference between ceramic and metal tools is in the hardness at elevated temperatures and the thermal conductivity (discussed earlier). Both of these are conducive to the use of higher machining speeds.

Cutting-speed tool-life tests have for a long time been considered as an important criterion in evaluating performance of cutting tools. Consequently, numerous investigators have evaluated ceramic tools in this manner and under a wide variety of conditions. Similar characteristic differences, however, between ceramic and metal tools appear to be indicated in the majority of cases. Figure 142 from Fersing (118) shows cutting-tool-life data obtained on soft steel of C-8 carbide versus oxide ceramic tooling.

The different slopes of the two tool materials indicate that ceramics are much less sensitive to speed than carbides. With different performance slopes for ceramic and carbides the lifelines will cross, in this case at about 500 fpm. At cutting speeds below this point, carbides have the performance life advantage and above this point ceramics show increasingly longer life as speed goes up. Above 1500 fpm the curves show a tremendous tool-life difference under these particular conditions.

In similar studies of carbide versus ceramic tooling Kibbey and Moore (119) found the crossover point to be between 800–900 fpm for 1045 steel at 180 bhn when employing a feed of 0.011 ipr and depth cut of 0.100 inch. See Fig. 143.

The statistical analysis of the test results showed that, in the 500- to 1500 fpm speed range, the life of both C-5- and C-8-carbide tools varied inversely as the third power of the cutting speed, whereas, within this range, speed had no significant effect on ceramic-tool life. This supported Fersing's findings that the life of ceramic tools is less affected by cutting speed than the life of carbides.

Similar crossovers probably exist under other cutting conditions—

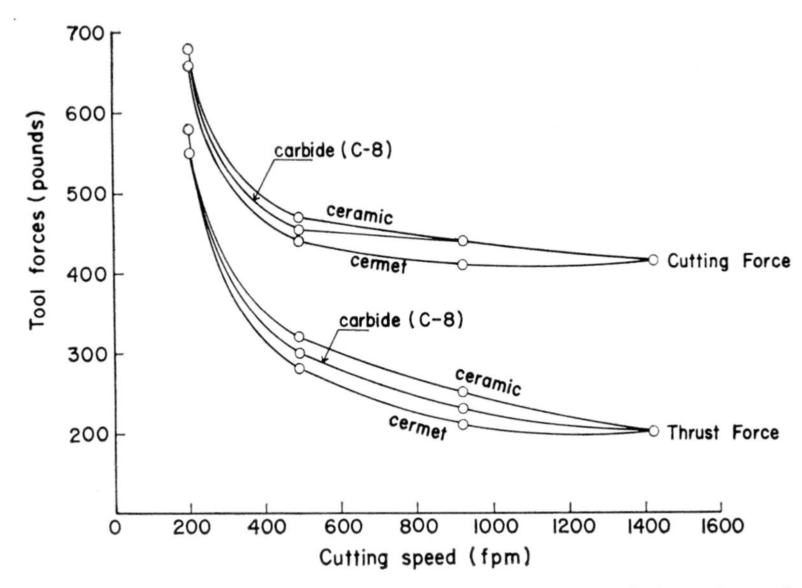

FIG. 140. Tool-force comparison curves showing cutting and thrust forces for various tool materials on steel (Krabacher and Haggerty, 9).

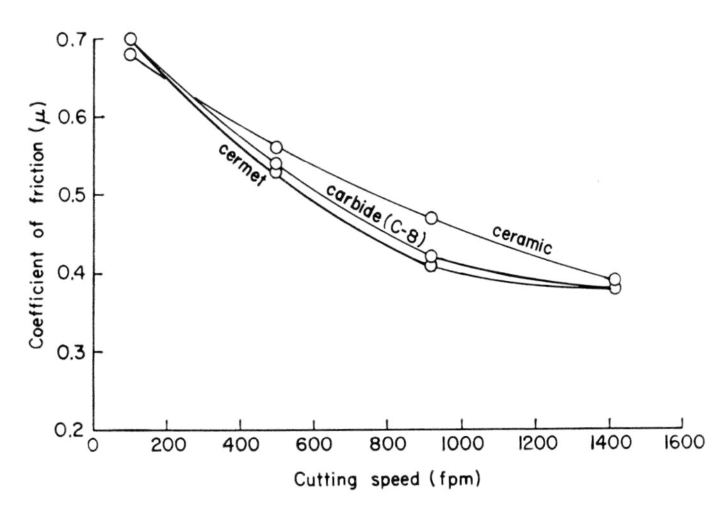

FIG. 141. Coefficient of friction comparison curves for various tool materials on steel (Krabacher and Haggerty, 9).

although the value is probably much lower for harder and tougher materials.

Thus, for economical performance of ceramic tooling, the higher speed ranges of from 2 to 10 times that normally used with metallic tooling should be used. As cutting pressures do not rise with increases

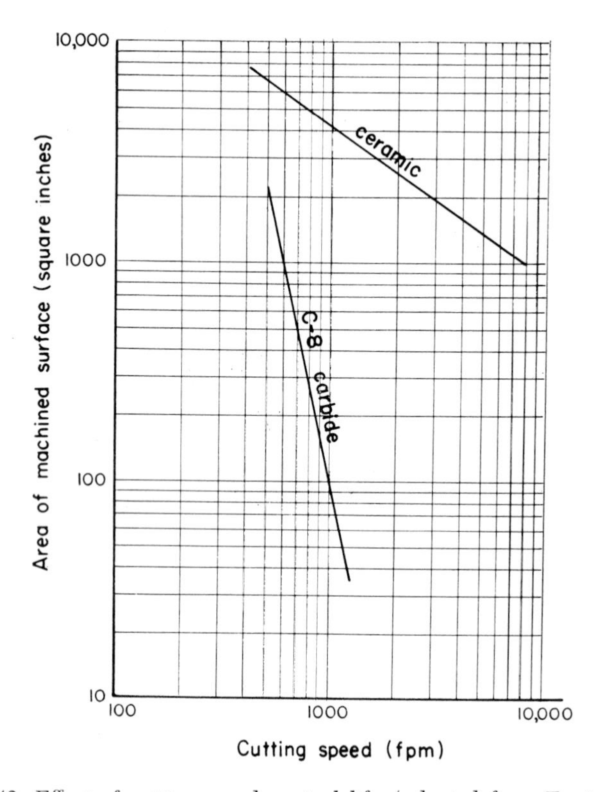

FIG. 142. Effect of cutting speed on tool life (adapted from Fersing, 118).

in cutting speed, the highest cutting speeds possible, commensurate with reasonable tool life and machine or work-piece limitations, should be used for the purpose of obtaining the shortest machining cycle.

Siekmann's (54) investigations have pursued this approach with tool life tests on AISI 1045 steel 170–180 bhn at cutting velocities from 500 to 18,000 fpm and while optimum speed for ceramic tools is shown to be as high as possible, the available horsepower and rigidity of machines in industry place a current practical limit on speeds that can be used. Most plants rarely use more than 25–30 HP for their high-speed lathes. This will accommodate a 0.100-inch depth of cut at a feed of 0.010 ipr, at a speed of 2000 fpm on a soft steel.

Thus, a basic range of cutting speeds using ceramic tools are suggested in Table XIX. Figure 144 shows recommendations of Carborundum Co. for cutting speeds for machining ferrous metals at different hardness levels. The graph shows that the optimum speed is

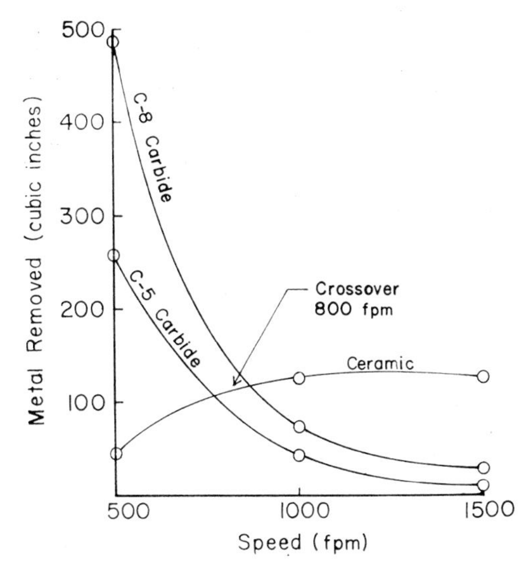

FIG. 143. Effect of cutting speed, carbide versus ceramic (Kibbey and Moore, 119).

very sensitive to hardness, and a change in hardness from 200 bhn to 250 bhn would change the optimum cutting speed from about 1100 fpm to 800 fpm.

2. Effects of Feed

The magnitude and effects of feed vary with and depend on other conditions that have a bearing on tool performance. At lower cutting speeds on soft-work material, feed has a relatively small effect on tool life within a normal loading range. As cutting speed or work-material hardness is increased, the effect of feed becomes more important. Also, the ratio of feed to depth of cut is important. Ceramic tool can take higher stock-removal cuts if the chip load is properly

TABLE XIX

RECOMMENDED CUTTING SPEEDS FOR CERAMIC CUTTING TOOLS BY MATERIAL CLASSIFICATION[a]

Material to be machined	Material condition or type	Roughing (Over 1/16-inch depth 0.015-inch to 0.030-inch feed)	Finishing (Under 1/16-inch depth Under 0.010-inch feed)	Recommended tool geometry (rake angles)	Coolant
Carbon and tool steels	Annealed	300–1500	600–2000	Negative	
	Heat-treated	300–1000	500–1200	Negative	N.R.[b]
	scale	300–800		Negative with edge hone	
Alloy steels	Annealed	300–800	400–1400	Negative	
	Heat-treated	300–800	300–1000	Negative with edge hone	N.R.
	scale	300–600		Negative with edge hone	
High-speed steel	Annealed	100–800	100–1000	Negative	
	Heat-treated	100–600	100–600	Negative with edge hone	N.R.
	scale	100–600		Negative with edge hone	
Stainless steel	300 Series	300–1000	400–1200	Positive and Negative	Sulfur base oil
	400 Series	300–1000	400–1200	Negative	

TABLE XIX (*Continued*)

Material to be machined	Material condition or type	Roughing (Over 1/16-inch depth 0.015-inch to 0.030-inch feed)	Finishing (Under 1/16-inch depth Under 0.010-inch feed)	Recommended tool geometry (rake angles)	Coolant
Cast iron	Gray iron	200–800	200–2000	Positive and negative	
	Pearlitic	200–800	200–2000	Negative	
	Ductile	200–600	200–1400	Negative	N.R.
	Chilled	100–600	200–1400	Negative with edge hone	
Copper and alloys	Pure	400–800	600–1400	Positive and negative	Mist coolant
	Brass	400–800	600–1200	Positive and negative	Mist coolant
	Bronze	150–800	150–1000	Positive and negative	Mist coolant
Aluminum alloys[c]		400–20000	600–3000	Positive	N.R.
Magnesium alloys		800–10000	800–10000	Positive	N.R.
Nonmetallics	Green ceramics	300–600	500–1000	Positive	
	Rubber	300–1000	400–1200	Positive	N.R.
	Carbon	400–1000	600–2000	Positive	N.R.
Plastics		300–1000	400–2000	Positive	N.R.

[a] From Carborundum Company (120).

[b] N.R., coolant is not required. If a coolant has to be used, it is recommended that the tool be flooded to eliminate the possibility of heat checking.

[c] On certain aluminum alloys ceramic tools have the tendency to develop a built-up edge.

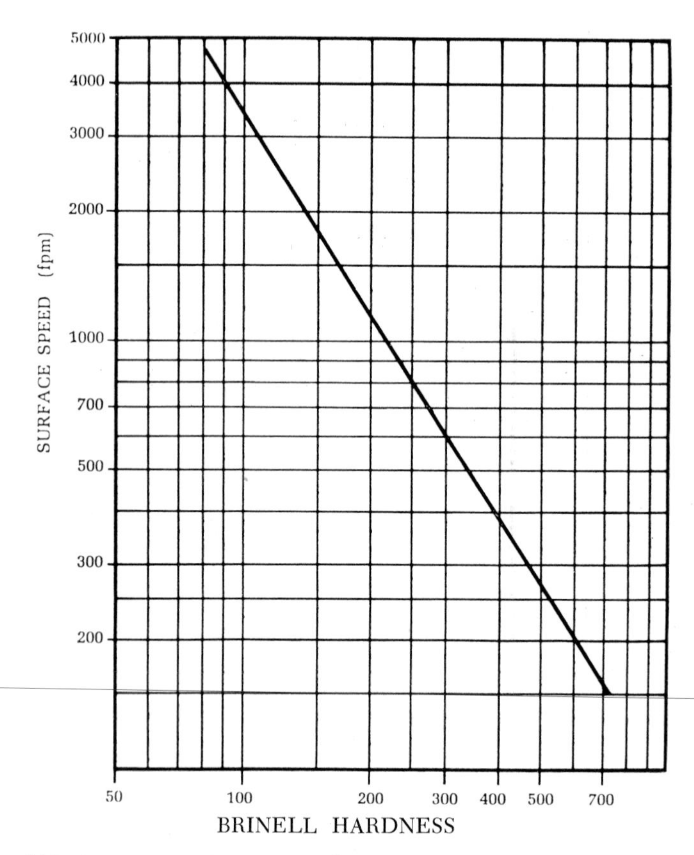

FIG. 144. Cutting speed recommendation for materials of different hardness (The Carborundum Company, 120).

distributed. That is, a heavier depth of cut at a lighter feed is to be preferred over a lighter cut and a heavier feed.

As all of the forces acting on a tool increase as feed is increased, a relative increase in wear, susceptibility to chipping and fracture, and consumption of horsepower are to be expected.

The authors in their tool-evaluation studies have found that in machining of 300-bhn 4340 steel, a 0.022-inch ipr feed is a limiting factor at 1500 fpm whereas at 1200 fpm, the same feed can be expected to give a substantial relative life. Moore and Kibbey (111) in their work with SAE 1045 normalized and annealed steel operating at a speed of 1500 fpm found that increases of feed from 0.006 ipr to 0.020 ipr produced from 2 to 4 times the tendency for the cutting edge to chip.

Similarly, Makarov (110) in Russia noted that doubling the feed from 0.004 ipr to 0.008 ipr caused an increase in relative wear of 38%.

The work of Okushima and Fujii (42) in Japan showed that under their cutting conditions the most favorable tool life was obtained with a feed rate of 0.004 ipr. Doubling feed rate dropped tool life approximately 31%.

All of these investigations, however, look at the effects of feed without considering the volume of stock removed in a given time, which is usually the major economic consideration in manufacturing. Therefore, for stock-removal operation, feed rates should be as high as conditions will permit, short of premature tool fracture. Generally, this dictates operating within the limitations of tool and holder design, rigidity of work piece and equipment, and available horsepower.

Experience has shown that feeds of 0.028 ipr on cast iron, 0.020 ipr on heat-treated steel, and 0.045 ipr on soft steel can be accomplished when other conditions permit. While cutting forces and consequently total horsepower do increase with increase in feed, the horsepower per cubic inch per minute drops off (54), thus this further supports the economics of use of maximum allowable feed, as shown in Fig. 145.

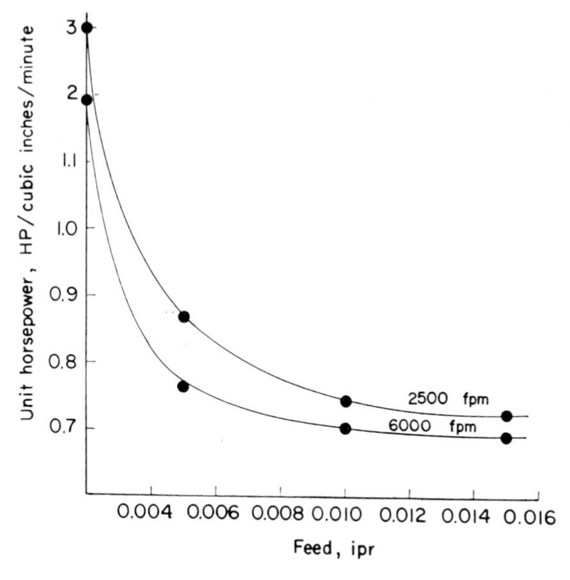

FIG. 145. Horsepower per cubic inch per minute versus feed rate (Siekmann, 54).

The exact feed rate best for each job must be established by test. However, good average stock removal feed rates are 0.020 ipr for cast iron, 0.017 ipr for heat-treated steel, and 0.021 ipr for soft steel.

As a guide for machining of heat-treated steels, generally recommended maximum feeds relative to depth of cut and speed are given in Table XX.

TABLE XX

General Recommended Machining Conditions for Heat-Treated Steels (Vascoloy Ramet/Wesson)

Hardness of steel	Depth of cut (inches)	Maximum recommended feeds	Recommended speeds (fpm)
Rc 40–Rc 48	To 1/32	0.030	300–1200
	1/32 to 1/8	0.025	300–1000
	1/8 and up	0.021	300–800
Rc 48–Rc 55	To 1/8	0.015	200–800
	1/8 and up	0.010	200–600
Rc 55–Rc 65	To 1/32	0.010	120–450
	1/32 and up	0.008	75–350

The feed rate on finish operations is almost always set to produce a specified surface finish on the work. For very smooth finishes the feed rate must be low; rates as low as 0.0008 ipr have been used to advantage.

3. Effects of Depth of Cut

Generally, the limitations on depths of cut for ceramic tools are the design and the size of the tool (see Table XVIII), rigidity of tool-holding devices, the machine tool itself, and the available horsepower.

In nearly all cases, the depth of cut will be determined by the amount of metal to be removed. Depth of cut up to ½ the width of standard throwaway inserts, should not affect material tool life. Actual experiments conducted by investigators throughout the world confirm the fact that varying the depth of cut has very little influence on wear or total tool life. These tests involved as much as a tenfold change in depth. It does not follow, however, that ceramic tools can take cuts of unlimited depth or even equivalent to certain high-strength carbide tools. A point is reached at which the tools so far developed will not withstand the overall pressure generated at the cutting edge. The rupture strength of modern ceramic tools is at best about 60% of the hardest carbide grades. However, with the proper tool design and employment of good machine tool practice to lessen the effect of lower rupture strength, cuts up to ½ inch in depth can be accomplished without serious effect of tool life. Some heavy gun machining operations are now considered standard for ceramic tooling where stock removal is in the range of 60 cubic inches/minute. This requires upwards of 50 HP depending on the velocity of machining and feed rate (see Figure 145).

While this is a very good stock-removal rate, it still leaves room for future advancement before attaining the maximum stock-removal rate of carbides, such as the operations at the Ohio State Foundry where a 500-HP lathe is taking cuts with carbide, absorbing up to 350 HP.

C. Equipment

1. The Machine Tool

The machine tool employing ceramic cutters is as important as the quality and characteristics of the ceramic. Modern machine tools on the market today can use ceramic tooling effectively. While it is obvious that progress made in the development of ceramic tools is and must influence the future trend of machining tool design, it does not follow that ceramic tools can only be used on machines of the latest design. New machines produce more parts but there are many operations running very successfully on older machines. In other words, the new machines have the power and the range of speeds needed to use ceramic tools most effectively. Very rigid conditions are required for the best application of these tools. Elimination of all sources of vibration is most desirable in all machines in which ceramic tools are run. This includes maintaining tight clutches, finely adjusted bearings, well-balanced chucks or driving dogs, tail stock, and slide ways in good condition, etc. Thus, it has been determined that machines in poor condition are generally unsuitable for employment of ceramic tools, especially if vibration and chatter are present. Insulation from adjacent machines or other equipment causing vibration also appears to be desirable and important.

This covers the general aspects of the machine tool for ceramic machining. There are, however, five major areas which can be discussed to further advantage. They are, namely, speed, rigidity, horsepower, vibration, and safety.

2. Speed

As has already been pointed out, to get maximum advantage from a ceramic cutting tool, that tool should be operated at its most efficient speed. As a general rule, we have seen that ceramics will perform quite successfully on heat-treated or high-strength steels at two to three times the surface speeds used with carbide tools. On the low-tensile steels much higher ratios are achieved under certain circumstances. It follows then from considerable field experience that machines having sufficient horsepower to achieve 3000 fpm can take most practical advantage of the ceramic tools on the market today. While it has been demonstrated that much higher speeds can be used and the optimum for certain materials may be upwards of 10,000 fpm, such operations must be kept in the specialty category for the present. For instance, there are lathes in existence having spindle-speed ranges from 2500 rpm to 5000 rpm which absorb 150 or more horsepower. These may be standard shop equipment in the future. In the meantime, however, it must not be presumed that because higher speeds are desirable, they are mandatory in the application of ceramic tools. When other required conditions are met, lower speeds can be used on machines incapable of greater speeds, if superior work finishes are desired and if work tolerances are such that the superior wear resistance of the ceramic is an advantage.

3. Rigidity

Rigidity in machining applies to a system of machine-work-tool of which the machine is a basic component. Speed and vibration are directly linked into the system. For instance, from doubling the speed the following effects can be expected.

a. Intensity of machine vibration will increase about four times.

b. Intensity of vibration due to an out-of-balance work piece or machine part will increase about four times.

c. Tool pressure on the work piece and machine will not change appreciably.

d. The extra speed will not damage the machine.

Thus, speed by itself is not a serious problem but attendant increase in vibrations necessitates careful balance of machine components and work piece to suppress the vibration. Also, clamping systems can aid particularly in the tool-holder setup; this will be discussed later in this chapter.

One possible way to increase basic rigidity in the future may lie in the redesign of structural machine components to replace iron by employing steel or other metals with higher moduli of elasticity.

From the research on ceramic tools, it has become apparent that the tail stock is usually the weakest point of the machine, particularly where a live center is used. On older machines one should pay attention to the condition of this part and the possibility of strengthening or replacing it.

4. Horsepower

Obviously, ceramic tools with their negative-rake angles and normal-high speed of operation consume significantly more power than positive-rake or slower-speed cutting tools. However, for the same geometries and speeds, significant differences have generally not been found in horsepower consumption for carbides and ceramics. A few investigators have noted a power advantage for ceramic tools in their lower operating range (less than 600 fpm), possibly this is due to a lower coefficient of friction in that range. The power required to cut material with ceramic tools increases linearly with speed and may be estimated by using the following standard formula (120):

$$\text{Horsepower (HP)} = \frac{\text{feed} \times \text{depth of cut} \times \text{fpm} \times C \times 12}{0.7}$$

Where C is a constant denoting variations in the material being cut, as shown in Table XXI.

In many cases it may be possible to install larger motors in existing lathes. Most lathes are capable of using larger motors than those in current use.

5. Vibration

The effects of excess vibration have already been recognized as more critical to ceramic tools than to carbides. Reduction of vibration results in increased tool-edge life and a better surface finish to the work piece. Nearly all investigators have observed the benefits of minimizing all vibrations to attain maximum performance from

TABLE XXI

Values of C for Various Materials for Estimation of Horsepower Requirements[a]

Materials	C values
Aluminum Magnesium Copper Soft brass and bronze Malleable iron Soft cast iron Plastics and nonmetallics	0.35
Free cutting steel Hard cast iron Chilled cast iron	0.40
Low-carbon steel	0.60
Medium-alloy steel Cast steel 400-Series stainless 303 Stainless Medium-carbon steel	0.75
High-alloy steel Hard brass and bronze Manganese steel High-carbon steel	0.85
Tool steel High-speed steel	1.0
300-Series stainless (except 303) High-temperature alloys	1.15

[a] From The Carborundum Company (120).

ceramics; and now, equipment designers are giving this consideration in their newer machines. Because most often, the nature of the machinery is responsible for vibratory conditions, it is most helpful for machines to utilize precision spindles, bearings, and ways. Rigid tool holders and proper tool clamping are a necessity and will be discussed in a separate section. Thus, the challenge of machining with ceramic tools appears to be to eliminate vibration to the maximum extent in order to obtain longer tool life. Ideal conditions of freedom from vibration and freedom from impact in a cutting process cannot be achieved in practical machining, but can be minimized in most cases if the problem source can be recognized and identified.

Most of the exploration into the science of metal cutting, involving the shear process and effects of vibration, has been carried out with metallic tooling. This work has been extensive (121–124) and much of the knowledge gained can be applied directly to ceramic tooling.

In general, there are two classes or types of vibrations that may produce chatter and affect ceramic-tool longevity. The two types of vibrations are listed below along with some of the major factors contributing to their creation.

1. Forced vibrations from:
   - Bearings (inaccurate)
   - Unbalanced parts
   - Belts (worn)
   - Gears (imperfect)
   - Pumps
   - Electric motors, etc.
2. Self-excited vibrations (self-induced vibrations) from:
   - Cutting force magnitude variation
   - Cutting force direction variation
   - Chip deformation and fracture variation
   - Work-piece deflection variation
   - Tool deflection, etc., variation

While forced vibrations cannot be entirely eliminated, they can, for the purpose of ceramic-tool machining, be reduced to an undisturbing minimum by proper designs, the use of well-balanced motors, the best bearings, and the utilization of counter damping forces or dashpot effects.

The latter system of reducing vibrations by damping benefits directly from such concepts as that of Hahn (122) even though it has not been extensively explored for ceramic tooling. Damping in a large measure will offset inherent ceramic-tool brittleness. While somewhat complicated, dashpot systems can and will be developed to convert dynamically unstable systems to stable systems. Frequently, a dashpot effect may be accomplished by a simple change in a machine-tool operation. A change in tail-stock setting or revision of feed to alter feed-back balance often will correct vibration of chatter.

Self-induced vibrations are a much more important factor in the performance of ceramic tools. They can seriously limit the life of ceramic tools if not recognized and dealt with accordingly.

The physical characteristics of the current ceramic materials make them susceptible to either vibration or chatter which are produced by unstable conditions. Therefore, if full potential of the tool is to be gained, cutting parameters must be selected which will produce as stable operating conditions as is possible and practical.

Frequently, cutting stability can be improved by supporting the work piece properly, stiffening the tool holder, repositioning the tool, changing chip dimension, or application of damping media to name some of the conditions that have marked effect.

Vibration can also be of such a complicated nature that a separate and thorough analysis is required, which is beyond the scope of this book and often beyond the scope of current technology. In the author's studies on damping, it has been found that vibrations of tools are reduced by effecting maximum area contact of the ceramic bit and the surface of the tool holder. This has been effectively accomplished by lining the tool holder with 0.001- or 0.002-inch-thick aluminum foil.

At Spring Garden Institute (125) the use of tool holders made from powdered metal compacts was found to have a profound effect on the damping of an unstable oscillatory system of cutting with ceramic tooling. A long series of controlled tests, run between cutting-tool shanks of steel and their exact duplication in powder metal, showed an average decrease in vibration of 42% for ⅛-inch depth of cut and up to 75% decrease at $\frac{1}{16}$-inch depth when powder metal was substituted for the traditional-steel shanks.

Apparently, the effects of vibration depend much on the operating frequency and direction (124). Also, not all vibrations are considered detrimental by certain investigators.

Vorinin and Markov (126) superimposed ultrasonic vibrations on a cutting tool when machining creep-resistant alloys. Their results showed that amplitudes of 0.004 inch in the radial direction yielded an optimum tool life which was greater than without vibration.

Poduraev and Zakharov (127) reported in 1959 that vibrations parallel to the feed direction and induced by a hydraulic oscillator mounted on the lathe carriage, appeared to increase tool life under certain conditions.

Thus, it is not necessarily inconsistent that both harmful and beneficial results could accrue from vibrations varied through a wide range of frequency and magnitude.

The work of Moore and Kibbey (98) of Ohio State University, working under sponsorship of the authors' employer, leaves little doubt that vibration plays a part in both tool wear and failure by chipping or fracture in the metal-cutting process. Details of the directional and variable rigidity tool holder employed to induce vibration is presented in Chapter 5. While these tests can only be considered as preliminary and qualitative in nature they do indicate a much greater effect from vibrations in the feed direction and from the higher frequencies than from vibrations in the cutting direction and the lower frequencies.

It may seem surprising that more comprehensive work has not been done in the field of vibration associated with the performance of ceramic tools. But the present lack of information stems only from the complexity of the problem, and the fact that the newness of the ceramic-machining medium has made other problems seem more important and easier to solve.

6. Safety

The higher operating speeds associated with ceramic tools make necessary some safety precautions not ordinarily associated with machining operations. At speeds above 600 fpm, some measures for the protection of operator and equipment from flying chips are required.

Speeds above 1000 fpm with substantial depths of cut generate hot chips that form high-velocity projectiles that can seriously affect operators and equipment performance. Safety shields over the chuck and on tool-post carriage have proved quite efficient in controlling the chip barrage. Very high speeds may require more elaborate guards (see Figs. 146 and 147).

It must be remembered that a chip that hits a large diameter chuck can be thrown with speeds much higher than the fpm of the cut.

While simple deflectors mounted on the tool post will keep most of the chips under control, it is necessary to have room to handle the increased volume of chips resulting from the higher operating speeds. Much can be accomplished by employing sheet-metal chutes to eliminate areas where chips will clog and become a hazard.

If machines are closely grouped, it is necessary to provide complete

Fig. 146. Tool-post chip deflector.

Fig. 147. Flying-chip safety guard.

enclosure of the work piece to prevent saturation of the shop with hot chips.

Operator errors become more serious at higher operational speeds. Thus, ceramic machining does require a high standard of attention to details of setup and operation. Poorly chucked or centered work, a dial incorrectly read, or other human errors in setup can result in a serious hazard to the operator or brutal punishment to the equipment.

D. The Fixtures

1. Tool Post

Tool posts, blocks, or turrets, in which tool holders are mounted, must provide rigid support for the ceramic bits. They form the link between the machine and the tool-bit holder and must be kept tightened. Only tool posts husky enough to prevent distortion in the base are worth considering for ceramic tool use. A poor tool post can make it difficult to hold size, can cause chatter, and can break tools.

2. Tool Holder

Because rigidity is necessary and beneficial whenever ceramic tools are used, it dictates the desirability of employing as large a tool holder and shank as possible.

Excessive deflection of tool shank or holder will result in unwanted vibrations and subsequent unsatisfactory tool life. The design of these holders should be selected for maximum mass and provide for a minimum amount of projection or overhang of the tool itself.

A good rule to follow is to maintain overhang between 50 and 100% of the thickness of the holder shank; in any case, the overhang should not exceed 150% of the shank thickness except for light cuts. See Fig. 148 for an example.

The mechanically clamped holder offers the greatest support to the ceramic tool, since negative-rake angles can be readily obtained and the mechanical chip breaker can be arranged to equally distribute the clamping forces. It is most important that the chip breaker be adjusted to curl the chip above the holder for proper chip breaking. Failure of proper chip-breaker adjustment will curl the chip loose causing the machined material or chip to contact the edge of the tool. This will undermine the tool tip resulting in severe cracking, edge chipping, or premature failure. Setting of the chip breaker, of course, depends on work material. However, one investigator during extensive ceramic-tooling studies at Watervliet Arsenal, has found it advantageous to make initial setting according to the formula: "Chip breaker distance from cutting edge = 4 × feed + 0.012 inch." He then makes finer adjustment from this point to produce the desired chip curl. Carbide chip breakers, held mechanically, appear superior to those fastened by brazing, and ease of adjustability is provided for a variety of work-piece materials.

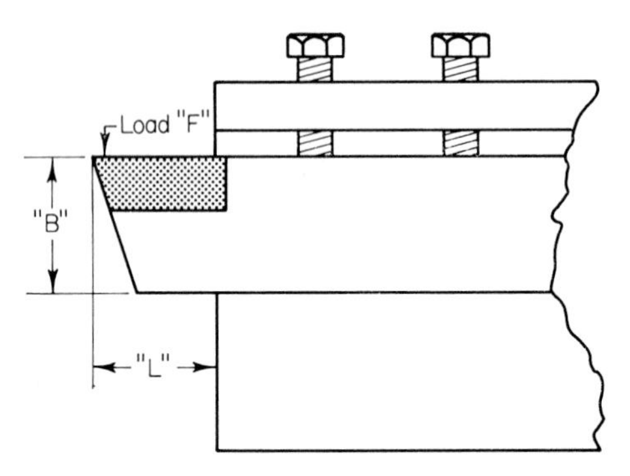

FIG. 148. Overhang recommendation (The Carborundum Company, 120).

In spite of the best practices in the setting of chip breakers, newly formed chips often curl so that they strike the ceramic tool along the cutting edge just beyond the portion engaged in the cut. In many cases this contact causes abrasion and chipping severe enough to affect tool life. A solution to the problem in our own work and that of other investigators has been to shape the chip breaker so that it covers and protects the cutting edge outside of the depth of cut. Figure 149 shows a sketch of how such a combination chip breaker is employed.

Precision-ground carbide seats or anvils are necessary for the proper support of ceramic tips. This provides a precision-mating surface and a high resistance to deformation under load. Some experiments have indicated a direct relationship between thickness of ceramic tool and the contact area with the seat to obtain optimum performance. In fact, some users have considered this sufficiently critical so that they lap the ceramic tip to the seat for complete contact. In any case, burrs, chips, or broken corners cannot be tolerated and the seat should be cleaned smooth or it should be replaced.

In addition, it has been found that if a thin sheet of soft aluminum foil or other soft metal (0.001- to 0.004-inch thick) is used as a shim between bit and anvil serves to distribute load and correct surface irregularities, fracture failures are reduced. Thicker shims are less effective and a shim above 0.005-inch thickness can actually be a detriment.

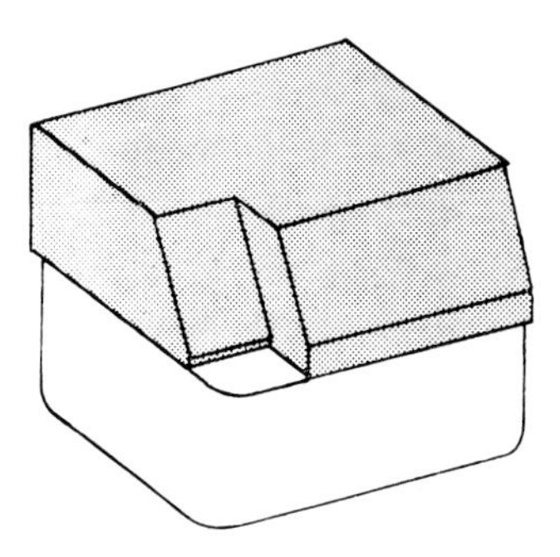

FIG. 149. Special combination chip breaker and cutting-edge protector.

The heavy solid-base tool-holder design shown in Fig. 150 is typical of many good tool holders available today and shows the elements necessary for the utilization of ceramic-tool hardness, high-temperature operation, wear resistance, and minimization of thermal shock and tensile stresses.

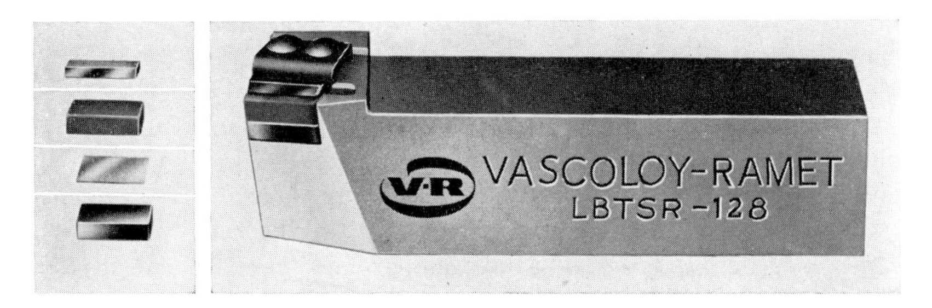

FIG. 150. Elements of a typical throwaway insert holder for ceramic tools.

Tool holders of materials which have higher moduli of elasticity than steel are under consideration but, thus far, only limited data have been collected which indicate the effect of this increased rigidity.

The Universal Cyclops Steel Corporation points out that for operation where rigidity and stiffness are a requirement, wrought molybdenum is 50% stiffer than steel of the same dimension.

In his work, Frommelt (128) has found that a copper-impregnated sintered-powder iron shank with a Young's modulus approximately three times that of steel shows particular benefit to the effective use of ceramic tools. Others, including the authors, have taken a preliminary look at a visco-elastic system for clamping vibrations that were setup in tool or shank, but thus far no systems have been uncovered that appear superior to the rigid setups.

3. Fastening

Methods of fastening ceramic tools to steel shanks fall into three general categories: mechanical clamping, cementing, and brazing.

a. Clamping

The clamp-type tool holder was first developed for cemented carbide tips to avoid stresses, introduced during brazing, and thermal stresses, arising from the different expansion coefficients of the carbide tip and the steel shank.

As ceramic tools are even more sensitive to these stresses, because of their lower tensile strength, it was natural to take advantage of the tool-holder development work already underway and proceed to adapt or redesign currently available clamp holders for ceramics. Most of the clamp-type holders use the multi-edged throwaway inserts which have been found more economical than regrinding. Figure 150 shows a typical "throwaway insert type of tool holder" especially adapted to ceramic tools. It has a carbide support anvil and a carbide-clamp block in the form of a chip breaker, with ground surfaces for maximum area contact with the ceramic insert in order to prevent flexing and localized clamping or cutting pressure. If the available tool holder does not provide a carbide seat-clamping surface, it should not be used unless a precision-ground insert is substituted into the holder.

Another technique of mechanical (128, 129) clamping involving powder metallurgy and copper impregnation has not been used extensively, but it has shown considerable promise under some circumstances. The tool-holder body, in this case, is of sintered powdered iron with a socket recess to accommodate the desired ceramic-bit shape. The ceramic tool insert is locked in place firmly and mechanically by the closing of the recess during the copper-impregnation phase.

b. Cementing

Cementing of the tool, directly to the steel shank with an adhesive such as an epoxy resin, has proved successful for certain light-machining operations (130). It is doubtful, however, that adequate support can be attained for other than finishing cuts on metals or moderate stock removal on certain other low-shear-strength materials.

An appreciable thickness and mass of tool bit is required to insulate the cement from the high temperatures generated at the cutting edge in order to preserve the fastening properties of the cement. While it appears that cutting tips have been cement fastened with success, it is still doubtful that the required rigidity was provided or that detrimental vibration was clamped sufficiently to compare favorably with the mechanical clamp-type holders.

Nevertheless, where space in a machining operation is a serious consideration, it may be desirable to cement the tool blanks to a steel shank. There are several types of epoxy-polymerizing types of resins available, that can be used and which have similar fastening characteristics.

The general procedure for fastening by this system is as follows:

1. Prepare both surfaces to be joined bya light sandblasting.
2. Apply a thin layer of epoxy-resin paste to both mating surfaces to be bonded.
3. Press the tool tip into position on the tool shank.
4. Slide the tool to position it and to eliminate any entrapped air.
5. Remove excess cement from the assembly.
6. Heat cure the bonding cement (usually 375°F–400°F for 1½–2 hours, but the specific recommendation of the manufacturer of the epoxy cement should be followed).

c. Brazing

The usual brazing or soldering procedures do not work for ceramic tools because of poor wettability between metals and ceramics under ordinary conditions (low affinity for most metals). The tools may be metallized on the surface by a number of techniques that will allow subsequent brazing to metal shanks. Very fine-metal powders of silver, nickel, iron, manganese, molybdenum, etc. mixed with some kind of organic-bonding agent (such as shellac) may be brushed onto the surface of tools which when heat-treated at an elevated temperature will leave a thin layer of metal. This layer is fired into the ceramic material and thus it makes intimate contact with and provides a suitable surface for soldering or brazing in the usual way.

A more advanced and sophisticated way of producing a stronger-metallized surface is by the active alloy or hydride process, a proprietary method applied by a number of companies specializing in the process. The process employs a metal hydride (usually of titanium or zirconium) as a wetting agent. It is carried out in a high vacuum or in an inert-gas atmosphere. Metallized surfaces, so produced, provide an extremely tenacious bond and have been failure tested at as high as 25,000 psi.

Mechanical attachment of a metal film by flame-spraying has also been tried but reliance upon mechanical interlocking of metal and ceramic and including the weak Van de Waal's forces, provides a relative low-strength joint compared to the other systems.

Whatever the metallizing process, the ceramic tip has to be further brazed to the shank; which is the major problem. Stresses are introduced during brazing and even larger thermal stresses arise in use, from the differential thermal expansion coefficient that exists between the ceramic tip and the steel shank. Thus, of necessity, a satisfactory brazing or soldering medium must be soft enough to accommodate the differential and still be strong enough to resist the machining forces applied. No such practical brazing medium, capable of taking substantial cuts, appears to be available at this writing.

Along this line some successful experiments have been conducted in the author's own plant by interposing still another material between the tool and the steel shank to equalize the differential of expansion. Certain metal carbides have coefficients of expansion closely matching that of alumina-ceramic tools. When they are employed as an intermediate, shim have appeared to successfully accommodate the differential in expansion during substantial stock-removal tests. However, as done experimentally, attaching the tool is difficult and may prove to be too expensive.

Chapter 7

Tool Evaluation

A. Requirements for a Test

The continued exploration concerning the mysteries in the process of metal cutting by chip-making is required for a better understanding in the future and improved machining with ceramic tooling. An immediate need, however, is for empirical tool evaluations that identify which tools perform best for a particular application, rather than why they perform. It is not possible to say which ceramic tools are best without first identifying best for what application. Each tool engineer desires the tool most effective for his purposes, but differing experiences have led to different ideas on how to determine this. Some tool engineers are willing to select tools on the basis of someone else's opinion but these are few in number. The average engineer would rather make a selection based on data, providing he has reason to accept the data as sound.

What aspects of tool performance are we looking for in tool evaluation? Most likely it will be one or more of the following:

1. Rate of tool wear
2. Total tool life
3. Finish produced
4. Dimensional accuracy maintained
5. Cutting forces generated
6. Rate of stock removal
7. Machining economics
8. Can the material be machined

Any of the above may be of major importance under particular sets of conditions. However, in most cases a combination of items 2, 3, 4, and 6 will provide a reasonable picture of machining behavior.

Testing of cutting tools naturally falls into three general classifications:

1. Laboratory testing under accelerated conditions
2. Laboratory testing under use conditions
3. Production testing

Tests 1 and 2 will, when properly carried out, usually give more accurate and precise information. The purpose of the laboratory type of tests is usually to exercise maximum control of machine conditions in order to yield comparative information of tool performance and develop operating parameters for introduction into production operations. It also serves to attain a better understanding of metal cutting and tool degradation.

Classification 3 is probably an easier type of testing and usually has the objective of producing good parts at an optimum rate. When production performance information is required, type-3 testing will be most reliable. Type-2 testing will be the next best and type 1 the least reliable. Production conditions are not readily duplicated or controlled in the laboratory.

Laboratory-type testing has developed the ceramic tool to its present state of usefulness and will in all probability be the criterion for future improvement or creation of new tool materials.

If a test is merely to establish a performance criterion for selection or standardization of tools, any of the classifications may be used provided a degree of control is exercised relative to the desired results.

Ceramic-tool evaluation has thus far been done mainly as lathe testing of single-point tools although there have been important studies of other machining operations such as milling, drilling, reaming, and boring. In laboratory investigations in which an accelerated picture of machining behavior was sought, machinability lathes were found to be extremely useful in developing optimum tool compositions and in establishing proper use of criteria such as tool geometry, holder design, and operating conditions.

Machinability lathes are rigid, precision, high-speed, high-powered machine tools equipped to electronically record the forces exerted on a single-point tool during chip production (see Fig. 151). A dynamometer permits measuring the three-component loads (tangential, feed, and radial) on a tool during the cutting operation (see Fig. 152). The three components are recorded continuously and permanently as the tool progresses in cut. The tangential force F_t and radial force F_r are mainly penetrating and frictional forces and are sensitive to tool geometry and wear. The feed force is particularly sensitive and as the tool

FIG. 151. Machinability Laboratory of the Metallurgical Products Department of the General Electric Company for evaluating ceramic and cemented-carbide cutting-tool materials (General Electric Company).

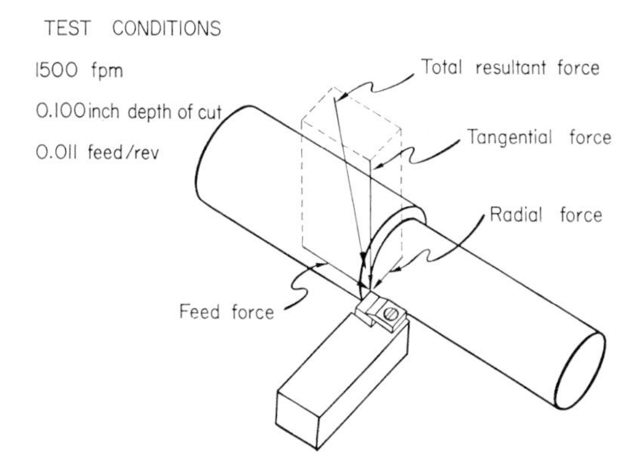

FIG. 152. Force components acting on a single-point cutting tool.

dulls, the force F_f, which is pressure required to push the tool into cut, increases in proportion to the dulling of the tool. The advantage of this type of testing equipment is that a visible-record is produced concurrent with the running of the test, and therefore interruptions for tool or cutting-edge inspection are unnecessary in order to observe the performance behavior of the tool.

1. Measurements of Desired Quality

Tool life is most often used as the criterion of tool quality. Five general methods of expressing tool life have been employed relative to the amount of cutting or machining that has taken place.

a. The cutting time in seconds or minutes
b. The volume of stock removed in cubic inches
c. The surface area of stock machined in square inches
d. The number of passes under a fixed set of conditions
e. The amount of tool wear under a fixed set of conditions (width of wear land)

There are five additional methods of establishing end points of cutting or machining tests.

a. Total destruction of tool
b. Development of a given wear land
c. Percentage increase of feed load over initial value
d. Initial chipping of tool
e. Operator's opinion of deterioration in cutting action

While all these methods of establishing end points have proved successful with metallic tools, certain of these methods have proved more adaptable to ceramic-tool testing than others during the author's investigations.

If the tool is allowed to run to total destruction or catastrophic failure the end point is definite and positive, but this is a hazard to the test equipment. The tool holder or work piece may be damaged, which would temporarily disrupt the test and necessitate some repair expense. This, however, is only infrequently the case and most catastrophic failures do no damage other than to the particular tool-cutting edge in use.

By running different tests to the same percentage increase of feed force over its initial value and by measuring performance in terms of square inches of surface developed useful comparisons are made. What percentage feed force should be employed for the best results creates quite a controversy. The authors, however, found 25% quite satisfactory for comparing and developing ceramic-tool compositions in the early stages of our work with soft steels. Initial chipping of tool has provided a satisfactory end point in certain types of tests, but this requires extremely careful observation by the test operator.

The method of determining the end point of tool life by the operator's opinion of excess tool deterioration is most consistent with what is done in actual production. It has proved both reliable and realistic. A qualified operator simply stops the test when he considers the tool to have failed. This subjective criteria has proved satisfactory in the majority of cases, because there is a definite point in the majority of cases at which the cutting action deteriorates radically short of catastrophic failure. This deterioration is simultaneously accompanied by one or more of the following which aid the test operator in his decision:

a. Sparking
b. A step in work-piece surface
c. A change in machining noise
d. A change in chip formation
e. A change in work finish

The tool is then examined visually and if a chip or fracture is observed, the selected end point is considered to be valid.

As a criterion of performance, operating a cutting test to a preselected terminal flank wear rather than measuring the amount of machining accomplished has probably been used by more investigators than any other system in studying ceramic tools. However, it is of doubtful value in judging the total tool life since ceramic tools of optimum physical characteristics usually fail by fracture and not by predictable progressive wear. Nevertheless, much useful information has been generated by this system. The width of wear land adopted as an end point has varied widely with different investigators. Moore and Kibbey (111) reported satisfactory cutting action with tools having flank-wear lands up to 120 mils but adopted 60 mils for their early tests. Gion and Perron (112) expressed preference for employing a terminal wear land between 15 and 30 mils. A number of others favor wear lands between 10 and 15 mils as terminal points.

2. Reproducibility

A problem which is immediately evident to anyone who has done ceramic-tool testing is that of data variability. This is a basic problem in engineering research of all kinds, and ceramics are particularly susceptible because of their low ductility which has already been noted. In strength testing of brittle materials a much higher variability in results is expected than in the testing of ductile materials. Even under laboratory conditions with the best tool-grinding practice and carefully controlled cutting conditions, test results have inherent variability. Therefore, to establish test results for a given set of conditions, it is obvious that a single set of measurements is not sufficient. The usual practice is to make several repetitive test runs and use the average of the test results. The number of test runs that should be made to determine tool performance within satisfactory confidence limits cannot be determined without prior experience. The data variability will provide the necessary clue in deciding the correct number of tests. For small variation, a few tests will suffice, but in tests where large variations appear, a larger number of tests are required to give a valid answer.

If the costs of testing were inconsequential, an investigator would simply make a sufficient number of tests to be sure to have enough data to insure valid results. This, however, is usually not the case and it is necessary to reach a decision with a minimum of time and expense. It would seem that the degree of experimental control of variables in a test would provide the control for the required number of tests. This is true up to a point, but strict control of test variables would largely determine data variability. For instance, Kibbey and Morris (131) reported that in working near a critical condition, it appeared that experimental errors as small as 1° in the angle and 0.001 inch in the width of the cutting-edge land were capable of causing tool-life results to vary by as much as 30%. This merely illustrates that critical conditions are to be avoided in setting up any test expected to give reasonably reproducible results.

The reproducibility of tool-life measurements in ceramic-tool testing leaves much to be desired. However, refined controls are reducing the variability, and useful information has been generated in many areas with as few as three to five duplicate runs. Because of the complex uncertainties which exist in test systems, it is often desirable to utilize statistical methods of experimental design and data interpretation.

3. Statistical Methods

As we have pointed out in the preceding chapter, the gathering of machining data involves a large number of variables that can affect tool life. To determine how any one variable affects tool life requires a large number of tests in order to offset the inherent data variability. This still may be the best way to get information, under certain circumstances, provided the cost can be tolerated and the interaction effects with other variables is taken into account. More often it is desirable to develop knowledge of the effects of a number of variables with a minimum of testing. Statistical analysis of a properly designed experiment often makes this objective possible.

The statistical analysis of variance technique has been used successfully by a number of investigators, particularly Moore, Kibbey, and Morris of Ohio State University and Mennell and Jeffery (132, 133) of Watertown Arsenal. It is not within the scope of this monograph to explain statistical techniques; but, significant references are cited and the benefits and uses of these techniques are outlined. For the non-mathematician or those not versed in statistical techniques, a small paperback "Facts from Figures" by Moroney (134) is suggested as a helpful source of information.

Analysis of variance may be described as a method by which the total variation in the data is separated into components in such a manner that their significance may be evaluated. The technique is most useful when there is considerable variation in the data or when there are many variables to be investigated, because the statistical significance of any variable may be assessed with the least possible number of tests. Variance is the measure of variability in the data; it can be attributed to individual factors or combinations thereof. The measure of variability is considered significant if it can be considered reliable to a certain confidence level, i.e., a reasonable numerical probability that the conclusion is correct. A 0.001 confidence level means that there is only one chance in a thousand that the variation attributed to a component is incorrect. Up to a 0.05 confidence level or a 95% assurance of a correct conclusion are results which are considered significant. It is the perogative of the individual to accept conclusions with a lower probability if he is so inclined. The authors feel that a 95% confidence limit is too restrictive in many cases of ceramic-tool life testing, due to excessive but inherent variability in test results and the expense of involved testing programs. It is more desirable to decide with a 10% chance of being wrong than it is to either not decide or to become bogged down in unjustifiable and lengthy test programs. Under some conditions we are delighted to accept a 20% confidence decision. Four to one are better odds than a practical engineer often has to accept. Multivariable testing is then an attempt to gain information about more than one variable during a test.

The success and value of the application of statistical analysis is largely based on individual opinion. Therefore, the reader can best assign his own values following careful consultation of the given references.

The authors, however, in their cooperative programs with Moore and Kibbey of Ohio State University, feel that for the number of tests involved, more information was obtained than would have been possible with standard single-variable testing. One of the great powers of this technique is the determination of interaction effects between the main variables. These effects often reveal physical processes which are occurring in the test system. Also, a significance could be attached to the variables, themselves, and the interactions of the important variables that were observed. There are, nevertheless, some disadvantages in the use of the analysis of variance technique. They are as follows:

1. Computation time is lengthy if the system is complex (i.e., requires a computer).
2. Prior information is needed to establish optimum replication and to determine what variables should be included in test.
3. The psychological trap of merely reporting the data as variances and correlation coefficients must be avoided. The data are not the end in itself, but are of value only as more quantitative means of revealing physical processes which occur in the system.

B. Test Materials

For the comprehensive study of the relative performance of different ceramic tools and the development of superior compositions, it is necessary to evaluate them on steels.

Since machinability is affected by both the type of steel and the condition of the steel, there is little agreement among investigators as to which material constitutes the best test material. In fact, it is probably not possible to select a best steel composition and condition unless it is first specified as best for a specific set of operating conditions and time of machining.

There is little doubt, however, on the part of all investigators that the steel used should be carefully selected for uniformity of hardness and other properties throughout a given work log and from log to log in a test. In other words, the physical conditions of microstructure and hardness must be as constant as possible to obviate excessively high or low results that will be introduced from steels and treatments selected at random.

Hardness and ductility are two factors important in the machinability of metals. These two factors are usually not available at optimum levels in the same work material nor are they necessarily required at optimum levels in test work where we want tool-life criteria in a minimum amount of time, i.e., an accelerated test.

1. Soft Steels

Soft steels such as SAE 1045 annealed and normalized have been quite satisfactory for tool-performance studies in the earlier stages in the comparison and development of ceramic-tool compositions.

As tools improved, the study of ceramic-tool life in straight-turning operations has become impractical on soft steels because of an excessive amount of work-material consumption and the time interval needed in order to get results. It was not unusual for the better tools to run in excess of 20 minutes at 1500 fpm, 0.100-inch depth, and 0.011-inch feed per revolution before reaching a 25% increase force and to have used up more than 100 pounds of a selected steel in the 200-bhn range.

2. Hardened Steels

The authors turned to hardened steels to accelerate testing for the more rapid development of better ceramic tools. At the same time, attempts were made to select a steel with optimum characteristics of uniformity in order to eliminate the variables in the work-piece material, insofar as possible.

The first investigations in this area were made with carefully heat-treated AISI 4340 to Rc 45. These investigations accelerated testing but they gave an average deviation of 48% in machinability performance results. A check of the hardness variation from the surface of a 6-inch diameter work piece to the internal center of the log showed a difference of 3.7 units on the Rc scale. Most probably, such a hardness variation was a major contribution to the excessive deviation in machinability test data.

To further reduce this variability, an AISI Type A-6 tool-steel material, having the analysis shown in the following tabulation, supplied by Universal Cyclops Steel Corporation under the identification of "Lo-Air" steel was selected for continued investigation.

ANALYSIS OF "LO-AIR" STEEL[a]

Carbon	0.73
Manganese	2.47
Silicon	0.32
Sulfur	0.11
Phosphorus	0.037
Chromium	1.00
Vanadium	0.12
Molybdenum	1.27

[a] Measured in percent.

Type A-6 tool steel has performed with an average deviation of 26% in test results, in other words, about half of that formerly attained with the 4340 steel. Examination of a slab cut through a heat-treated 6-inch-diameter work log showed a maximum variation of one-point Rc from periphery to center. Thus, this material has been accepted by the authors as the preferred work stock for their investigation. Hardness level is also important and Rc 50 appears to be optimum. Both Rc 45 and Rc 55 give significantly wider spreads in test results.

The relative costs of work material, of course, enters the picture; but, in general, reliability of test results is of most importance and will usually far outweigh any cost considerations for materials. The cost of AISI Type A-6 steel which was found to be optimum is approximately $0.75 per pound as compared to less than $0.20 for low-grade soft stock, or approximately $0.40 to $0.50 for standard alloy stock.

3. PROBLEM OF TOOL-LIFE MEASUREMENT

The problem of measuring tool life is not knowing how to predict or accurately establish it, except by running actual tool-life tests under the specific conditions for which the information is desired.

Some of the more important variable factors influencing the problem are now recognized in the following six areas:

1. Definition
2. Measurement
3. Selection of end point
4. Operating conditions
5. Work-material uniformity
6. Tool-material uniformity

While a tool engineer might, in general, define tool life as the length of time a tool functions properly, in reality he will have many ways of defining it, depending on the desired characteristic from the cutting operation, such as rate of stock removal, size control, surface finish, or cutting economics.

The measurement of tool life is most often in minutes; however, this is not meaningful unless operating parameters are given so the amount of stock removal or number of parts completed can be visualized. Consequently, the volume of stock removed or area of surface machined are also often criteria for measuring tool life.

Selection of the end point of a tool-life test is probably the most critical variable and to determine it positively and accurately is very difficult. Tools ordinarily reach the end of their useful life by one of two mechanisms, wear or complete fracture. In the case of ceramic tools, a third wear mechanism needs to be considered which is identified as minute chipping or microspalling. Also, ceramic tools are more prone to reach a total tool life by fracture than by wear. Because tool life based on total tool failure is undesirable for a number of reasons, such as damage to the test setup, numerous other end-point criteria have been employed. Most of these have already been discussed in an earlier section of this text. They include wear-land basis, cutting-force basis, surface-finish basis, etc., none of which have proved entirely satisfactory or reproducible with respect to predicting total tool life.

Operating conditions, work material, and tool material are important examples of the numerous factors and variables which do influence tool life. If a tool-life test is performed on an accelerated basis, these factors become even more critical; and now to obtain data of any significance, precise control of the variables is required.

Nevertheless, because ceramic-cutting tools have been developed to a point where conventional tool-life tests have become so costly that relatively few tests can be conducted in a reasonable time and at a reasonable cost, the development of accelerated testing procedures is mandatory.

Thus, in spite of the problems presented, the accelerated tool-life test can be and is being used, with the proper recognition of variables, to promote the development of better ceramic tools as well as generate information concerning their practical use.

C. Test Methods

Although the present quality of ceramic tools is much higher than the earlier manufactured ceramic tools, the technology of producing and using these tools is still new and not completely understood. Therefore, we must be more than usually concerned with the parameters of accelerated testing and the reliability of the figures obtained.

A number of accelerated testing systems, judiciously performed, have aided the development of materials and their field application significantly. The nature of the results from any of these systems of testing depends on the work materials employed and the testing conditions selected.

1. Ohio State University Method of Moore and Kibbey

Moore and Kibbey's early work (84) indicated tool-wear rates were not conclusive in determining tool differences known to exist. Apparently total tool failure, which usually is chipping fracture, is necessary to show consistent results. Consequently, their investigative effort became concerned with the development of short-time methods for total failure of ceramic cutting tools. It was evident to them that without such a test, the orderly development of new tool materials could be limited to the extent that many compositions that could be valuable would not be tested.

The current optimum test, evolved following many investigations and discussions with the authors, utilizes a cyclic-cutting operation which is mechanically operated under laboratory control with special equipment. Involved is a series of multiple short passes along a long-work log which allow the tool to stop briefly against the shoulder between passes and dwell with the nose radius in contact with the turned surface. In other words, it is an interrupted feed test which greatly amplifies the number of work entries and the severity of thermal shock conditions. The method is one of the fastest and most consistent of anyone that has been tried. The best cycle timing appears to be 12 cycles per minute with a cutting-time to dwell-time ratio of 1 to 8. Cycles per minute apply to the number of cuts made per minute of a preselected length. Cutting ratio is the actual time of cutting as opposed to the dwell time of tool on work while not cutting, i.e., $1/8$ ratio means the tool is cutting $1/8$ of each cycle time and dwelling the remaining $7/8$ of the time. To further clarify this, the word "dwell," here, means the cutting edge of the tool is left in contact with the moving work during the period it is not fed along the axis to remove material. The procedure has been found satisfactory for checking tools during the machining of both hard and soft steels, and there is reasonable confidence that tool-life differences of 20% or more will appear significant with a minimum of about five tests.

Equipment to carry out such a testing method is of necessity quite special and numerous special devices are required to fit the machinability lathe for this system of ceramic-tool testing. The machine used for this work is a Warner and Swasey turret lathe, modified for continuously variable high-speed operation by being powered with a direct-current motor drive through a gearless head stock. Special devices include a special driving plate which transmits torque to the work through hardened steel pins, a positive-tailstock lock, special guards to protect the operator and moving parts of the machine, and an electrically timed and controlled cyclic tool-feed system. This latter item involves the following changes in a normal machinability lathe operating system:

1. The design and installation of a clutching system for the feed screw that can be cycled positively and rapidly
2. The development of a solenoid-operating mechanism to actuate the clutch
3. The development of an electromechanical system to allow a wide selection of cutting cycles per minute and any desired ratio of cutting time to tool-dwell time
4. The provision of an indicator system to record the number of cycles to tool failure

In addition, the ceramic cutting tool is mounted in a tool-force recording dynamometer setup; an operator's panel is included which contains controls for starting, stopping, varying the machine speed, and controlling the feed-rod clutch. Even with this test method a short-time test requires relatively high cutting speeds. Speeds of 1000 fpm to 3000 fpm have been the rule, depending on the hardness of work log. The multivariable testing approach has been employed, whenever possible, in order to gain a maximum of information in a minimum of time. The following example (98) will serve to illustrate the practical use of the test method.

Example

Objectives

To evaluate the effects of cutting-edge land angles and widths on the performance of ceramic tools.

Controlled variables

1. Tool material: hot-pressed alumina—1-, 3-, and 7-micron average grain size
2. Work material: 1045 steel at 2500 fpm, Lo-Air steel, Rc 51, at 1000 fpm
3. Edge-land angle: 20°-, 40°-, and 60°-width cutting direction
4. Edge-land width: 0.002 inch and 0.008 inch

Fixed conditions

1. Method of operation: interrupted feed
2. Cycles per minute: 12
3. Cutting time to total-time ratio: ⅛
4. Feed: 0.011 inch
5. Depth of cut: 0.040 inch
6. Tool-nose radius: 1/16 inch
7. Tool position: double-negative 5° rake angle, 10° lead angle.

Results in following tabulation

NUMBER OF CUTS

Work material	Tool (micron-grain size)	0.002-inch land width Angle to cutting direction			0.008-inch land width Angle to cutting direction		
		60°	40°	20°	60°	40°	20°
1045	1	48	52	43	38	59	18
	3	59	67	54	51	22	30
	7	21	17	12	24	24	2
Lo-Air	1	124	32	1	163	63	5
	3	89	39	48	139	62	1
	7	13	40	11	165	9	48

Statistical analysis of this data reveals the following significant results:

1. The edge-land angle shows high significance but its real importance is best evaluated by examination of the work-material edge-land interaction.
2. The interaction indicates that on soft steel (1045) little difference in tool life is caused by a change of land angle.
3. The interaction indicates that on hard steel (Lo-Air) the land angle has a strong influence on tool life.
4. The best land angle of those tested for cutting the hardened material is 60° with the cutting direction. With this value, the tools had a life six times better than those with a 20°-land angle.
5. The results of this test indicate that a narrow edge land is most desirable when cutting soft material.
6. Similarly, a wider edge land is necessary for good tool life when cutting harder materials.
7. Since only three values of cutting-edge angles and two widths of cutting edges were employed in this test, there is no assurance that any of the values are optimum or that some other configuration of edge land might not be still more durable.

Thus, it is obvious from the example that a great deal of useful information is obtained, within a short time and at a reduced test cost, with the procedures discussed. However, all data are not so clear-cut as that presented here. Some data collected under other ratios and operating cycles present higher variability which makes accurate conclusions more difficult. Nevertheless, the test method has proved extremely useful in evaluating the developmental approaches to better ceramic tools. Some of the areas of uses and indications are as follows.

1. It has been used to evaluate 1-micron, 3-micron, and 7-micron grain size hot-pressed-alumina tools machining both soft and hard steels. Indications are that there is an advantage to the larger crystal-size tools (7 microns) on long low-speed cuts. Under more severe conditions, the small crystal sizes (1 micron and 3 microns) began to show superiority. The 3-micron grain size, however, appears to be the better all-around tool.
2. It has been used to evaluate cutting-edge preparation. Indications are that cutting-edge lands prepared with the radius are superior to those with a flat surface; furthermore, the size of the radius is important. In the tests conducted at 0.011-inch feed per revolution a 0.002-inch radius performed significantly better than larger radii.

3. It appears to indicate that different grades of ceramic tools may be eventually required to handle effectively a wide range of jobs.

2. Watertown Arsenal—Norton Method

The investigators, in the early work at Watertown Arsenal on materials developed by the authors, recognized the importance of selecting tool materials and machining conditions before they are introduced into production. The logical and most accurate method of testing was, of course, to machine under the given use conditions until the tool failed or until the tool machined for as long as the time required for commercial use. This, however, was found to take several hours, to use up many pounds of metal, and when many tools were compared or many machining conditions evaluated, the full tool-life tests became prohibitively expensive.

Consequently, as ceramic tools improved in quality, it became mandatory to devise evaluation methods which reduced the effort in testing tools. Of the several ways of accelerating tool-life tests, the use of a harder work piece was selected to increase the severity of test conditions to shorten life. This alone, however, did not make a useful test because of major variability in results. It was further necessary to discover a more uniformly structured work material, the proper heat-treatment procedures, and optimum hardness level. Thus, the finalized test became one employing A-6 tool steel at 50 Rc-hardness level for straight cylindrical turning under the following machining parameters: speed, 1000 to 1200 fpm; depth of cut, 0.080 inch; feed per revolution, 0.011 inch to 0.015 inch. Under these conditions, a reasonably rapid tool failure is achieved; it usually is less than 5 minutes for total tool life.

The machine used for this testing method is a Jones and Lamson 25 horsepower 2½-inch-turret lathe modified for machinability testing by being powered with a DC drive for continuously variable high-speed operation up to a spindle speed of 2000 revolutions per minute (see Fig. 153). Several special devices fit this machine for ceramic-tool testing. To insure constant speed, the lathe is equipped with a servo-system that measures and compensates for speed drop at the beginning of each cut, a driving plate which transmits torque to the work through steel-drive pins, a safety-tail stock, and a strain-gage tool dynamometer.

In this work the end points of total tool life are all determined by the operator's opinion as outlined under Section 6,A. The primary use

Fig. 153. Machinability test lathe (Watertown Arsenal).

of this test method has been for a screening test to detect any improvement in materials and cutting-edge configurations.

Example 1

Objective

To evaluate the effect of grain size of a ceramic tool on tool life.

Variable

Tool material: hot-pressed alumina 1-, 3-, and 7-micron average grain size.

Fixed conditions

1. Work material: Universal Cyclops Lo-Air tool steel, 6-inch diameter × 30 inch, heat-treated to Rc 49
2. Depth of cut: 0.080 inch
3. Feed: 0.015 inch
4. Cutting speed: 1100 fpm

5. Edge land: flat 60°, 0.005–0.007-inch wide
6. Tool geometry: double-negative 5° rake, 10° lead angle

Results in following tabulation

Accelerated Life Tests

	Group I (1 micron)	Group II (3 microns)	Group III (7 microns)
Tool life (seconds)	416	303	48
	229	219	70
	220	291	194
Average	286	271	104

A tool-life-measurement criterion of seconds of operation was chosen for simplicity, only. It is certainly all right for others to have used volume of material removed, area machined, length of chip, etc. These or any other measures could easily be obtained by multiplying the number of seconds by the appropriate constant.

Whereas this test was to determine the effect of grain size, the results in seconds tell us that the larger grain size gives an inferior life and that the two small-grain sizes are considerably better but not very different from each other. However, from other studies it is known that 1-micron material is apt to be more brittle; this and other tests have led to the production of 3-micron-range tools as the best all-around tool. This does not mean that there are not specific areas and conditions where either 1-micron or 7-micron ceramic tools may excel—most probably there are. Using this method for studying cutting-edge lands, the following is an example of tool-life comparison between differently prepared lands.

Example 2

Objective

To evaluate the effect of chemically polishing a standard flat-edge land.

Variable

Edge-land preparation: standard flat-ground land 60° 0.005–0.007 wide and the same land chemically polished identified as the Logan land.

Fixed conditions

The same as for Example 1 except for a work-piece hardness of Rc 51 and a speed of 1200 fpm.

Results in following tabulation

ACCELERATED LIFE TESTS

	Group I (Standard cutting-edge land)	Group II (Logan land)
Tool life (seconds)	53	267
	66	116
	116	404
	90	188
	76	167
	117	193
Average	86	222

This shows a tremendous advantage to chemically polishing the cutting lands under these particular conditions. However, no such advantage was shown when these same tools were tested by the Ohio State University cyclic method. This probably means that the polish has a particular advantage for straight and continuous turning, but is of little advantage on work involving the shock of many entries.

Furthermore, it has been observed with the Watertown Arsenal method that in order to obtain reliable comparisons of test data, it is necessary to maintain the same ratio of entries to surface area machine for each test.

3. OTHER TEST METHODS

Of the several other test methods devised to accelerate and reduce the effort in testing of ceramic tools, the most widely accepted systems involve machining to only a fraction of the full tool life. These systems usually machine to some predetermined degree of physical tool wear or preselected load on the tool-cutting edge.

The selection of the test method depends on the suitability for the particular investigation being conducted, the accuracy and convenience required, and largely on the convictions of the investigator.

Physical tool-wear criterion is most often taken as the terminal flank wear-land dimension. Currently, this is probably the most popular system both in the United States and abroad. An example of the useful information gained (54) from this method is illustrated in Fig. 154.

This log-log plot of tool life versus cutting speed is from test results of machining performed on an ultrahigh-speed, high-powered machinability lathe. It indicates a straight line relationship for both a typical high-grade ceramic tool and high-performing cemented carbide tool. However, the slopes are quite different which results in

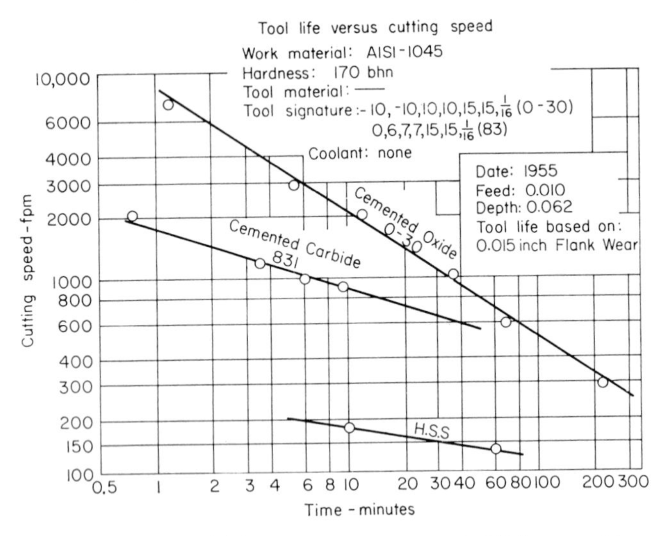

FIG. 154. Tool life versus cutting speed (Siekmann, 8).

quite different Taylor formulas where velocity of machine (V) $\times$ tool life raised to the power of the slope (T^n) is equal to a constant. The ceramic and carbide slopes are respectively 0.69 and 0.30, which give corresponding numerical formulas of $VT^{0.69} = 13{,}400$ and $VT^{0.30} = 1670$.

An analysis of the practical significance of the positioning and degree of these slopes indicates that longer tool lives can be expected from ceramics running at similar speeds to carbides and that relatively higher speeds for the ceramics will produce even greater economic advantages. This is true for the conditions selected and for speeds above 400 fpm, but it could be reversed at lower speeds. One of the problems in conducting this sort of test is the possibility of biasing results by numerous interruptions of machining tests to measure the wear land. This situation is minimized to a considerable extent if the assumption is made that wear land is approximately directly proportional to surface area machined. Also, the wear land is frequently irregular and this is difficult to measure accurately enough to give consistent tool-life results.

Another accepted tool-life criterion utilizes measurement of increase in the forces acting on the tool. The feed force is a convenient criterion of tool wear because increases in this component are approximately proportional to the amount of machining for many machining applications. Also, many significant occurrences affecting tool life, such as chipping, vibration, breakage, etc., all show up as deviations on the running plot of tool forces during machining. Therefore, this running plot is helpful in predicting tool life.

The optimum increase in feed force that can be used as a test criterion is dictated by the test parameters and the investigator's discretion. Increases in feed force have been successfully employed in a range from 15 to 50%.

Figure 142 illustrates a typical test (118) by this criterion and the accompanying text discusses results and conclusions. The index for determining the length of test cuts for the carbide tools was 25% and for the ceramic tools 15%. These produced approximate wear lands of 0.020 inch and 0.016 inch respectively. This latter figure of 0.016-inch wear land for the ceramic was selected because beyond this point for this particular ceramic breakdown became rapid and irregular.

There are, of course, many other variations of test methods which have been employed by a myriad of investigators to study tool wear versus work accomplished or product characteristics produced, but we still have no standardized accelerated test procedure. Until agreement is reached on a unified test procedure, reliance will be placed on individual approaches for advancing ceramic-cutting materials and optimum cutting practices.

Chapter 8

Industrial Experience

Industry is always anxious to cut costs and increase production. Consequently, it very eagerly accepted ceramic-tool samples for testing when they first appeared in the mid-1950's. The test results and practical applications of ceramics for machining presented a paradox: ceramics could outperform cemented carbides in most applications and on most materials as determined by test results, but in many cases they could not outperform cemented carbides on the machine-shop floor. Even if we exclude heavy-impact cutting, such as milling or interrupted cuts on steel, the same conclusion generally holds true.

Industry found that in most cases ceramics would not replace carbides on a one to one basis. Ceramics were utilized in volume only where they had a unique advantage such as in machining cast iron or hardened steels. Patient engineering of individual jobs has subsequently shown that ceramics can be generally more useful to the tool engineer if care is taken in their application in regard to the choice of cutting parameters, tool-edge preparation, and machine-tool maintenance. This care is needed because the ceramic is a more brittle tool material than carbide; the ceramic also has a lower tensile strength than the carbide. In the future, the strength of ceramic materials will undoubtedly improve and tools made from these materials will be available to the tool engineer. When this occurs, the application of these materials in a shop will not be so critical, and ceramics will be used more readily. For this discussion on industrial utilization of ceramics in metal cutting to have a lasting value, it is necessary for us to consider problems both of immediate usefulness and utilization possibilities under ideal conditions—the latter is likely to be commonplace in the not too distant future.

At present among users, there is a difference of opinion as to the relative merits of ceramics. While we can cite examples from the literature and from our own experience as to where ceramics can be profitably used, we always have to return to that sobering thought that the failures are not published. An impartial guide to the quantitative amounts of tool materials being utilized is the estimate of dollars which are being spent for the various materials. Only about 2½% of the total dollars spent for cemented carbide and ceramics is being used for ceramic tools. This estimate is higher when only the throwaway inserts are considered; then it is in the vicinity of 4% of the dollar volume for ceramics. This degree of utilization is not true for every application across the board.

Currently, ceramics have virtually no application in milling cutters on steel, but are extensively used for turning cast iron. At present, use of ceramics is specialized; in the future, it will be more general. The purpose of this chapter is to discuss both, as exemplified by actual user information rather than projected speculations. We are concerned then with the present status of ceramic tools as well as that of the immediate future.

A. Economics

This is motive. From the tool-engineer's view and from a managerial view, the motivation behind manufacturing-engineering studies is to increase profitability. Usually, this can be done by finding cheaper methods of shaping a part, often by cheaper machining methods, and sometimes by changing from a carbide to a ceramic cutter. In essence, this is true because of the greater durability of ceramic cutters and their insensitivity to higher cutting speeds, both of which tend to reduce manufacturing costs. Whether or not this is true in detail requires an individual analysis. The purpose of this discussion on economics is to point out how the ceramic material affects manufacturing economics, how this differs from that of cemented carbides, and how this difference might be put to practical use.

1. Mathematical Basis of Cost Analysis Using Ceramics

The total manufacturing costs can be obtained by adding the following four contributing factors [according to Gilbert (135)]:

a. Idle costs
b. Cutting costs
c. Tool-changing cost
d. Tool-regrinding cost

By an analysis using Taylor's (136) empirical tool-life equation $VT^n = C$, Gilbert derived the following expression for computing the cost per piece:

$$\text{Cost / piece} = K_1 \times \text{idle time} + K_1 \frac{L\pi D}{12fV} + K_1 \frac{L\pi DV(1/n - 1)}{12fc(1/n)} TCT + K_2 \frac{L\pi DV(1/n - 1)}{12fc(1/n)}$$

where:

K_1 = Direct labor rate + overhead rate \$/minute
K_2 = Tool cost per grind, \$/tool
L = Length of part, inches
D = Diameter of part, inches
V = Cutting speed, fpm
f = Feed per revolution, inches
T = Tool life, minutes
TCT = Tool-changing time, minutes
c = Constant from Taylor equation
n = Exponent from Taylor equation

Most of these factors are the same for both ceramics and carbide with the exception of the exponent and constant from the Taylor equation. This will influence the derivative of the equation so as to produce quite different optimum-cutting parameters to minimize costs or maximize productivity.

This equation is predicated from the empirical Taylor relation which is generally true for a wide variety of tool materials if the tool-life criterion is wear failure. Ceramics have a propensity to fail by mechanisms other than wear, and where this occurs the Gilbert equation for cost computation will not be valid. Ceramics often fail by fracture which is controlled by a fatigue process. This will impose upon the tool-life-velocity relation a statistical function relating to the probability of fracture failure, rather than the less variable wear process. The probability of fracture would correlate with some function of the tensile stress acting on the tool tip. This expression would not necessarily contain a linear relation with velocity, feed, or depth of cut, but will likely be a complex composite of material, geometrical, and cutting parameters; the quantitative expression of which is currently beyond our knowledge.

2. Economic Significance of Ceramic Materials

The exponent of the Taylor relation "*n*," which depicts the tool behavior, has been measured by Gilbert (137) and appears with the computed optimum tool life for a minimum part-cost *Tc*, a maximum production *Tp*, and the minimum-cost cutting speed *Vc* in a typical example.

Table XXII was prepared by Gilbert. He assumed an equal cost of $0.50 per tool, a labor overhead rate of $6 per hour, and a tool-changing time of 2 minutes. It is evident from the data that ceramics require high horsepower, high-rpm machines for optimum performance. This does not imply that the ceramics cannot necessarily be used at lower speeds with economic advantage. The data indicate

TABLE XXII

Optimum Tool-Cutting Conditions[a]

Tool material	n	$1/n - 1$	Tool life (minute)		Vc, fpm
			Tc	Tp	
High-speed steel	0.125	7	35	14	107
Tungsten carbide	0.250	3	15	6	701
Ceramic	0.5	1	5	2	3500

[a] From Gilbert (137).

that manufacturing costs can be minimized with ceramics in an operation where the tool edge rapidly deteriorates due to wear at very high-cutting velocities. These velocities are beyond the capacity of most lathes for small parts and certainly are beyond current-shop practices. These velocities are also difficult to achieve if the part or chuck is out of balance due to the resulting vibrations. They are also beyond the chicken point of most machine-tool operators. Without basic redesign of machine tools, utilizing novel concepts which tend to alleviate these problems, it is not likely that ceramic tools can be utilized at their maximum efficiency. This does not imply that ceramics are not economical at practical cutting conditions.

Figure 155 shows graphically the solution of cost allocation for each factor in Gilbert's equation for an "*n*" value corresponding to a single-point carbide tool.

Figure 155 shows that the cutting cost is reduced with speed, but the tool and regrinding costs are rapidly rising with speed so that the resultant total cost goes through a deep minimum, and the economic-cutting speed is adjustable only between about 150 to 350 fpm.

Figure 156 shows the same information for a ceramic cutter with the same values for the parameters except the "n" and "c" values were taken at 0.5 and 5000, respectively, so that they correspond to the performance of O-30 tools as scaled from Siekmann's curves. [Siekmann (138) has measured n and c at 0.69 and 13,400 from other data on the O-30 tool.]

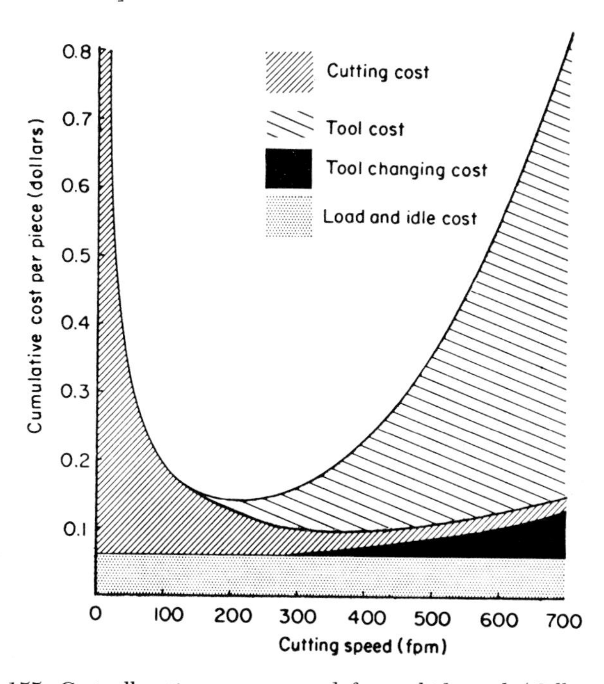

FIG. 155. Cost allocation versus speed for carbide tool (Gilbert, 137).

Since the load and idle costs and the cutting-cost factors contain the same parameters, these are not affected and remain the same for both examples. However, the tool-changing costs and the tool and regrind costs have been markedly reduced over the speed range productive load and idle costs. Also, since the tool and regrinding in the illustration so that for all practical purposes they have vanished. The total cost will continue to decrease with increasing speed, and asymptotically approach the fixed charges dictated by the non-

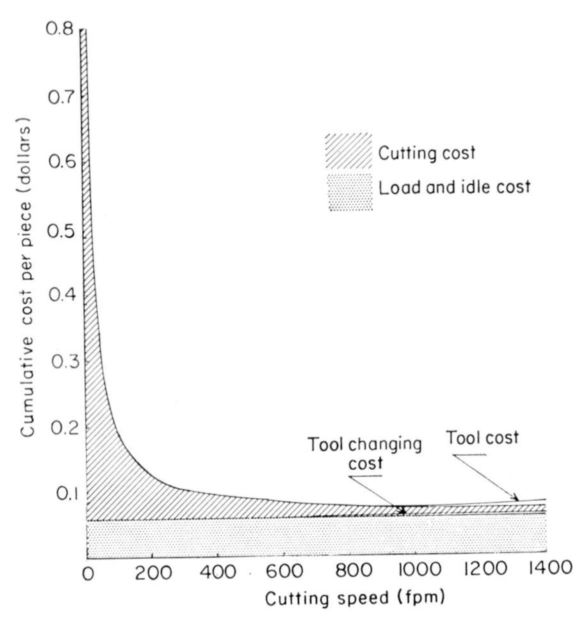

FIG. 156. Cost allocation versus speed for ceramic tool (Gilbert, 137).

costs vary linearly with speed ($n = \frac{1}{2}$), the machine-tool operator can increase cutting speed and productivity far beyond the limits of our illustration without significant alteration of the unit costs of production. In this case of machining at high speeds (>500 fpm) and using ceramic cutters, the production costs are almost independent of:

1. Cutting cost
2. Tool-changing costs
3. Tool costs
4. Tool-regrinding costs
5. Cutting speed
6. Production rate

Practically, this is all free—unless a fracture failure occurs, in which case the preceding arguments are not valid.

An analysis of machining cast-iron pulleys using ceramic and carbide cutters has been made by Schmidt *et al.* (91). Their data, presented by Gilbert, appear in Figs. 157 and 158.

In this case, the use of the ceramic makes the cutting costs and tool costs negligible, and manufacturing costs are essentially independ-

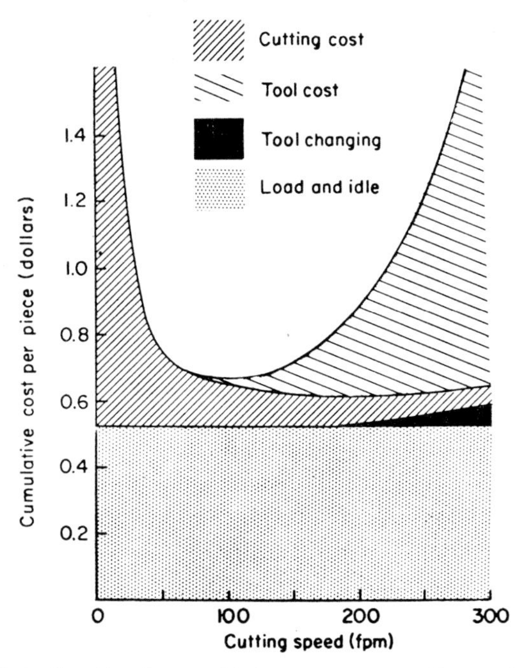

FIG. 157. Cost allocation for machining a cast-iron pulley with a carbide tool (Schmidt *et al.*, 153).

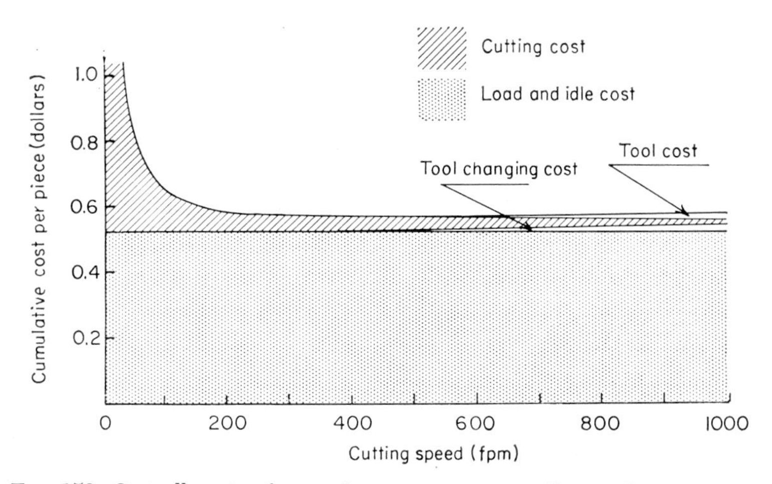

FIG. 158. Cost allocation for machining a cast-iron pulley with a ceramic tool (Schmidt *et al.*, 153).

ent of cutting speed over the range studied. The machine operator is free to maximize production without being penalized by excessively rapid tool deterioration. In this particular case, the example illustrates the futility of further advances in tool materials beyond the ceramic. Where is the motive? This is not true, of course, for other machining problems or on work-piece materials other than cast iron.

The high exponent of ½ in the Taylor equation indicates the insensitivity of ceramic wear with cutting speed. This exponent is characteristically about ¼ for carbides and ⅛ for tool steel. This means that as cutting technology advanced to each new material, the utility was expanding as a geometric progression in the exponent! This is an explosion! Ceramic cutters are so good now on a wear criterion that there is little impetus to search for new materials. However, there is ample motivation for improving the strength of ceramic tools in order to reduce the incidence of premature fracture.

By inserting the exponent of ½ into the Gilbert cost equation the following expression is derived:

$$\text{Cost/piece} = K_1 \times \text{idle time} + \frac{KL\pi D}{12fV} + \frac{KL\pi DV}{12fc^2}\,TCT + \frac{KL\pi DV}{12fc^2}$$

The last two terms, which are a measure of tool and tool-changing costs, are only related linearly to cutting speed and over the speed range of practical interest represent only a small fraction of the total cost allocation. From a practical standpoint the cost per piece is linearly related to the length and diameter of the piece, and inversely proportional to the feed and cutting velocity. Since we are not penalized for increasing the speed, but for increasing feed rates tool failure is greatly accelerated. The operator almost invariably machines at higher velocities with ceramics so as to increase productivity. The instances in the literature, reporting on the successful application of ceramics, usually show an increase of cutting speed of about threefold when a job is switched from carbide to ceramics.

3. Examples of Machining with Ceramics

Many examples exist which illustrate the high cutting-speed advantage of ceramic tools. Some of these illustrations show tenfold increases in cutting speed, but on commonly machined materials this advantage is somewhat less. Perhaps a more typical example would be the experience of an automotive manufacture in machining SAE 5135 steel-transmission gears (139) where the operation included

Fig. 159. Turning and facing SAE 5135 with ceramic tool (General Electric Company, 149).

turning the OD and finishing 3 faces, as shown in Fig. 159. The performance data using a popular ceramic tool in this operation is shown in Table XXIII.

In this example where the productivity is increased by 50%, fewer machines can do the same amount of work saving capital expenditures, amortization costs, maintenance costs, floor space, and other

TABLE XXIII

Ceramic Tool Performance Cutting SAE 5135

Speed:	970 fpm
Feed:	0.013 inch/rev
Depth:	0.025 inch
Pieces per grind:	1200
Hardness:	170–207 bhn
Increase in tool life:	4 × carbide
Increase in cutting speed:	2 × carbide
Increase in production:	50%

general overhead costs. This can cut into the base of the Gilbert cost equation and effect a substantial reduction in the cost level which the cost per piece asymptotically approaches. The increased productivity is most important in an integrated high-capacity production line, and least important in a small-job shop where the machines are not being fully utilized. In our particular example, the conversion to ceramic tools resulted in the elimination of one machine from the line.

The higher productivity can be the principal benefit in the utilization of ceramic tools, but whether or not this benefit is evident depends upon the accounting system which is in effect. Any accounting system is at best only a mathematical model of a financial complex in which the debits, credits, and allocation of these two different sources, is described. Like other mathematical models it is useful, and like all models it is only an approximation. The futility of balancing accounts to the penny is evident when a sophisticated estimate of corporate wealth might well have a probable error of $\pm 5\%$. The impact of increased unit productivity by the use of ceramic tools would perhaps represent a less significant financial perturbation to a bookkeeper than it would to a sophisticated and knowledgable accountant. Accounting systems are by the pragmatic necessity of their function conservative in nature, resistant to change, and rigidly standardized. Without a firm financial anchor, management would be hard put to evaluate performance. Unfortunately, a high-modulus mathematical model often cannot accommodate a perturbation outside of its conservatively construed matrix, and a new development of radical character will be unrealistically evaluated by an obsolete measure. The accounting system may not be realistic in a new situation which was not anticipated when the system was derived. This can, and often does, lead to a controversy between the engineering and the financial departments.

With the assumption that the financial evaluation of performance does measure the real advantage gained by ceramic cutters, the insensitivity of the ceramic economics to cutting speed is most evident in the case of facing cuts which range from high speeds on the OD to slow speeds near the center of the face.

Figures 157 and 158 which show the costs of machining cast iron illustrates this point. When facing with carbide, the instantaneous cost varies as the tool cuts on a decreasing diameter and on a decreasing cutting speed. The cost will go through the minimum, and up the other side of the curve on Fig. 157. The cost rocks back and forth on the curve depending upon the diameter. On the other hand, when using ceramics the costs are almost independent of cutting speed above 200 fpm, and the facing cut is economically optimized over the entire cut.

A practical example of this is in the finish facing of a cylinder head of gray-cylinder iron A.S.T.M. SA-278, class 35. This operation was taken from the experience of the Fuller Company using a popular ceramic tool; the part produced is shown in Fig. 160 (140).

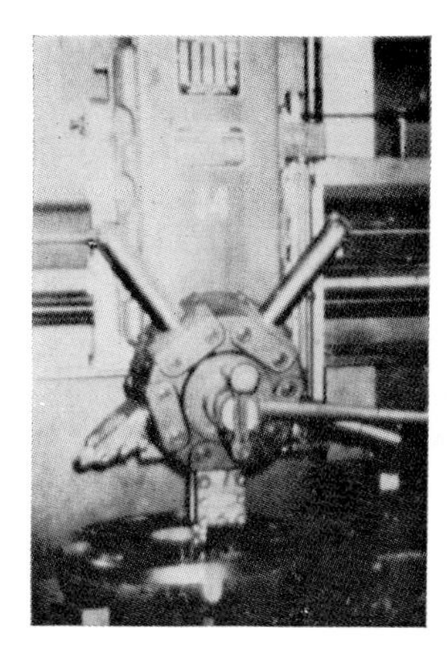

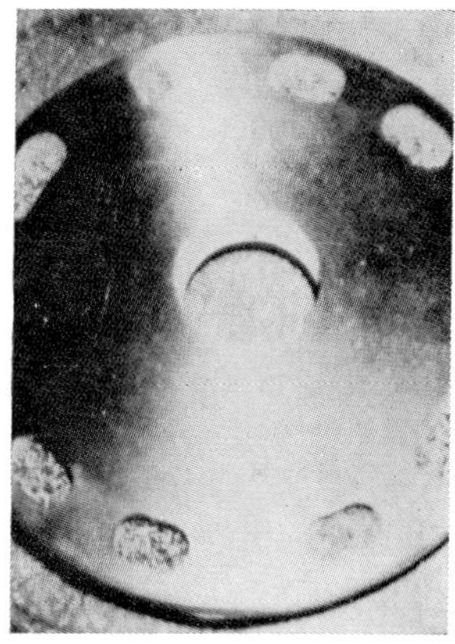

FIG. 160. Facing gray cylinder iron with ceramic tool (The Carborundum Company, 140).

The part has a 18.187-inch OD $\times$ 2.687-inch ID. This results in a severe change in cutting speed depending upon the diameter plus a serious interrupted cut due to the holes. The data comparing machining with carbide and ceramic appear in Table XXIV.

Figures 157 and 158, which appeared earlier, show that the cost insensitivity of ceramics with cutting speeds offers a great advantage for facing operations across large diametric changes. The carbide cutter will start on the OD of the piece at a cutting speed which places unit costs high upon the right-hand limb of the curve—off scale of the illustration. As the cut progresses, the unit costs gradually diminish until an optimum speed is reached at approximately 100 fpm. The unit costs then increase slightly along the other limb of the curve until the ID of the piece is reached at 46 fpm. This is not so for the ceramic. The cutting starts at a high-peripheral speed, also off scale, but with a

TABLE XXIV

COMPARATIVE CERAMIC TOOL PERFORMANCE FACING GRAY CYLINDER IRON

	Carbide	Ceramic
Surface speed (minimum fpm)	46	210
Surface speed (maximum fpm)	316	1418
Spindle speed (rpm)	67	300
Feed (inch/rev)	0.015	0.010
Depth of cut (inch)	0.010	0.010
Machining time/piece (minutes)	7.71	2.4
Pieces/cutting edge	12	100

flat response of cost with speed. As the surface speed is reduced due to the smaller diameter of the cut, the unit costs remain essentially constant until the minimum speed of 210 fpm is reached with only a slight rise in the curve as the ID of the piece is reached. It is possible to machine over a wide variety of speeds with minimum unit costs when using ceramic tools. This enables the tool engineer to select optimum cutting conditions on other beneficial criteria, such as surface finish, production rate, or tolerance. The ceramic can free him from the restrictions of a deep minimum in Gilbert's cost curve, which will allow him an additional degree of freedom of choice in optimizing his manufacturing system.

Similar instances illustrating the economy of ceramic tools can be also cited for machining both soft and hard steels. It is common to find the doubling of cutting speed with the use of ceramics on steel as compared with cemented-carbide cutters. There are also instances where the improved surface finish that is produced with ceramics allows the elimination of steps in the manufacturing process, such as the grinding of previously turned parts. One example was that of producing the oil-well tool from SAE 4142 steel (141) at Rc 30 to Rc 35 as is shown in Fig. 161.

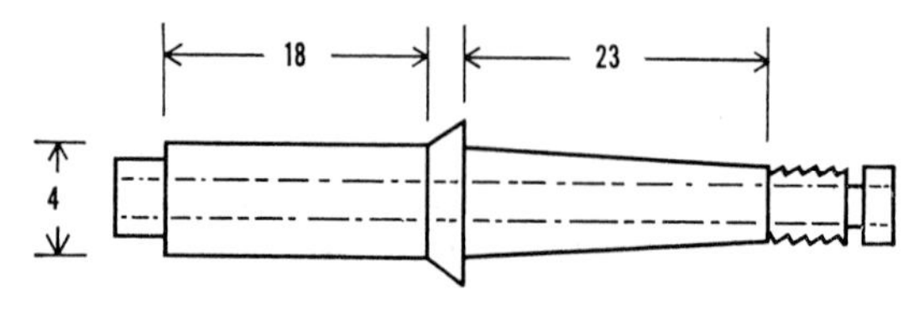

FIG. 161. Finish turning SAE 4142 steel at Rc 30–Rc 35 with ceramic tool (General Electric Company, 141). (Measurements in inches.)

This job is machined using a cemented-oxide tool at the top speed of the machine tool at 635 fpm. The tolerance on surface finish from the grinding operation was 32 microinches and the ceramic was able to stay well within this tolerance by producing a 25 microinch finish. The previous grinding cost was $7.50 per part and this was reduced to $2.01 by using the more rapid metal removal rate which is an inherent advantage of ceramic turning tools.

The efficient production of high-quality surfaces is an additional bonus that the manufacturer can collect when he is able to switch to ceramic tooling. Sometimes, as in the case cited above, the grinding operation can be eliminated if the tolerances are not hypercritical. Wherever this is possible, a very large economic advantage exists.

Using both ceramic and cemented-carbide tools, Ansell and Taylor (142) have studied the effects on surface finish over a wide variety of machining conditions. They have shown that the surface finish, as measured across the grooves, is largely determined by the geometry of the tool and the cutting conditions. However, the finish measured along the direction of the grooves is sensitive to the tool material and accounts for the brighter appearance of parts machined with ceramics. Figure 162 shows their data; the average surface finish (center line

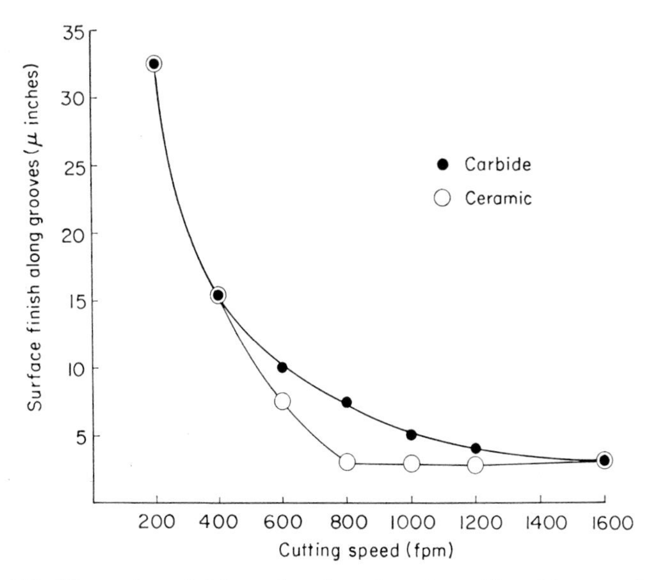

FIG. 162. The surface finish produced as it varies with cutting speed for carbide and ceramic tools (Ansell and Taylor, 142).

average) is plotted against cutting speed for both ceramics and carbides. The feed rate varied from 0.002 to 0.035 inches/rev at both 0.010-inch and 0.020-inch depth of cut.

These data were obtained on 0.4% plain carbon steel in a facing cut on the end of a tube 15 inch OD × 12½ inch ID. Most of the cuts would properly be classified as finishing cuts, except perhaps the

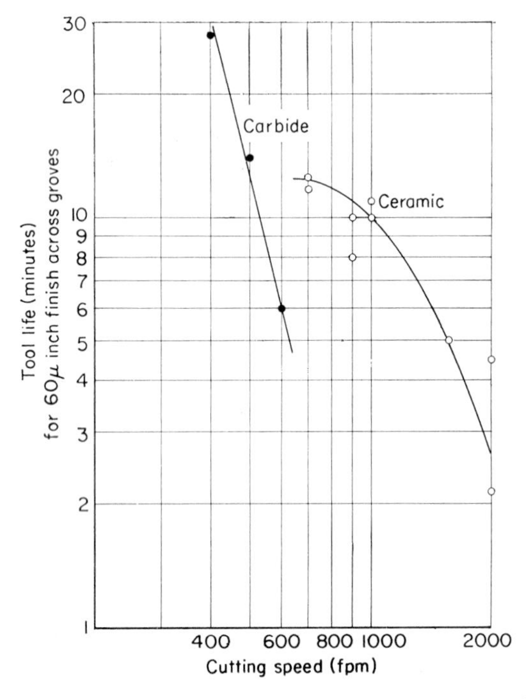

Fig. 163. Tool life based on 60-microinch finish for ceramic and carbide tools (Ansell and Taylor, 142).

ones using the larger feed rates. Figure 162 shows that the ceramic has a large advantage in producing smooth-surface finishes over the speed range of approximately 600 to 1100 fpm. This happens to also be the speed range of great practical interest, particularly for machining steel.

The difference between ceramics and carbides for producing surface finish is even more pronounced if the effects of prolonged wear are introduced as an additional complication. Ansell and Taylor have shown that the surface finish deteriorates with time as the tool is used for cutting. They established a tool-life criterion, on this basis, for both carbide and ceramic cutters used for finishing the machining of cast iron. These data appear in Fig. 163 where the tool life is considered to be the time at which a surface finish of 60 microinches is produced and is plotted against cutting speed.

It can be seen from the curves that the ceramic has the advantage by about 2 : 1 over carbide in cutting speed to produce an equivalent tool life. The ceramic is capable of functioning at speeds in excess of carbides and yet it still is able to retain a useful tool life. This is a practical criterion for tool life in such applications as that cited above in machining the hardened steel part shown in Fig. 161. The machine operator may well find that useful tool life is limited by a deterioration in surface finish rather than by the usual criterion of wear or fracture. Interestingly, the exponents of the Taylor equation were 0.3 for the carbide, and 0.55 for the ceramic; these values are just about the same as those that are found by a wear criterion and they suggest that the tool wear controls the surface finish deterioration, as would be expected.

4. Fracture Failure Economics

The foregoing discussion on economics assumes that the type of failure which occurs is smooth wear and that tool life is predictable within reasonably narrow limits. With ceramics, and carbides as well, the tool engineer often finds that matters are not this simple. This is not important in itself, as a wear failure is no less a cause of the cessation of the machining than is fracture. What is of importance, however, is that fracture is less predictable, and also it can seriously alter the shape and character of tool-life speed curves. This, of course, alters the cost analysis with a set of new criteria.

If we disregard those fractures which are the result of excessive optimism on the part of the operator, and if we disregard those fractures which result from careless practices or other unexplainable random causes and consider only those fractures which result from the accumulated fatigue damage in the ceramic tip, the tool life will then follow a distribution function like any other fatigue data; and the ceramic can be effectively used within control limits which are dictated by a particular job. These control limits may only have an incidental relation to wear processes.

Moore and Kibbey have shown that on a total tool-life criterion the ceramic does indeed behave differently than it does on a wear criterion. Their data (Fig. 164) are plotted along with Siekmann's data for wear characteristics for ceramic, carbide, and high-speed steel.

Moore and Kibbey used as a failure criterion on 1045 steel either the incidence of a fracture on the tool tip which destroyed the cutting action or wear-land development with side loads to more than double with accompanying unsatisfactory chip formation—whichever occurred first. The results in Fig. 164 indicate that there is general concurrence

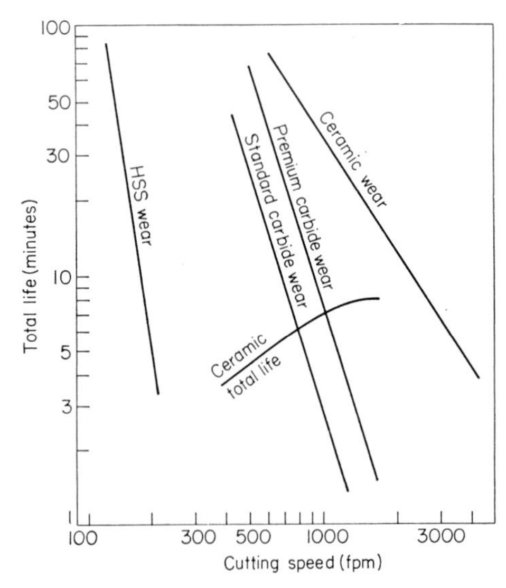

FIG. 164. Comparison between wear and total tool life for ceramic and carbide tools.

between the carbide tests of Siekmann and those of Moore and Kibbey, indicating that a wear criterion controlled tool failure in both cases. The discrepancy between Siekmann's ceramic-tool data and that of Moore and Kibbey is dramatic. This discrepancy results from the difference in tool-life criteria which were used for end points; Siekmann using wear and Moore and Kibbey using fracture. Both are proper procedures; the one used depends upon the test objectives. Since the exact character and shape of the fracture-criteria curve is not known with any great degree of exactitude, there are hazards in predicting tool behavior beyond the actual test speeds, and hazards in generalizing behavioral patterns beyond those actually experienced. The statistical analysis which was made by Moore and Kibbey on the data from which these results were abstracted led them to the following conclusion, "In the speed range of 500–1500 fpm the life of both sets of carbide tools varied inversely, approximately as the third power of the cutting speed. In the same speed range (500–1500 fpm), speed had no significant effect on the life of the ceramic tools." If we accept this statement quantitatively, with due apologies to Moore and Kibbey who more realistically qualified their statement, certain implications on machining economics naturally follow.

The Moore and Kibbey data at 500 fpm seem low in terms of tool life when other experience is considered. The data at 1000 and 1500 fpm when connected with a straight line, fit the "ideal" tool requirement with the amount of stock removal being constant per cutting edge and independent of cutting speed. In the Taylor equation the exponent becomes 1 and for our case the constant becomes 9700 and 9600 for 1000 and 1500 fpm respectively. The following discussion is predicated on the assumption that the tool is "ideal" by this criterion and the Taylor equation is

$$VT = C = 9650$$

The total cost equation of Gilbert is altered by making the factors of tool-changing costs and tool and tool-regrinding costs completely independent of cutting speed with Gilbert's equation reducing to: where the ceramic tool with a Taylor exponent of ½ enabled the last

$$\text{Cost / piece} = Ki \times \text{idle time} + \frac{KL\pi D}{12fV} + \frac{KL\pi D}{12fc} TCT + \frac{KL\pi D}{12fc}$$

two terms to become linear with speed. As we have shown previously, the total tool life consideration in our particular example further reduces these expressions to speed independence, and the previous observations that the costs per piece were "practically" independent of speed, do in reality become speed independent of the tool and tool-changing costs.

This is not of any great practical significance in itself, at the cutting speeds normally used, since these costs were already so low that they were only minor contributions to the total costs. This can become increasingly important, of course, as cutting speeds are further increased, or as ceramics become adaptable to very high speed milling applications.

Of greater practical significance is that the fracture tool-life curve for ceramics is displaced to a lower level on the performance diagram.

This causes the ceramic and carbide curves to cross at cutting speeds between about 600 and 800 fpm for soft steel. This crossover indicates that the carbide will outperform ceramics at speeds lower than this, and that the ceramic will function to advantage at speeds in excess of these values. In practice, on high-shear strength materials this relation holds approximately true, and very few instances can be found in the literature where the cutting speeds are below these values. This crossover speed can vary with the work-piece material, with the crossover being at much lower speeds on hardened steels.

The lower level of fracture tool-life values that are shown for ceramics in Fig. 164 largely account for the resistance of industry to accept ceramic tools for general use. A 10-minute tool life is shorter than customary in common practice, and can complicate a production operation even though the economics may favor the ceramic. This short tool life interferes with habit. Nonetheless, this does remain the principal area for future tool development, and an increase of two-fold in the "average" tool life could lead to a much wider acceptance of the ceramic cutters. This is well within the range of possibilities.

B. Materials

1. Cast Iron

Cast iron is noted for the rapid tool-wear characteristics which it exhibits when machined. This is particularly true if high cutting speeds are used. The normal tendency of cast iron to abrade conventional metallic tooling is aggravated by high cutting speeds.

The rapid tool wear probably results from two sources: the graphite or free carbon in the metal and the scale on the surface of the casting. It is likely that the free carbon can react with carbide tools to form solid solutions of WC in C which will remove layers from the tool surface as the reaction occurs. Industrial experience in graphite machining has shown that ceramics are less susceptible to this rapid wear than carbide.

The ceramic tool has four characteristics which make it desirable in machining this type of work-piece material:

1. It is inherently harder than most other tooling and it has high wear resistance over an extended temperature range.
2. It is very resistant to high temperatures and does not deteriorate in the manner of other types of tooling when run at high speeds.

3. It has little tendency to weld to either the chip or the work piece and it leaves a smooth bright work finish.
4. It is less reactive with carbon.

Because of these characteristics, both edge wear and cratering are prevented for extended periods or large numbers of manufactured parts. Therefore, the users of these tools are realizing one or more of the following operating advantages:

1. Better tool life
2. Higher speed cutting
3. Better control of size
4. Greater flexibility because of the wider range of operating speeds
5. Better finishes

a. Stock Removal Operations

The scale on cast iron often contains both iron oxide and entrapped sand particles which make this scale very abrasive. The scale thus severely tests the wear resistance of the tool material. In addition, the scale is rough and has a tendency to impact on the leading edge of the tool.

While ceramic tooling has the necessary resistance to wear, industry has found it necessary to design both holder and tool geometry to give the cutting edge maximum strength in order to gain freedom from chipping, fracture, and to promote trouble-free service. To accomplish these results, a number of recommendations can be made that have been developed from several years of field experience. These recommendations are:

1. The cut should be continuous. Severe interruptions on deep cuts can cause problems with ceramic tooling.

2. A heavy-duty holder should be used. It should have a shank of substantial cross section, a solid-carbide seat, and a loose or floating clamp. (See Fig. 150.)

3. A heavy insert should be used. For rough surfaces, $\frac{1}{4}$-inch-thick inserts are a minimum; a $\frac{5}{16}$-inch-thick insert is usually employed, and a $\frac{3}{8}$-inch or more should be used on the more difficult cuts.

4. An aluminum-foil shim or other soft metal 0.002–0.004-inch thick should be used under the tool to best distribute the load and cushion it from vibration and shock.

5. The insert should be honed on all cutting edges. Any part of the cutting edge which is to remove scale should be heavily honed. Tools

may be prehoned by the manufacturer or hand honed on the job. (See Fig. 137.)

6. Before starting the cut with ceramic tools, it is desirable to chamfer the beginning and end of any part that is badly out of round. This reduces shock on the tool at entry into, and exit from, the cut. These are the most critical points for tool performance.

7. The feed usually should not exceed 0.028 ipr. Higher feeds have been used, but 0.020–0.028 inch are usual. On some cuts lower feeds may be necessary.

8. Speed usually is 600–1200 fpm. Higher speeds may be used if the part is in good balance.

9. Tool holders should be maintained in top condition. Replace damaged seats or clamps and if the pocket in the holder becomes damaged, replace the holder.

When these recommendations have been followed, good results have been achieved in a variety of cast irons. The observance of good machining practices that are normally followed when using any tooling also contributes to obtaining maximum performance with ceramic tools. As with any other type of tooling, the machinist should not stop the tool in a cut or allow it to dwell in the cut. Dragging the tool back over a machined surface will also reduce tool life.

Some rather remarkable stock-removal performances on cast iron have been achieved recently through the use of ceramic tools. For example, the Cooper-Bessemer Corporation (143) has the job of machining Meehanite gas-engine pistons at 285 bhn with ceramic tools on both the roughing and finish cuts. The castings and finished parts are shown in Fig. 165. The machine tool used was a 50-HP Warner and Swasey Turret lathe, and the machining was done under the conditions shown in Table XXV.

A high rate of stock removal for ceramics and for current machine tools is 133 cubic inches per minute. While this example may be exceptional, it does illustrate the capacity of ceramic cutters to take heavy cuts when other conditions permit. In our example the ceramic functioned at speeds and stock removal rates 6 times that of carbide, with a corresponding reduction in machining time. The ceramic operation also produced an improved surface finish, which is a common added bonus. The general tendency in using ceramics for heavy-stock removal is to rely on speed increases rather than higher feed rates. This makes sense. The high strength of carbide or tool steel enabled the machine tool operator to utilize heavy feeds for stock-removal purposes. Master machinists trained their apprentices with the phrase "the money lever is in the feed—not the speed." This became a truism with technological support. The ceramic alters this. It has a lower tensile strength, but is insensitive to increases in cutting

FIG. 165. Cast-iron gas-engine pistons machined with ceramic tools (The Carborundum Company, 148).

TABLE XXV

COMPARATIVE CERAMIC TOOL PERFORMANCE MACHINING CAST-IRON PISTONS

	Carbide	Ceramic
Spindle speed (rpm)	70	422
Surface speed (fpm)	256	1547
Feed, roughing (ipr)	0.023	0.023
Feed, finishing (ipr)	0.006	0.006
Depth of cut (inch)	To 3/8	To 3/8
Machining time (minutes)	11.2	1.86
Pieces per edge	3–4	3–4
Stock-removal rate (cubic inches/minute)	22	133

speed. The "truism" is no longer true. With ceramics, "the money is in the speed—not the feed," and for this statement we now have impressive technological support. Stock-removal cuts using ceramics are characteristically taken at high speeds, moderate feeds, and whatever depth of cut is appropriate for the job and machine tool, from moderate to deep.

b. Finishing Operations

While many precautions are recommended for roughing cuts in cast iron, few are needed in the finishing operation. Even interrupted cuts are not a problem on most finishing operations. However, the following are some practical notes to finishing operations that can prove helpful in working with ceramic tooling on CI.

1. Both continuous and interrupted cuts are practical.
2. Finish obtained can be held to 35 microinches and may make possible elimination of subsequent grinding operations.
3. A substantial increase in tool life over other tools can be expected.
4. Speeds can be used to the limit of machine and work piece.
5. Tool holders should be kept in good condition. Burred or otherwise damaged seats and clamps should be replaced.

From the evidence at hand, it would seem that any company machining cast iron should review the possible benefits of using ceramic tools.

One of the best examples of finishing cuts on cast iron is the machining of cast-iron brake drums and clutch plates by the automotive industry, and this particular application has become standard for ceramic cutters. In 1961 approximately 60% of all the brake drums turned out by one manufacturer (144) were machined using ceramics.

FIG. 166. Finishing operation with ceramic tools on cast-iron transmission-brake drums (Vascoloy Ramet/Wesson).

The utilization of ceramics would be even higher except that in some cases the surface finish produced is too good and then, carbides are preferable. Figure 166 shows a contour-boring operation on transmission brake drums at 895 fpm, 0.012 inch/rev feed, and a 0.015-inch depth of cut.

In this cam-controlled cycle the ceramic tool faces the lip of the drum, bores it, and then moves to the center of the drum and faces the entire inside of the bottom (145). In general, the use of ceramics has allowed a two- or threefold increase in cutting speed and about a twofold increase in tool life in the finishing of cast iron. So, not only does the tool cut faster, but it also gives longer service at 1200 fpm than carbides do at less than half this cutting speed.

2. Soft Steel

Ceramic tool performance on this type of material is expected to be good.

Soft steels are currently being machined by ceramics at speeds from 500 to 2000 fpm, with feeds ranging from 0.004-inch to a 0.024-inch ipr. Many of the production cuts are finishing applications, but heavier cuts are being taken to depths of 5/8 inch at 0.020-inch feed.

At the present state of the art, it is not unusual to utilize 30 to 40 HP with ceramic tooling. There are instances where carbides utilize upwards of 150 HP from 250-HP lathes and future plans call for industrial use of up to 500-HP lathes. This is not yet for ceramic tooling and we must wait for further evolution in ceramic tool development to operate in this area or in some of the lesser horsepower ranges where carbide tooling is optimum. However, if it is desired that an operation be faster and produce a better finish, better tool life, better size control, or allow flexible machining parameters of other parts on the job, ceramic tooling is logical for consideration. Also, one tool producer has noted that with ceramic tools cutting mild steel (1020) there is less of a tendency to tear than with conventional operations.

On steel, severe interrupted cuts do not seem to be practical at this time. The cut should be continuous, but need not be free from cyclic loading such as produced by an out of round parts. Until further property advancements are made with respect to ceramic tool strengths (which is most probable), it will probably remain as a complementary material to carbide tooling.

In general, at the lower speeds carbides are likely to outperform ceramics, at intermediate speeds ceramics can perform as effectively as carbides, and at higher speeds, generating elevated temperatures, ceramics will be superior to metallic tooling. Thus, characteristics of equipment and specifications of a specific job will dictate the tooling selection for soft steels. Where suitable conditions are met, the ceramic can outperform other materials and therefore it is a considerable advantage to the manufacturer. One such example is in the finish turning of AISI 1050 at 180 to 220 bhn (146). This operation is shown in Fig. 167.

The data on the performance indicated that ample motivation was present to warrant the use of the ceramic (Table XXVI).

FIG. 167. Finish turning of AISI 1050 steel with ceramic tools (General Electric Company, 146).

TABLE XXVI

CERAMIC TOOL PERFORMANCE MACHINING 1050 STEEL

Speed (fpm):	715 (increased 100%)
Feed (inch/rev):	0.0125
Depth (inch):	0.015–0.030
Pieces/insert:	29
Production:	Increased 50%
Tool life:	Increased 30%
Finish:	Improved

In our experimental studies, we have machined similar materials at 1500 fpm with the tool cutting upwards of 6000 cubic inches of steel before failure. This was on straight turning with 0.011-inch feed/rev and 0.100-inch depth of cut. Although this is a finishing type of operation, the stock removal rate was quite high and tool life very satisfactory.

3. Hard Steel

The development of the ceramic tool to its present degree of perfection has made it possible, for the first time since the beginning of metal cutting, to machine fully heat-treated steels.

Table XXVII gives the expected conditions for cutting hardened steels above Rc 40 up to Rc 65 (147). This table outlines some of the operating parameters used as starting points when setting up to machine in Rc ranges above 40.

TABLE XXVII

Conditions for Machining Hardened Steels

Hardness of steel	Depth of cut (inches)	Maximum recommended feeds (inch/rev)	Recommended speeds (fpm)
Rc 40–Rc 48	To 1/32	0.030	300–1200
	1/32 to 1/8	0.025	300–1000
	1/8 and up	0.021	300–800
Rc 48–Rc 55	To 1/8	0.015	200–800
	1/8 and up	0.010	200–600
Rc 55–Rc 65	To 1/32	0.010	120–450
	1/32 and up	0.008	75–350

Thus, with this background, practical machining is taking place on hardened steels at economical speeds and feeds while holding size and finish without any increased difficulties over machining of soft steel.

This advance in the science of metal machining happened as the strength properties of the ceramic tools were advanced by research into tool structures and grain sizings. Furthermore, the single most important characteristic of ceramic tools is that they are able to withstand, without significant loss of strength, the elevated temperatures that occur when steel of high hardness is machined. In industry, by using the fine feed and the speeds shown in Table XXVII, it has been possible to hold a 20 microinch finish on steels harder than Rc 40. Many individual pieces have recorded finish as low as from 6 to 10 microinches.

To achieve these results the following practices have been found most desirable and necessary:

1. Maintain holders in good condition. Replace damaged or worn seats, clamps, and chip breakers.
2. Use only tools with honed lands as shown in Fig. 137 that have the maximum physical properties with respect to strength.
3. Do not stop the tool in the cut, or drag it back over a machined surface.
4. The cut should not be fully interrupted. Moderate machining of intermittent cuts, such as occur when a work piece is out of round, will be possible at lighter feeds and lower speeds. Full interruptions due to holes, slots, or cutouts will likely cause chipping of the tool.
5. Use heavy tool holders for stock-removal cuts.
6. Use only solid-carbide seats under tools.
7. Use a shim of aluminum foil or similar soft metal under stock-removal cuts.
8. Use thicker inserts for heavier cuts. (See Table XXVII.)
9. Use square or rectangular inserts where possible, as this shape is considered 50% stronger than the triangular ones.
10. All tools for cutting hard steel have a negative rake and the cutting edge must be honed.

By following the above 10 points plus good common-sense machining practice, one can perform production operations on hard steel with a marked reduction of machining time or the elimination of grinding. Thus machining of hard steel becomes a relatively new approach where engineers can design parts for turning, with a potential of reducing manufacturing costs and at the same time improving the quality of the part.

Figure 168 shows a bearing race made of 52,100-steel hardened to Rc 61 and machined with a ceramic tool at 300 fpm and 0.005-inch feed per revolution.

The part has a 20-microinch finish, and for some applications,

FIG. 168. Finish turning of steel at Rc 61 (Vascoloy Ramet/Wesson).

grinding can be eliminated on jobs of this type. Prior to the ceramic, this part could not be turned at all as grinding was the only process capable of machining steel this hard.

Another type of hardened ferrous metal which is successfully machined with ceramics are the cast alloys and cast steels which are commonly used for mill rolls. Figure 169 shows a 60-inch diameter, 80-inch long backup roll of cast steel (148) at about 55-shore sclero-

FIG. 169. Cast steel roll finished with ceramic tools (The Carborundum Company, 148).

scope which was machined using ceramic cutters. The conditions for this operation is shown in Table XXVIII.

Ceramics have been very successfully employed in machining applications of this type because of the great advantage they have over carbides on hard materials. In roll turning, the finish produced by the ceramic is sometimes adequate for the purpose, and in this case the roll grinding can be eliminated.

TABLE XXVIII

MACHINING CAST STEEL ROLL[a]

Surface speed	865 fpm
Feed	0.0455 inch/rev
Feed	2.5 inches/minute
Depth of cut	0.040 inch
Machining time/roll	32 minutes
Rolls/edge	1
Rolls/tool	8

[a] From The Carborundum Company (148).

Stock removal rates on chilled iron-mill rolls at Rc 23 to Rc 34 have been reported (149) up to 154 cubic inches per minute where carbide cutters achieved 75 cubic inches per minute. These results were on an unusually large lathe taking a 1-inch depth of cut at 456 fpm. They do indicate high stock-removal rates are possible with ceramics, if the machine tool has sufficient capacity.

4. Nonferrous Materials

Bronze, brass, copper, molybdenum, tungsten, plastics, carbon-graphite, and other nonferrous materials are processed successfully by machining with ceramic tools. Table XXIX gives the degree of success expected with these materials.

Tungsten is a particularly good example of a case in which ceramic tools perform with ease, whereas other cutting-tool materials usually have difficulty.

On the other hand, little or no advantage is gained by attempting to employ ceramic tooling on aluminum, titanium, nickel, or aluminum bronze. While aluminum can be cut, it has a high affinity for alumina and tends to create built-up cutting edges. This nullifies any advantage over carbide tools. Titanium belongs in the group of materials that can be identified as "gummy" and as tough which produces accelerated galling wear to ceramic tooling. It is suspected that there may be a detrimental chemical reaction with the tool at the elevated temperature generated by the cutting action. Nickel and alumina bronze, also "gummy" in nature, tend to break down the edge of the tool by progressive minute chipping.

It should be remembered that the relief angles have to be reduced for the hard materials. Better cutting and superior finishes can be produced with neutral to positive rakes. These can be employed on the softer nonferrous and nonmetallic materials.

TABLE XXIX

MACHINING NONFERROUS MATERIALS WITH CERAMICS

Material	Tool life	Usual speeds
Carbon-graphite	Excellent	200–1000 fpm
Plastics	Good	300–3000
Tungsten	Excellent	150–800
Tantung	Excellent	60–140
Molybdenum	Fair	500–800
Copper	Excellent	600–2000
Titanium	Poor	Not recommended
Brass	Good	To 3000
Bronze	Good	To 3000
Aluminum bronze	Poor	Not recommended
Hard rubber	Excellent	To 1000

5. HIGH-TEMPERATURE ALLOYS

Excellent results are obtained when ceramics are used to machine certain types of high-temperature alloys and superalloys, machining of other types result in a mediocre performance at best.

These materials may be roughly grouped into two general categories.

I. Hard-cobalt base alloys and all chromium-base stainless steels, such as the stellites and 400-series stainless steels.

II. Softer, work-hardening, nickel and nickel-iron base alloys which are characterized by Inconel Hastelloy C, A 286, 300-series stainless steels and similar materials.

Group I, with the cobalt-base alloys, is a good operating area for ceramic tooling. Negative rakes, large lead angles, and large radii, appear to be the best for cutting these alloys. Conventional grades of carbides have problems with this group and tend to chip or wear excessively.

Group II, with the nickel and nickel-iron base alloys, is a poor operating area for ceramic tooling. Almost all of this type of alloy has a tendency to work harden, is gummy, and has high shear strength which requires a positive geometry in a strong tool material. Such a system tends to cause early tool failure in most of the present-day ceramic tooling.

C. Type of Operation

Ceramics have been experimentally applied in a wide diversity of machining operations. Industrial experience, however, has shown ceramic tools to be most useful in single-point turning, facing, and boring. The subject of this section is to illustrate that no inherent reason prevents the diversified use of ceramics; but practical experience has shown a greater degree of utility in particular areas and operations.

1. Turning

a. Continuous Cuts

Experience has shown that straight turning in continuous cuts is one of the best applications for ceramic tooling. Both roughing and finishing of rolls, shafting, large gear blanks, gun barrels, and tubing are all typical examples of applications accomplished with excellent results. In most of these operations high stock-removal rates, better size control, and superior finishes have been achieved in addition to more economical cutting.

Table XXX summarizes the industrial experiences in the straight turning of cast irons, soft steels, hardened steels, and nonferrous materials.

b. Interrupted Cuts

Experience has shown that cuts should not be fully interrupted with ceramic tooling because of the destructive nature on the tool-cutting edge. Fully interrupted cuts are possible on cast iron only for light finishing. Partially interrupted cuts such as those which occur when the work piece is out of round can be accomplished at reduced feeds and speeds on cast iron, steel, or even hardened steels. Since the ceramic material has a lower tensile strength than carbide or tool steels, it is more prone to fail by a nose fracture or by progressive chipping of the cutting edge. This tendency can be minimized by proper edge preparation and selection of machining conditions. The edge of the cutter can be greatly strengthened by grinding a small land or by tumbling a small radius so that the stress on the edge is more favorably distributed. The size and angle of the land or size of the tumbled radius can be fairly critical for each application, and at present this will probably have to be determined empirically. Tools can be purchased with a variety of edge preparations so the burden of tool preparation does not necessarily fall upon the user.

As an illustration of the improvements which can be produced by edge preparation, we have prepared a 5½-inch diameter fine-grained-case iron log by milling four longitudinal slots ⅝-inch wide; we machined this log using ceramic tools. Figure 170 schematically shows the log and tool for this operation.

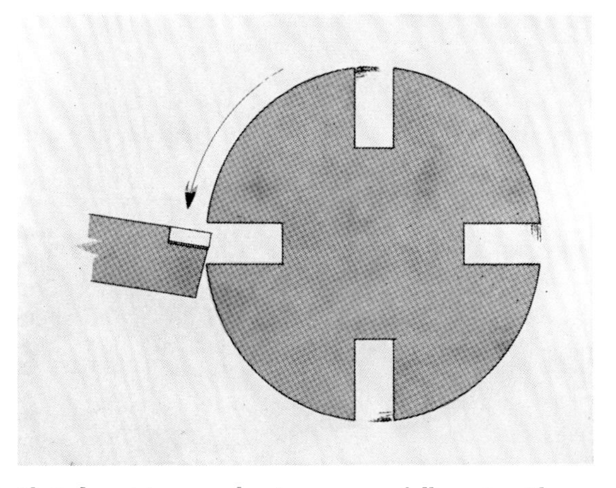

FIG. 170. Slotted cast-iron work piece successfully cut with ceramic tool.

This condition represents one of the most severe interrupted cuts possible on cast iron. The tool tip is impacted four times each revolution, and a conventional tool with a ground land will fail almost immediately upon entry. The tool performance can be greatly improved by either chemically polishing a small radius on the tool edge with the borax fusion, or by tumbling a small radius on the edge with abrasive media. Coupled with a 45° lead angle, the chemically polished tool

TABLE XXX

Example	Operation	Material	Part	Size (inch)	Speed
1	Rough contour turn	Alloy iron	Tire-rim roll	15–18 OD	371
2	Finish turn	Nodular CI Rc 35	Steel-mill roll	32 D × 60	510
3	Finish turn	Nodular CI Rc 35	Mill-roll journals	24 D × 16.5	330
4	Finish turn	Alloy iron Rc 49	Steel-mill roll	18.5 D × 54	290
5	Finish turn	Alloy iron Rc 52	Steel-mill roll	16.5 D × 40	130
6	Rough and finish contour turn	Alloy iron Rc 47	Rod-mill roll	$10\frac{3}{8}$ D × 30	140 (average)
7	Finish turn	Alloy iron	Camshaft journals	2 D × $\frac{3}{4}$	370
8	Rough and finish turn	Meehanite	Piston	14 D × 18	1547
9	Finish turn	Cast steel Rc 30	Steel-mill roll	$21\frac{5}{8}$ D × 87	820
10	Turn	Cast steel Rc 37	Mill-roll journals	17 × 50 × 21 14.5 × 17	110
11	Contour turn	Cast steel	Bar mill	12 D × 38	220–440
12	Finish turn	Cast steel Rc 35	Back-up roll	46.2 D × 90	965
13	Turn	1020 steel forging	Gear blank	9.50 D × $\frac{1}{2}$	2060
14	Turn	1020 steel	Rollers	$12\frac{1}{2}$ D × 179	688

TURNING EXPERIENCE USING CERAMIC TOOLS

Feed (ipr)	Depth (inch)	Stock removal machining time	Finish	Comments
0.015	1/4 (average)	—	Excellent	Machining time cut from 15–3 hours
0.050	0.020–0.030	62.6 minutes (3 cuts)	—	Total taper 60 inches, 0.003 inch
0.014	0.0025	22.6 minutes	Good	Less than 0.002 inch taper
0.071	0.030	16 minutes	Good	Previous machining time 54 minutes
0.050	0.030	27 minutes	Good	Previous machining time 53 minutes
0.007–0.020	1/32–1/8	7 hours 45 minutes (11 cuts)	Good	Previous machining time 23 hours 30 minutes
0.012	0.017	0.26 minute	—	Time reduced from 0.34 minutes; tool life up 8 to 1
0.023	to 3/8	1.86 minutes or 133 cubic inches/minute	Good	Previous stock removal rate 22 cubic inches/minute
0.019	0.060	32 minutes	—	Previous machining time 105 minutes
0.034	3/8	161 minutes	—	Precious maching time 284 minutes; tool life up 2 to 1
0.008	0.030	35 minutes	—	Previous machining time 7 hours 55 minutes
0.047	0.035	24 minutes	45–50 rms	Taper less than 0.001 inch
0.0028	0.015	—	35–40 rms	75 pieces per cutting edge; chatter eliminated
0.018	0.080 0.015	—	Excellent	Polished operation eliminated size hold within 0.0005 inch; time cut by 68 minutes

TABLE XXX – Continued

Example	Operation	Material	Part	Size (inch)	Speed
15	Turn	1020 steel	Hot-rolled tubing	$8\frac{1}{2}$ D × 36	1750
16	Turn	1020 steel	Hot-rolled tubing	8 D × 50	1450
17	Turn	4340 Rc 42	Gun barrel	8–12 × 24	420
18	Turn	AMS 6427 Rc 48	Hollow cylinder	$9\frac{1}{2}$ × 100	434
19	Contour turn	Alloy steel Rc 51	bell-shaped component	13–$8\frac{1}{2}$ × 10	300
20	Turn	HYCC Rc 58	Punch		75
21	Turn	52100 Rc 61	Boaring race	30 × 1	300
22	Turn	Tool steel Rc 60	roll	$13\frac{1}{2}$ D × 30	440
23	Turn	Hardened steel Rc 71–72	mill roll		200
24	Turn	Aluminum	Bearing bracket		3000
25	Turn	Tungston	Experimental log	6 D	350
26	Turn	K Monel	Experimental log		2650

Turning Experience Using Ceramic Tools

Feed (ipr)	Depth (inch)	Stock removal machining time	Finish	Comments
0.014	0.100	—	Good	13 pieces per cutting edge
0.040	0.050	—	Good	Machining time reduced from 6½ minutes to 2 hours
0.020	⅜	Approximately 60 cubic inches/minute	Good	Stock removal doubled; machining time reduced; better size control; and tool life improved
0.008	0.0375	—	60 rms	Taper less than 0.001 inch: could not be done economically any other way
0.017	0.500	30 cubic inches/minute	—	Doubled stock removal with improved tool life
0.010	⅛		—	Salvaged 2000 punches; too costly to grind
0.005	0.025	—	20 rms	Grinding eliminated
0.005	0.015	50 minutes	Good	Machining time reduced to ⅓; grinding eliminated
0.005–0.007	0.030	—	—	Reduced grinding; overall machining time reduced 20–30%
0.025		—	—	Reduce machining time
0.030	0.030	—	—	Promising experiment
0.0125	0.100	—	Excellent	

was able to cut over the entire length of the log without failure using 0.0165 inch/rev feed, 1200 fpm, with a 0.060-inch depth of cut.

This illustration dramatically suggests directions that can be taken to alleviate interrupted cut problems which cause tool breakage, and even though these results are experimental they do demonstrate a capability for difficult machining jobs using available materials and processes.

Figure 171 shows an actual case where an interrupted cut has been taken on cast-iron chuck bodies (150).

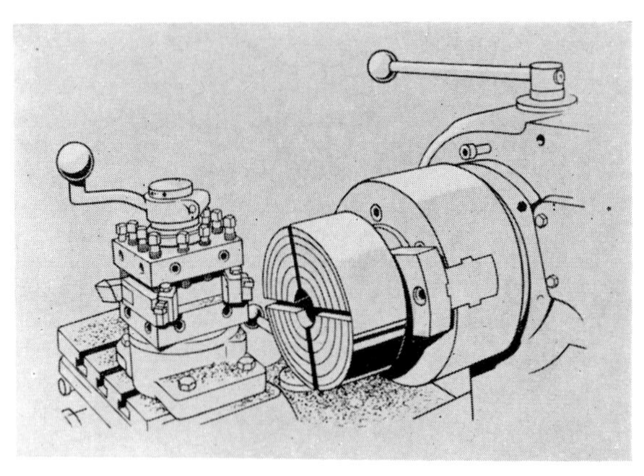

FIG. 171. Cast-iron chuck body being machined with a ceramic tool (Gulton Industries, 150).

The ceramic functions in this application at 800 to 1200 fpm, 0.011 to 0.016 inch/rev feed; as compared to 350 fpm and 0.022 inch/rev to 0.027 inch/rev feeds for carbide tooling. The carbide tooling required two passes while the ceramic was able to produce the surface finish required in a single cut, and thereby a considerable advantage was gained. Tool life was about the same for both tools. Interrupted cuts of this type are still rare and the usual experience has been less satisfactory.

c. Facing Cuts

As was discussed earlier in this chapter, facing cuts offer a real advantage when made with ceramic tools because of the ceramics insensitivity to cutting speed. This is another very satisfactory area of application with ceramics. The cutting speed can in most cases be set at a reasonable value for the smaller diameter without fear that the speed will be too high on the larger diameter.

Figure 172 shows a cast-iron clutch disk (151) which has to be faced to a 37- to 50-microinch finish.

The ceramic tool does this job at 625 to 146 fpm, 0.005 inch/rev feed, and 0.020-inch depth of cut; on a cut ranging from 10- to 2⅜-inch diameter. Over 200 disk faces are machined with every index of the ceramic-tool cutting edge, and the use of ceramic tooling obviated a large capital expenditure for a face grinder.

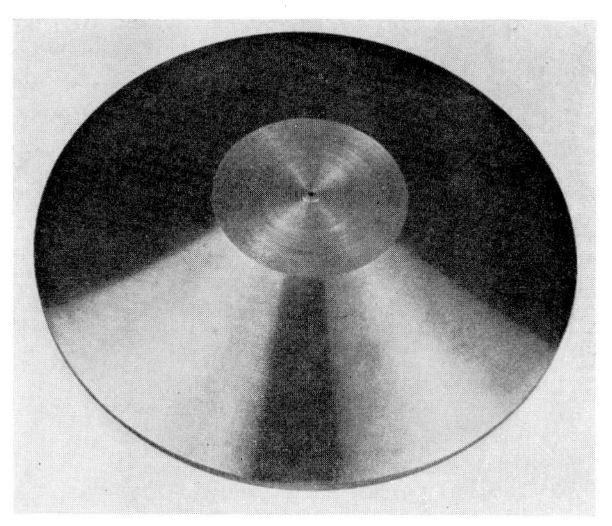

FIG. 172. Cast-iron clutch disk faced with ceramic tool (General Electric Company, 151).

Facing cuts are also possible and practical on steel, hard steels, or any other material which can be cut with ceramics. Operational gains with facing cuts have been parallel to those in the straight turning of these same materials.

2. BORING

Many boring operations have taken advantage of the beneficial operating characteristics of ceramic tools. Precision finish cuts, performed at high speeds, have been particularly suitable for the boring operation.

Boring, however, has been, for the most part, restricted to the larger

ID's so that the tooling can be made sufficiently massive and rigid to enable operation without excessive bending or vibration. This has been found to be an important consideration for boring tools, because if the ceramic insert is subjected to added bending stress or vibration, injury to the cutting edge can result.

One of the best examples is the finish boring of cast-iron automotive brake drums where tool life has been increased by 5 to 1, a secondary polishing operation eliminated, and machining time cut by ⅓.

In the boring of steels, ceramics have found a significant place by being able to machine and produce superior finishes on fully heat-treated steels between Rc 50 and Rc 60. In the majority of cases this has not only saved considerable time but has also eliminated a finishing operation by grinding.

Holmstrom (152) has investigated precision boring using oxide tools and his results appear in Table XXXI.

TABLE XXXI

PRECISION BORING WITH CERAMICS

Material	Speed (fpm)	Lead (inch/rev)	Depth of cut (inches)	Tool life (miles)	Wear land (inches)
Cast iron	500	0.010	0.010	9	0.015
Cast iron	1000	0.010	0.010	7	0.015
4150 annealed	1000	0.005	0.010	2	0.006
	1000	0.005	0.010	8	0.020
	2000	0.005	0.010	7	0.020
	5000	0.005	0.010	4	0.020

The results reported in this table are not radically different from expectations in finish turning, yielding tool lives from 1½ hours to a rather remarkable 4 minutes at 5000 fpm.

In Table XXXII is summarized some of the reported industrial experiences with boring using ceramic cutters.

3. MILLING

Milling operations with ceramics on a general basis has not yet been established. However, industrial experience and test programs place ceramic milling close to the realm of practical and economic tooling for a number of types of operations.

The relatively low transverse rupture strength and sensitivity to intermittent cuts for ceramics indicates that special attention to tool-

TABLE XXXII

INDUSTRIAL BORING WITH CERAMIC TOOLS

Material	Part	Size	Speed (fpm)	Feed inch/rev	Depth (inch)	Stock-removal machining time	Finish (rms)	Comments
Cast iron Rb 92–Rb 98	Brake drum	11 inch ID × 2¼ inches	875	0.015	0.022	0.43 minutes	80–120	Machine time cut ⅓, tool life doubled
Cast iron	Cylinder liner	11⅝ inch × 22 feet	1015	0.009	0.250	7.63 minutes 27.4 inches^3/minute	—	Machining time reduced by ⅔
Steel Rc 42	Aircraft component	2.2498 inch ID	640	0.014	1/32 inch	—	40	Tool life increased, faster operation
Steel 4140 Rc 50	Sleeve	5 inch OD × 4 inch ID	1200	0.005	0.050	—	8	Eliminated grinding
Tool steel Rc 64–Rc 66	Flanged sleeve	—	135	0.0046	0.008	—	—	Machining time drastically reduced, grinding eliminated
Soft low carbons steel tubing	Automotive tubing	1.84 inch ID	1460	0.005	0.025	0.15 minutes	40–50	Cutting time reduced to almost half, finish much improved

ing and machine conditions is required to obtain successful milling operations with ceramics.

Experience indicates that suitable cutter geometry and contact conditions should be employed to insure that initial contact between cutter and work piece occurs behind the cutting edge. If this is done by proper adjustment of radial rake, axial rake, corner angle, and angle of entry into the work, with a rigid cutter body in a rigid machine tool, some excellent results can be achieved.

In general the shallower cuts and finer feeds which involve smaller tool forces and ligher impacts give the best performance.

Relatively lower tool forces are essential to most effective use of ceramic tools, and even higher cutting speeds than presently available would be expected to help the situation.

Furthermore, Schmidt *et al.* (153) found a narrow flat cutting-edge land to reduce detrimental chipping. This was confirmed by Weller (154) in his tests which showed flat lands also to be superior to rounded lands.

The most extensive industrial use of milling with ceramics has been with cast iron but satisfactory results have also been achieved with aluminum, soft steel, and heat-treated steels.

The speed of cut and surface finish has been shown to be superior with ceramic milling but there is still much to learn about their most effective application before general use is achieved. Nevertheless, all indications point to practical, feasible, and economical use with continued buildup of experience.

Figure 173 shows Krabacher's (155) data on the comparative milling performance of carbides and ceramics on cast iron. These two curves indicate that the same wear-resistant advantage of ceramics over carbides is present in milling as well as in turning. This assumes, of course, that premature fracture does not occur. All investigators have found that edge preparation is essential for ceramic-milling cutters and they list edges with both small chamfers and also with tumbled radii. Our own limited experience in milling cast iron indicates that a 0.002-inch radius on the cutting edge and a $\frac{1}{32}$-inch radius on the tool nose yielded the best results when milling a rough bar of cast iron. With this tool geometry the fly cutter enabled us to cut at 1100 fpm, 0.100 inch $\times$ depth of cut, and a 0.012-inch chip load per tool. Deviations from this cutting edge or tool-nose geometry to larger radii caused excessive loading and tool failure by fracture. Others have found a 0.003-inch wide land at 45° advantageous.

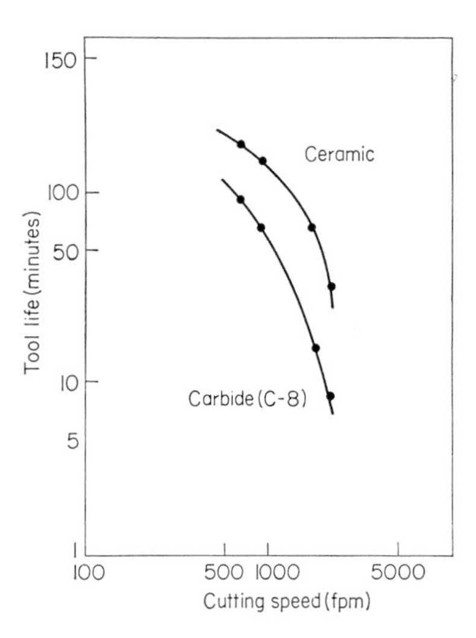

Fig. 173. Milling cutter life with speed on cast iron for carbide and ceramic tools (Krabacher, 155).

The use of ceramics for milling steel has been experimentally demonstrated but the results are generally so marginal that there is little practical application. Figure 174 shows Krabacher's data on milling steel.

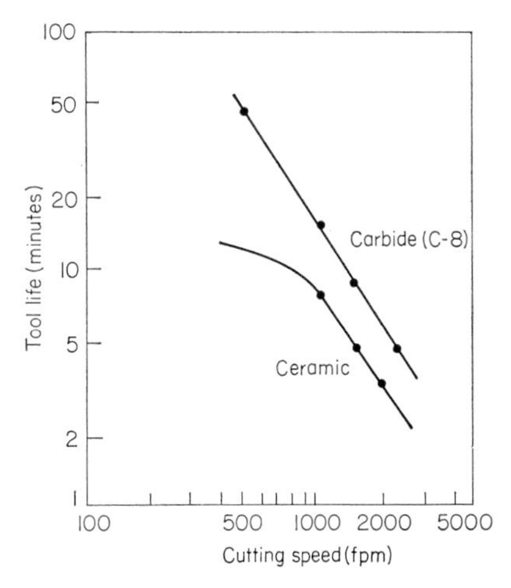

Fig. 174. Milling cutter life with speed on steel for carbide and ceramic tools (Krabacher, 155).

TABLE XXXIII

MILLING WITH CERAMICS

Material	Part	Size (inch)	Speed (fpm)	Feed	Depth (inch)	Stock removal machine time (seconds)	Finish (rms)	Comments
Cast iron	Cylinder head	—	3930	18½ in/min	0.010	—	25	Little wear of cutter after machining 70 heads
Cast iron	Test block	—	1750	0.006 inch/tooth	0.060	—	—	Higher speed and better tool life than with carbide
Pure nickel	Test block	—	3000	0.006 inch/tooth	0.060	—	—	Tenfold increase in stock removal, twofold decrease in tool life
7178–T–6 Aluminum	Panel	36 × 860 × 1	7500	To 120 inches/minute	0.030	—	—	—
Cast iron	Pad	2½ × 7	1710	15¾ inches/minute	⅛ to ¼	26	40–50	20% reduction in machining time
Chrome-Moly Steel Rc 38	Forging	—	800	4½ inches/minute	0.010	—	32	Eliminated grinding
SAE 4340 Rc 42	Test block	—	375	5 inches/minute	¼	—	80	Improved finish and speed

The curves indicate that the ceramic is inferior to the carbide; therefore there is little point in using ceramics for this purpose. Krabacher has also shown that the ceramic exhibits less wear than carbide in milling steel above 1500 fpm with a much flatter curve in the plot of flank wear versus cutting speed. The ceramic, therefore, has a potential use for this application with the development of a stronger material. Table XXXIII summarizes the experience in milling using ceramics.

4. Miscellaneous Operations

Ceramics have been used for a variety of other operations such as drilling. Because of the complex cutting action of the common-twist drill and its sensitivity to design and operating conditions, only a few superficial attempts have been made to apply ceramic cutting edges. To date, none have indicated any substantial promise. A design to render adequate support to the ceramic without excessive bending load is the major problem.

Gun drills of the straight single-flute design appear to offer a much better potential for ceramic tipping. A number of these have been constructed and are being tested but no results are as yet available. However, the technique is expected to increase output eventually and create finer finishes.

Only one report is available for planing using ceramics; this is the work of Hallberg (156) using 4340 steel at 400 bhn and planing at 300 fpm. The data indicated that ceramics could function at infeeds of 0.011 inch with a depth of cut up to ⅛ inch without failure. While this is not particularly impressive it does indicate the possibility of using ceramics for this type of operation. There are physical difficulties in obtaining the cutting speeds at which ceramics function most economically when using reciprocating table-or-tool motions. These difficulties would tend to limit cutting speeds to lower values where carbides and tool steels function well, and ceramics would not necessarily represent a great advantage unless the chemical or physical character of the work piece favored the use of the alumina cutter.

One additional operation which arouses repeated curiosity is the use of ceramics in hot machining of difficult metals. The high-temperature resistance of the ceramic would inherently favor their use in high-temperature cutting operations. This is especially true since the interfacial temperature between the tool and work varies proportionally with the work-piece temperature which is artificially maintained by resistance, induction, or arc heating. Dickter *et al.* (157) have shown that ceramics can be used for high-temperature machining of a hot-work die steel at Rc 60. In their tests the tool life was increased thirtyfold as the temperature of the work piece was raised from 76°F to 600°F using a cutting speed of 500 fpm. This represented an increase of tool life from a very short 30 seconds to a usable 15 minutes. At a temperature of 650°F no metallurgical changes occurred in the work piece so the test bar could be cut fully hard without any additional heat treatment and remachining. Only light feeds up to 0.006 inch were useful for this material; higher feed rates caused rapid wear while feed rates above 0.010 inch shattered the tool. The conclusions of their report indicated that hot machining was indeed practical from both an economic and a technological viewpoint, but that results on a variety of materials including refractory alloys did not always show an advantage for the technique.

Our own limited experience with hot machining of 18–8 stainless steel showed that heat shock of the cutting tool can become a serious problem at temperatures about 700°C. This problem can be relieved by preheating the tool prior to entry into the work piece and destructive thermal shock can be avoided.

Since hot machining appreciably lowers the forces acting on the tool, the machine tool with a given horsepower can remove stock at a higher rate than was formerly possible. This advantage, plus the advantage gained from longer tool life on some materials at higher temperatures, provide motives for continued research in hot machining. The high-temperature properties of the ceramic would tend to favor its application in this research. At present this has not been reduced to practice.

Meier (158) has reported on the use of ceramics for threading AISI 4140 bars hardened to Rc 55. Because of the exposed fragile ceramic tip which is necessary, the tools will fracture unless the cutting conditions are light. Meier reported that when using a tool ground to a 0.008-inch radius and shaped to provide appropriate clearances, the ceramic cut satisfactorily at 182 fpm with a depth of cut of 0.010 to 0.005 inch per chasing pass.

Chapter 9

The Future

Ceramic tools are used successfully in a wide variety of machining applications. This indicates that the available ceramic tools have physical properties which are adequate for these services. However, the widespread application of ceramic tools has not materialized as yet. In order that existing ceramics expand their serviceability in a general sense, it will be necessary for industry to retool with machines which can routinely operate in the "ceramic cutting range"; it will also be necessary for a considerable amount of individual tool engineering on each job, or each type of job where ceramics are to replace another type of tool material. Under these circumstances, it is understandable that growth will be slow unless technological perturbations rudely interfere with the normal course of events. With the present production engineering trends, progress in the development of machine tools will result through greater stress on their control and programming. As was shown in Chapter 3, the details of edge preparation can exert a profound influence on tool behavior and the preliminary designs of cutters; Albrecht's compound-edge lands or Logan's chemically polished edge-land combination, for example, could well point the way to a completely new level of development for the cutting tool itself. If these concepts are generally adopted, the existing ceramics could be applied to a wider range of routine machining services. Since alumina-based ceramics are inherently more efficient materials for chip making than cemented carbides, mixed carbides, or titanium carbide, or any other refractory hard metal or tool steel, the continued success and growth of alumina-cutting tools as compared with carbides is assured. Much of this growth is dependent upon reinvestment for modern machine tools, redesign of machine tools, and detailed tool engineering; therefore, this growth will be slow, unless better tool materials are developed. The consequences of improved ceramic tools and the massive impact they could have on the metals industry are the subjects of the next section.

A. Consequences of Improved Ceramic Materials

The development of a ceramic material with improved strength and fatigue properties would tend to alleviate the principal shortcomings of ceramics as they now exist for metal cutting. This would allow a more widespread use of ceramics for this purpose. The technology of alumina and its intrinsic properties, which are dictated by its structure and composition, would favor the continued development of alumina for cutting tools rather than a departure to a different material. Still, other materials are possible future competitors and will receive consideration. New tool materials will also influence machine-tool design, in the same way cemented carbide started the generation of new designs particularly suited to fully utilizing the properties of the cutting tool. The increase in efficiency which can be expected from such a material will also decrease the motive behind research directed at processes competitive with metal cutting; and where it is applicable, it will decrease expansion into these areas. The increase in physical properties of the tool will allow single-point machining to displace grinding in particular instances, and will limit the expansion of grinding into stock-removal applications and abrasive machining. Any new metal-cutting process is limited in growth by the percentage of the total cost the actual metal-removal comprises. Each particular case requires its own analysis. An improved ceramic cutter could and probably will have profound effects on metal-shaping technology. This conclusion will be examined in detail.

1. Alumina as an Improved Cutting Tool

The properties that make alumina uniquely attractive as a cutting tool arise from the conservative physical laws of nature, and as such are not susceptible to large variation. Melting point, chemical reactivity, and, in the limiting case, strength all arise from the kinds, number, and arrangement of atoms in the sapphire crystal. The number of chemical bonds, the valance of the atoms, and the closeness of packing result in a unique material which has more capacity for efficient metal cutting than any other material known. The deformational properties of sapphire also aid in determining tool utility in that multiple easy-slip systems do not exist and therefore make deformational wear and fracture nucleation correspondingly difficult. The deformational properties are structure sensitive and are basically determined by the atomic arrangement of the crystal. The atomic arrangement of the crystal is an inherent property—and again alumina is a conservative choice of a material. The thermodynamics of a chemical reaction are governed by a conservative physical law, and the chemical wear resistance of alumina is a direct result of these laws. Again alumina is a conservative choice. The extensive use of alumina in grinding wheels attests to its success as a chip-making tool almost to the exclusion of other materials. Exceptions do exist. The properties which allow alumina's success in a grinding wheel are the same properties which allow its success in a single-point tool. The essential difference is that a single-point tool has a carefully controlled geometry, engineered to maximize efficiency, while the grinding wheel is a statistical cutter but with the power of self-regeneration. Prior to the middle 1930's, it was not possible to utilize the inherent advantages of alumina because the technological strength of the material was too low. Increases in strength to values approaching 90,000 psi in transverse rupture and 550,000 psi in uniaxial compression did allow the successful application of ceramics to cutting steel and much experimental evidence indicated that the inherent advantages of alumina could indeed be realized in an actual machining case. This conclusion was strongly verified in the machining of cast iron where cutting forces are low, and verified in individual cases of machining steel where cutting forces marginally approach the strength of existing materials. Why was this so surprising at the time these results were presented? Actually, alumina is a conservative choice, and being a conservative choice another jump in utility is expected when strength, fatigue, and impact properties are improved to values that are no longer marginal in the case of machining steel. An increase in strength to about 200,000 psi in transverse rupture will allow ceramics to replace significant amounts of cemented carbide for turning applications on steel, and significant amounts for the milling of cast iron. The ceramic will still be excluded from heavy-impact service because it will probably still retain its brittle character. When ceramics are developed with transverse-rupture strength approaching 300,000 psi, the ceramic will have the capacity to encroach upon cemented-carbide markets in steel-milling applications. Carbides will retain, without difficulty, those applications where they have a unique advantage such as ductility in very heavy impact, or the advantage of being readily brazed to steel for particular configurations, or where the carbide offers a chemical advantage such as perhaps in the machining of titanium. The tacit assumption is made that an increase in transverse-rupture or tensile strength will be accompanied by a corresponding increase in fatigue strength. While this is generally true, it is not true in particular instances. If this is one of those particular instances, the degree of sophistication will need improvement. The crux of the question is really related to the probability of achieving these strength increases and not to the significance of them, once allowances for sophistication have been achieved, of course.

Gilman (159) has considered the significance of strong ceramic materials and concludes: "Since cutting tools often fail because of overloading in tension, such things as lathe bits, drawing dies, and extrusion dies represent another large group of devices that could be strikingly improved by materials with ultra-strength and high hardness." The maximum strength that is theoretically possible can be estimated, and Gilman's estimates for various materials appear in Table XXXIV.

Alumina, by this criteria, can have a strength no greater than 3.8×10^6 psi. This is a value a hundred times higher than that of the usual sintered alumina articles, and 40 times higher than transverse strengths of currently available ceramic materials. This leaves room for possible improvement. Alumina is also much higher in the table than any other oxide and is only exceeded by TiB_2, WC, and diamond.

Alumina whiskers with strengths of 2.2×10^6 psi have been described by Brenner (160). This at least confirms the fact that Gilman's estimate cannot be high by an appreciable factor. Gilman points out that the grain boundaries constitute a fundamental weakness which will limit the strength to lower values than that which is predicted by theory. On the basis of the number of atoms missing in a high-angle grain boundary the maximum strength can be no higher than 65% of theoretical or about 2.5×10^6 psi. Perhaps the biggest problem—and one that is generally recognized—is the thermal-contraction anisotropy that occurs when a sintered compact is cooled or heated. The stresses which arise from this source can be very large and do cause grain-boundary separation which can act as crack nuclei. Inspection of the photomicrographs in preceding chapters indicates that both transcrystalline and intercrystalline fracturing does occur in tool-bit materials. The implication of the intercrystalline fracturing is that these boundaries were deleteriously prestressed by thermal-contraction anisotropy. This effect will further reduce the maximum attainable strength from 2.5×10^6 psi to some unspecified but considerably lower value. In terms of the numbers which have been discussed, the increases we need in order to be able to produce a new class of cutting materials are relatively modest. An individual transverse-strength value of 155,000 psi has been observed on a polycrystalline alumina sample so the maximum strength must lie between 1.5×10^5 psi and 2.5×10^6 psi. Since a strength sufficiency for a cutting tool lies well at the lower end of this range, it is likely that such materials can be produced.

TABLE XXXIV

POSSIBLE STRENGTHS OF VARIOUS CRYSTALS[a]

Crystal	Young's modulus (mpsi)[b]	Density g/cm³	Maximum strength (5% strain; mpsi)	Strength: density ratio (arbitrary units)
Diamond	170	3.5	8.5	48
WC	104	15.8	5.2	7
TiB_2	94	4.5	4.7	21
Al_2O_3	76	4.0	3.8	19
TiC	72	4.9	3.6	15
SiC	71	3.2	3.5	22
B_4C	66	2.5	3.3	26
ZrB_2	64	5.6	3.2	11
W_2C	62	17.3	3.1	4
W	60	19.3	3.0	3
$MoSi_2$	55	6.0	2.8	9
Mo	54	10.2	2.7	5
B	51	2.3	2.6	22
BeO	51	3.0	2.6	17
FeS_2	50	5.0	2.5	10
ZrC	50	6.8	2.5	7
NbC	50	7.8	2.5	6
Be_2C	46	2.4	2.3	19
Be	45	1.8	2.2	25
MgO	35	3.5	1.8	10
Si	23	2.3	1.7	10
Steel	28	7.8	1.7	4

[a] From Gilman (159).
[b] Million psi.

The experiments by Stokes (161) on NaCl bicrystals with tensile strengths of about 1×10^5 psi encourage us to assume that proportional strengths are possible in alumina, yielding values well in excess of the criterion for a cutting tool. It is highly probably that a polycrystalline alumina with a transverse rupture of 3×10^5 psi can be produced. Since the strength increases are relatively modest, a scientific "breakthrough" probably will not be required and a technological approach to the strength problem could yield the desired result.

It is very likely that improved ceramics will be forthcoming. The impact of these materials on machining, in particular, will be profound.

2. Carbides and Other Refractory Hard Metals as Improved Cutting Tools

The search for improved cutting materials among tool manufacturers is still largely centered on the hard carbides. Advantages are sought by alloying systems with increasingly complex compositions to facilitate the generation of particular properties. An increasing number of compositions are offered to the tool engineer. The cemented-carbide materials are, at this time, among the most remarkable of structural materials with extremely high hardness and strength. They are the most sophisticated of cutting-tool materials. The use of cemented carbide is well entrenched because of its performance; attempts made to replace carbide with any new tool material should be viewed with skepticism. Carbide might be partially replaced because of its chemical properties. The carbide is oxidizable and is soluble in metals. The carbide cement is alloyable in metals and is also susceptible to softening at high-machining speeds. These limitations, with the possible exception of the latter, are inherent ones relating to the kinds of atoms and their arrangement, and all of the sophisticated compositional perturbations and thermal treatments will not exert any great effect on the end result. None of these materials have been successful as abrasives in grinding wheels for these reasons, and the single-point machining case is directly analogous.

Since wear is predominantly chemical in nature, there is not a great deal that can be done in a general way to move the carbide materials over to the oxide performance. Research on carbides, nitrides, or borides, to offset the encroachment of ceramic tools, is destined to result in failure for reasons that are scientific and conservative.

3. Oxides Other Than Alumina as Improved Cutting Tools

Although alumina is particularly attractive as a cutting tool for a wide variety of reasons, other oxide materials cannot be excluded. Such refractory oxides as BeO, ZrO_2 or $MgO \cdot Al_2O_3$ have melting points higher, or as high, as alumina; they are exceedingly stable chemically, and the spinel has been reported by Palmour (162) to have uniaxial compressive strengths of up to 5×10^5 psi. Some pertinent physical properties of refractory oxides have been extracted from a more extensive table of Kingery (163) and is shown in Table XXXV.

TABLE XXXV

PHYSICAL PROPERTIES OF SOME REFRACTORY OXIDE[a]

Oxides	Melting point (°C)	Modulus of elasticity (10^6 psi)	Thermal conductivity[b]		Linear thermal expansion[c]	Specific heat capacity[d]
			100°C	1000°C		
Alumina	2030	53	0.069	0.014	8.6	0.26
Zirconia (4% CaO)	2550	22	0.005	0.005	10.0	0.14
Beryllia	2570	45	0.50	0.046	8.9	0.50
Thoria	3050	21	0.022	0.007	9.0	0.06
Ittria	2410	—	(0.02)	—	9.3	0.13
Spinel	2135	34.5	0.033	0.013	8.8	0.25
Urania	2800	25	0.020	0.007	10.0	0.06

[a] From Kingery (163).
[b] Calories $sec^{-1} °C^{-1} cm^{-2} cm$.
[c] 10^{-6} inches/inch/°C.
[d] Calories/gram/°C.

Of these materials, zirconia, thoria, yttria, and urania have high thermal expansion. All of the oxides with the exceptions of alumina and beryllia have significantly low thermal conductivity. All of the materials, except alumina, beryllia, and spinel, have a low heat capacity. Pure zirconia has a crystallographic inversion at around 1100°C to 1250°C which can cause cracking of sintered compacts. All of the materials except alumina, beryllia, and possibly spinel would be inferior in thermal shock because of these properties. Spinel has a multiplicity of slip planes which allows deformation of a bulk material, and as a result might be less wear resistant at high cutting temperatures. Spinel has a microhardness much less than alumina or beryllia and unless it is suitably alloyed to restrain slip the low hardness would exclude it for use as a tool.

Future choices of materials for development into ceramic-tool compositions are alumina, beryllia, the compound crysoberyl $BeO \cdot Al_2O_3$, or, possibly, spinel $MgO \cdot Al_2O_3$. Alumina is the least expensive of these, is the most developed and is nontoxic.

4. Diamond as a Cutting Tool

Since diamonds can be successfully synthesized and the conditions of growth controlled, it should be possible to produce a cryptocrystalline dense diamond object—analogous to a sintered alumina—which could be used as a cutting tool. The extreme hardness of diamond, and the fracture resistance impacted to the polycrystalline aggregate could produce a material of rather unique properties. Structures of this type occur naturally as Framesite or Balas diamond which commands a premium price for uses requiring the maximum wear resistance. Since diamond is oxidizable, it can invert to the graphite structure, and since carbon is soluble in iron, the advantages of diamond over alumina as a cutting tool are seriously lessened. Duwell and McDonald (71), in abrasive quality tests in which the metal removed to abrasive wear is plotted, concluded that alumina and diamond act similarly even though the diamond is much harder. It is likely that a polycrystalline diamond structure of strength equivalent to an oxide ceramic will not offer sufficient advantage to justify its greater cost. Reactive metals such as beryllium or titanium, or gummy metals like pure copper, where the dead sharpness of the cutting edge is critical, are possible exceptions.

5. The Influence of Improved Ceramic Tools on Grinding

In this case the material, alumina, is in competition with itself. In each instance the relative merits of single point cutters or geometrical cutters versus statistical cutters will have to be judged on the basis of economic advantage. The single-point cutter, or milling-type cutter, can remove stock at a higher rate than a grinding wheel. A properly designed tool configuration in a rigid machine can produce a very good bright finish to a tolerance acceptable for most applications. Existing ceramic tools have in some instances eliminated extra grinding steps in a manufacturing process. It is likely that the inherent efficiencies in geometrical cutters versus statistical ones will make additional inroads, once superior oxide materials are developed. The use of grinding wheels for stock-removal purposes is destined to wither, both in precision grinding and in billet grinding or snagging. It is likely that grinding will be partially replaced in those instances where it is proceeded by a geometrical cutter machining operation, if the tolerances are not hypercritical. The development of new and more rigid machines will permit closer tolerances and better finish in the work piece, and the development of superior and more wear-resistant tools will furnish the economic motive to design such machines. A limitation on the finish which can be obtained with a geometrical cutter is the chip-induced vibrations which cause a topographic pattern in the work-piece surface. This is also true of the statistical cutter, but the pattern can be of a smaller scale. Grinding will not be appreciably affected in those areas of minimum oversize machining, very close tolerance, very fine finishes, cut-off applications, tool-room work, and machining of hard brittle materials. It will also not be appreciably affected in those particular areas where grinding offers a unique advantage in handling, or where the work piece cannot be revolved at a high speed. The chief effects of improved ceramic tools on grinding will be the limitation of growth into stock-removal applications and the provision for a slow attrition in other instances where an extra handling step can be eliminated by a more sophisticated geometrical cutting operation.

6. The Effect of Improved Tool Materials on Machine Tools

The history of metal cutting clearly shows that the development of a new tool material provides the motive to design a new generation of machine tools. In each case, from carbon steels, to high-speed steels, to cemented carbide, advances were made in the speed and rigidity of machine tools. Even with current ceramics, and most certainly with improved ones, a new set of requirements must be met by the machine to fully utilize the potentials of the cutting tool. The tool leads machine design. The ceramic of the future will have higher strength than its existing counterpart, but it will still be brittle and sensitive to surface preparation. The ceramics performance will be optimized in a machine tool that operates at very high-cutting speeds, minimizes vibrations, and provides maximum rigidity.

It will be increasingly difficult to obtain higher cutting speeds in the generation of cylindrical or conical surfaces. Particularly with large work pieces, the lack of dynamic balance in many instances prohibits the use of higher surface velocities. In order to obtain efficient cutting speeds, a new generation of machine tools, half-lathe and half-milling machine, will require development and will be developed. These machine tools will be analogous to the cylindrical grinding machine where the statistical cutter—the grinding wheel—is replaced with a milling-type head containing the geometrical cutter—the ceramic tool. The use of very high cutting speeds—a few thousands of surface feet per minute—will presumably aid in producing an acceptable surface finish on the work piece. In many instances the greater strength of the new ceramics will allow the use of positive rake angles where this is desirable. Ceramics can be brazed to metals with the generation of a reasonably strong bond. Relieved from the limitations of clamp-type holders, ceramics could be used for broaches, drills, and other operations that do not allow the use of bulky tool holders. This brazing is more difficult than that used to fasten carbides to steel and will probably remain an operation best performed by a tool manufacturer or specialized industry. Resharpening of ceramic tools will probably not be possible in the average shop because of the requirements on surface preparation and chemical polishing. These considerations will naturally work against the rate at which ceramic tools can enter these fields as well as impose limitations on future versatility.

The effects upon milling machines will parallel those of lathes. Similar requirements of horsepower, speed, and rigidity should be met if improved ceramics are to be fully utilized. A primary difference between milling and turning is that in milling the tools are impacted twice during every revolution of the cutter. These impacts are both physical and thermal, and both positive and negative. A fatigued ceramic such as the one shown in Fig. 114, Chapter 5, will immediately fail if it develops this much fatigue damage during milling although it was performing satisfactorily in turning with the damage illustrated in the figure. The cyclic impact loading of a milling cutter may well be the primary source of tool damage—improvements in machine rigidity and vibration control might be secondary effects. If this is true there will be less motivation to control these conditions to a greater extent in milling machines. However, this may not be true.

The vibration experiments of Moore and Kibbey (98) which were presented in Fig. 120, Chapter 5, showed that vibrations were much more harmful in the feed direction than they were tangentially. The primary amplitude of the vibrations produced when impacting a milling tooth on the work piece will be analogous to the tangential vibration in turning, and thereby will not be as harmful per specific energy content as incidental vibrations in other directions. The direction dependency was an order of magnitude; if the vibrations could be completely filtered, the directional dependency would undoubtedly be even greater.

Recommended cutting speeds on milling machines are comparable to those recommended on lathes. *The Tool Engineer's Handbook* (62) recommends cutting speeds for carbide cutters of between 180 and 400 fpm on cast iron, 250 to 500 fpm on malleable iron, and 200 fpm on 4150 steel. Ceramic tools can increase these milling cutting speeds just as they increased cutting speeds in turning. Data from this same source indicated that carbide-cutter life drops from 43 minutes at 600 fpm to 5 minutes at 1500 fpm. A study by Krabacher and Haggerty (9) indicated the feasibility of milling cast iron with ceramic tools at high speeds. Their data showed that the ceramic was superior to carbide at all speeds using a total tool-life criterion and that ceramics can operate at about twice the speed for equivalent life. They also found that a honed land on the cutter edge markedly increased tool life and decreased sensitivity to angle of engagement.

The foregoing illustrates that the potential advantages of ceramics in turning are also potential advantages in milling, and that future milling-machine design should be cognizant of the impact that improved ceramic materials will make on machining. The improved ceramic will probably still be brittle, and the particular effects of this in milling should be a subject of intensive study as soon as better ceramics become available.

B. The Consequences of Improved Machine Tools on the Application of Existing Ceramics

The extensive laboratory tests performed by us and a myriad of other investigators indicate that under controlled conditions the existing ceramic tools—at least the better ones—have a chip-making capability and versatility beyond that obtained in practical use in the field. If we assume that these test results and the field results are all reported by men of technological acumen, we are left with a paradox.

An investigator in the laboratory is apt to have a specialized machine which is instrumented and maintained in good working order. Sometimes it is constructed with design features aimed at eliminating extraneous results in tool-life testing, and as a result could not be considered typical of machines encountered in a production department. The fact that such machines indicate a wider utility for ceramics than that which is actually obtained, encourages us to predict that better machine tools will aid the ceramic in its latitude of service. Machine tools which are faster, more rigid, and have suppressed vibration should permit a moderate expansion of ceramics into areas where they cannot now operate.

1. Design of New Machine Tools

Ceramic tools have the primary advantage of being relatively temperature (speed) insensitive, and the primary disadvantage is that they are brittle. The mechanical design engineer must be cognizant of these two facts and design his machine accordingly. In general, the machine tool should be capable of high speeds, it should be rigid, and it should be free of excessive vibration. The greater rates of stock removal that are possible at higher cutting speed will generally necessitate higher horsepower. The data presented in Fig. 9, Chapter 1, show that ceramics have an advantage over cemented carbide at speeds in excess of 800 fpm. Successful cuts have been taken by Moore and Kibbey up to 3000 fpm on normalized 1045 steel where 600 cubic inches of stock were removed. A machine tool, specific for ceramics, should have the capacity of attaining approximately these speeds.

The data on vibration which were presented in Fig. 120, Chapter 5, indicated the vibrations in the feed direction and also those vibrations at the higher frequency are especially harmful. These vibrations should be suppressed in the machine design. Carefully controlled experiments, at Watertown Arsenal and by Moore and Kibbey at Ohio State on the same tools and same types of work pieces, often failed to duplicate results or conclusions. The only significant difference in these tests, in our opinion, were the machine tools. In our opinion, the only meaningful differences between them were the amount and possibly the character of machine vibrations. The effects on tool behavior were often large, and by inference we can project that quieter production machine tools will greatly increase the utility of ceramic tools.

Rigidity and vibrations in the radial direction can have a noticeable effect on work-piece dimensions and surface finish. A particular attraction of ceramic geometrical cutters is that they have the capacity of eliminating finishing operations. The tolerances due to low wear rates and the finishes that can be produced at high stock removal rates have in some instances eliminated finish cuts or grinding operations. Further advances in this direction will require machine tools with design and manufacturing excellence that permit the tool engineer to fully use the capacity of the ceramic.

Trends in machine specialization and numerical control favor the ceramic tool because specialized and high-velocity machine operations are now possible using numerical control at production rates faster than a human operator can function. The ceramics main contributions are capablity of higher cutting speeds and productivity. A numerically controlled production machine should be able to function without difficulty, as the ceramics dependability is greatly enhanced in a properly designed machine. It would be a mistake to use a ceramic tool in an automated setup to cut steel, unless the rigidity and vibration of the machine were minimized.

2. Applications of Ceramics Using Improved Machine Tools on Cast Iron

Because of the abrasive character and low-shear strength of cast iron, ceramics have received their greatest application in the shaping of cast-iron parts. The introduction of ceramics into this area was relatively easy because the advantage of ceramics over carbides was so great. The trend to replace carbide with ceramics will continue by attrition in individual instances. Better machine tools should accelerate this attrition. This coupled with some sharp tool engineering on cutting-edge geometry should allow ceramics to make sizable inroads into cast-iron milling and interrupted cuts in turning.

3. Applications of Ceramics Using Improved Machine Tools on Steel

The preponderance of favorable test results indicates that ceramics can be successfully used in the machining of steel if they are applied with the use of good machine tools. Applications of ceramics to machining steel are becoming more frequent in the machining literature as newer machine tools become available and tool engineers learn how to apply ceramics in particular jobs. Ceramic-tool manufacturers are beginning to supply tools with edge configurations that are often desirable when machining steel. Further improvements in lathe design will provide an additional stimulus to further the application of ceramics to steel. Since the strength of existing ceramics is marginal on steel, improvements in design will not radically alter machining practice as we now know them, but rather will allow ceramics to make inroads in finishing to moderate cuts. Existing ceramics will not be able to make much progress in severe interrupted cuts or in milling of steel.

An example has been selected to illustrate what can be done when a good ceramic and a modern machine tool are coupled to increase productivity of a steel part. Figure 175 shows a view of the part that requires manufacture.

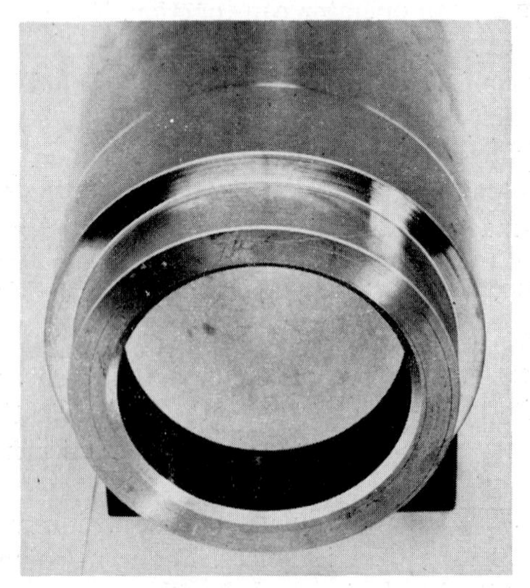

Fig. 175. Face machined by a ceramic tool. Steel artillery part showing the surfaces on the end of the piece which require machining (Frankford Arsenal, 164).

The part is about 3½ inches in diameter and the end shown must be turned, bored, faced, and chamfered. The part is made of either FS 5135 with a minimum-yield strength of 110,000 psi and a hardness not to exceed 320 Brinnell, or 1010 cold extrusion with a minimum yield of 65,000 psi. The part is produced for artillery ammunition by Frankford Arsenal in Philadelphia (164).

The machine tools used are the Amcot Model "C" Production lathe and the Amcot Model "C 6" Speedmaster lathe. This equipment is specifically designed for operation in the ceramic tool-cutting range with specially designed spindle bearings and a prime-mover motor capable of the rapid accelerations necessary in high-speed production work. It is capable of delivering 60 HP into the work piece. The components are dynamically balanced and the power drive is designed without gears to minimize vibrations. The spindle can operate at up to 2000 rpm, or slightly higher(165).

Figure 176 shows the lathe with a machined part just removed from the collet.

Figure 177 shows the part being machined at high cutting speeds with VR97 ceramic tools.

FIG. 176. The model "C-6" Speedmaster Lathe is a high-speed lathe used in ceramic tooling (Frankford Arsenal, 164).

Fig. 177. A ceramic tool-turning diameter. Steel part being machined at high-cutting velocities (Frankford Arsenal, 164).

Production information on the performance of this machine and the ceramic tool is compared with production performance using a good but less sophisticated machine tool and cemented-carbide cutters. This information appears in Table XXXVI. The operation is to turn and face the band seat using the FS 5135 steel.

These data represent a 340% increase in tool life in the earlier operation and a 480% decrease in cycle time permitting one machine

TABLE XXXVI

Comparative Performance between Carbide and Ceramics in the Machining of Steel[a]

	Carbide	Ceramic
rpm	375	1100
Feed	0.008	0.013
Depth of cut	0.020 to 0.048	0.020 to 0.048
Cycle time (min)	0.48	0.10
Tool life facing (average, pieces/insert)	80	270

[a] From Frankford Arsenal (164).

tool to do the work of almost five by the older method. The cuts are all uninterrupted and light.

When the modern lathe and ceramic tooling was used to finish turning the bandseat and to bore, chamfer, and face the part, a tool life of 133 pieces/insert was obtained for turning and facing; 532 pieces/insert on boring gave a cycle time reduced to 0.17 minutes—just a third of the previous figure. One machine tool with one operator does the work of three. These machine tools have been used with ceramic tooling at speeds of up to 2235 fpm for machining steel.

These results, and others we might have selected instead, portend the future of existing ceramic tools and illustrate the influence of machine tools on their application. The obsolescence of a large portion of the machine tools which were acquired during the World War II and the Korean War will necessitate large-scale replacement of these tools in the near future. When this situation is faced by each shop and by each tool engineer on the line, careful consideration will have to be given to the future trends in machining. Careful consideration should also be given to the areas to which ceramics can be applied, and to the machines which can improve the utility of the ceramic.

REFERENCES

1. Singer *et al.*, "A History of Technology," Oxford Univ. Press (Clarendon), London and New York, 1956.
2. F. Singer and H. Thurnauer, Sinter alumina: I. Theoretical aspect. *Metallurgia* **36**, No. 215, 237–242 (1947); Sinter alumina: II. Production and application. *Ibid.* pp. 313–315.
3. E. Ryschkewitch, Ceramic cutting tool. U.S. Patent 2,270,607 (1942).
4. N. Pavlushkin, Microlite. *Znanie-Sila* pp. 22–26 (1953).
5. Watertown Arsenal Rept. No. RPL 23/2, Minutes of symposium on ceramic cutting tools, (1955).
6. W. M. Wheildon, Notes on the development and performance of ceramic cutting tools. Presented by J. K. Sjogren, at *58th Ann. Meeting Am. Ceram. Soc., 1956*
7. M. E. Merchant, Future trends in materials removal techniques. SAE Preprint T40, 1960.
8. W. M. Wheildon, Ceramics for cutting purposes, *in* "Modern Materials" (H. H. Hausner, ed.), Vol. 2, pp. 107–142. Academic Press, New York, 1960.
9. E. J. Krabacher and W. A. Haggerty, Performance characteristics of ceramic tools in turning and milling. *ASTE Tech. Paper* **145**, Book 2 (1958).
10. H. J. Siekmann, E. W. Goliber, and K. W. Stalker, A round-up on tomorrow's tool materials. *Am. Machinist New York* pp. 160–172 (1956).
11. D. R. Kibbey and H. D. Moore, Cutting tool comparisons at high speeds. *ASTE Tech. Paper* **305**, Book 2 (1960).
12. E. W. Goliber, Ceramic and cermet compositions containing TiO. Paper presented at *66th Ann. Meeting* Am. Ceram. Soc., *Philadelphia, Pennsylvania, 1960.*
13. E. W. Goliber, personal communication.
14. G. C. Kuczynski, L. Abernethy, and J. Allan, Sintering mechanism of aluminum oxide, *in* "Kinetics of High Temperature Processes" (W. D. Kingery, ed.), M.I.T. Press, Cambridge, Massachusetts, 1959.
15. R. L. Coble, Diffusion sintering in the solid state, *in* "Kinetics of High Temperature Processes" (W. D. Kingery, ed.), M.I.T. Press, Cambridge, Massachusetts, 1959.
16. J. E. Burke, Recrystallization and sintering in ceramics, *in* "Ceramic Fabrication Processes" (W. D. Kingery, ed.), M.I.T. Press, Cambridge, Massachusetts, 1958.
17. P. Schwarzkopf and R. Kieffer, "Cemented Carbides." Macmillan, New York, 1960.
18. C. Agte, R. Kohlermann, and E. Heymel, "Schneidkeramic," Akademie Verlag, Berlin, 1959.
19. J. T. Jones, P. K. Maitra, and I. B. Cutler, Role of structural defects in the sintering of alumina and magnesia. *J. Am. Ceram. Soc.* **41**, 353–357 (1958).
20. J. E. Burke, Grain growth in ceramics, *in* "Kinetics of High Temperature Processes" (W. D. Kingery, ed.), M.I.T. Press, Cambridge, Massachusetts, 1959.

21. R. L. Fullman, "Boundary Migration During Grain Growth," Am. Soc. Metals, Cleveland, Ohio, 1952.
22. W. D. Kingery, Diffusion in oxides, *in* "Kinetics of High Temperature Processes" (W. D. Kingery, ed.), M.I.T. Press, Cambridge, Massachusetts, 1959.
23. I. B. Cutler, Nucleation and nuclei growth in sintered alumina, *in* "Kinetics of High Temperature Processes" (W. D. Kingery, ed.), M.I.T. Press, Cambridge, Massachusetts, 1959.
24. H. J. Smothers and H. J. Reynolds, Sintering and grain growth of alumina. *J. Am. Ceram. Soc.* **37**, 588–595 (1954).
25. H. P. Cahoon and C. J. Christensen, Sintering and grain growth in alpha alumina. *J. Am. Ceram. Soc.* **39**, 337–344 (1956).
26. E. W. Goliber, U.S. Patent 2,873,198.
27. E. Ryshkewitch, "Oxide Ceramics," p. 219. Academic Press, New York, 1960.
28. P. J. Jorgensen and J. H. Westbrook, Role of solute segregation at grain boundaries during final-stage sintering of alumina. *J. Am. Ceram. Soc.* **47**, 332–338 (1964).
29. R. L. Coble and J. E. Burke, Sintering in ceramics. *Progr. Ceram. Sci.* **3**, 197–251 (1963).
30. R. L. Coble, Sintering alumina: Effect of atmospheres. *J. Am. Ceram. Soc.* **45**, 123–127 (1962).
31. P. Duwez, F. Odell, and J. L. Taylor, Recrystallization of beryllium oxide bodies at 2000° C. *J. Am. Ceram. Soc.* **32**, 1–9 (1949).
32. D. R. Wilder and E. S. Fitzsimmons, Further study of sintering phenomena. *J. Am. Ceram. Soc.* **38**, 66–71 (1955).
33. O. J. Whittemore, Jr., A. G. King, and J. C. Logan, U.S. Patent 3,093,498.
34. R. R. Van der Beck, A. W. von Mickwitz, and L. G. Scheinman, How oxide cutting tools are made and what they do. *Ceram. Ind.* (1957).
35. R. L. Coble and J. S. Ellis, Hot pressing alumina-mechanisms of material transport. *J. Am. Ceram. Soc.* **46**, 438–441 (1963).
36. P. Murray, D. T. Libey, and J. Williams, The hot pressing of ceramics, *in* "Ceramic Fabrication Processes" (W. D. Kingery, ed.). M.I.T. Press, Cambridge, Massachusetts, 1958.
37. R. F. Walker, Mechanism of material transport during sintering. *J. Am. Ceram. Soc.* **38**, 187–197 (1955).
38. G. E. Mangsen, W. A. Lambertson, and B. Best, Hot pressing of aluminum oxide. *J. Am. Ceram. Soc.* **43**, 55–59 (1960).
39. L. M. Foster, G. Long, and M. S. Hunter, Reactions between aluminum oxide and carbon, the Al_2O_3-Al_4C_3 phase diagram. *J. Am. Ceram. Soc.* **39**, 1–11 (1956).
40. G. F. Scott, unpublished research.
41. J. Taeyaerts, Reduce diamond grinding. *Cutting Tool Eng.* (1961).
42. K. Okushima and Y. Fujii, On ceramic cutting tools. *Bull. JSME* (*Japan. Soc. Mech. Engrs.*) **2**, 217–223 (1959).
43. A. G. King, The influence of microstructure on the mechanical properties of dense polycrystalline alumina, *in* "Mechanical Properties of Engineering

Ceramics" (W. W. Kriegel and H. Palmour, III, eds.). Wiley (Interscience), New York, 1961.
44. A. A. Griffith, The Phenomena of rupture and flow in solids, *Phil. Trans. Roy. Soc.* **A221**, 163 (1921).
45. J. C. Logan, unpublished research.
46. R. L. Coble and W. D. Kingery, The effect of porosity on the mechanical properties of sintered alumina. *J. Am. Ceram. Soc.* **39**, 377 (1956).
47. L. J. Trostel, Jr., Strength and structure of refractories as a function of pore content. *J. Am. Ceram. Soc.* **45**, 563–564 (1962).
48. R. C. Brewer, Appraisal of ceramic cutting tools. *Engr. Dig.* **18**, 381–387 (1957).
49. J. F. Quirk, N. B. Mosley, and W. H. Duckworth, Characterization of sinterable oxide powders: I. BeO. *J. Am. Ceram. Soc.* **40**, 416–419 (1957).
50. W. B. Crandall, D. H. Chung, and T. J. Gray, The mechanical properties of ultra-fine hot-pressed alumina, *in* "Mechanical Properties of Engineering Ceramics" (W. W. Kriegel and H. Palmour, III, eds.). Wiley (Interscience), New York, 1961.
51. R. M. Spriggs, J. B. Mitchell, and T. Vasilos, Mechanical properties of pure, dense aluminum oxide as a function of temperature and grain size. *J. Am. Ceram. Soc.* **47**, 323–327 (1964).
52. W. D. Kingery and J. Pappis, Note on failure of ceramic materials at elevated temperatures under impact loading. *J. Am. Ceram. Soc.* **39**, 64–66 (1956).
53. N. H. Cook, Cutting tool temperatures. *ASTE Tech. Paper* **21**, (1957).
54. H. J. Siekmann, The use of an ultra high speed, 150 horsepower lathe for machinability studies. *ASTE Tech. Paper* **82**, Book 2 (1958).
55. J. B. Wachtman and L. H. Maxwell, Plastic deformation of ceramic-oxide single crystals. *J. Am. Ceram. Soc.* **37**, 291–299 (1954).
56. P. W. Bridgman, The effect of hydrostatic pressure on the fracture of brittle substances. *J. Appl. Phys.* **18**, 246–258 (1947).
57. P. W. Bridgman, "Fracture and Hydrostatic Pressure," pp. 246–261. Am. Soc. Metals, Cleveland, Ohio.
58. P. W. Bridgman, Effect of high shearing stress combined with high hydrostatic pressure. *Phys. Rev.* **48**, 825–847 (1935).
59. F. G. Satkiewicz, "Experiments on plasticity of magnesium oxide and calcium oxide under compression, *in* Mechanical Properties of Engineering Ceramics" (W. W. Kriegel and H. Palmour, III, eds.). Wiley (Interscience), New York, 1961.
60. H. Palmour, III, W. W. Kriegel, and J. J. DuPlessis, Microbrittleness anisotropy in thermally etched sapphire, *in* "Mechanical Properties of Engineering Ceramics" (W. W. Kriegel and H. Palmour, III, eds.). Wiley (Interscience), New York, 1961.
61. S. Kobayashi and E. G. Thomsen, The role of friction in metal cutting. *J. Eng. Ind.* **82**, 324–332 (1960).
62. "Tool Engineers Handbook." ASTE, McGraw-Hill, New York, 1959.
63. P. Albrecht, New developments in the theory of the metal cutting process. Part I. The ploughing process in metal cutting. *J. Eng. Ind.* **82**, 348–358 (1960).

64. N. W. Thibault and H. L. Nyquist, The measured Knoop hardness of hard substances and factors affecting its determination. *Trans. Am. Soc. Metals* **38,** 271–330 (1947).
65. L. P. Tarasov and N. W. Thibault, Determination of Knoop hardness numbers independent of load. *Trans. Am. Soc. Metals* **38,** 331–353 (1957).
66. A. G. King and W. M. Wheildon, Physical properties of ceramic tools and their relationships to tool performance. *ASTE Tech. Paper* **303,** Book 2 (1960).
67. A. G. Metcalfe, Why oxide tools can cut faster. *Am. Machinist* (1956).
68. General Electric Company, Metallurgical Products Dept., Tech. Data Sheet (1958).
69. G. Economos and W. D. Kingery, Metal-ceramic interactions: II. Metal-oxide interfacial reactions at elevated temperatures. *J. Am. Ceram. Soc.* **36,** 403–409 (1953).
70. M. C. Shaw and P. A. Smith, Workpiece compatibility of ceramic cutting tools. *Trans. Am. Soc. Lub. Eng.* **1,** 336–344 (1958).
71. E. J. Duwell and W. J. McDonald, Some factors that affect the resistance of abrasive grits to wear. *Wear* **4,** 372–383 (1961).
72. E. J. Duwell, Friction and wear of single-crystal sapphire sliding on steel. *J. Appl. Phys.* **33,** 2691–2698 (1962).
73. L. F. Coffin, Jr., Some metallurgical aspects of friction and wear, *in* "Friction and Wear" (R. Davies, ed.). Elsevier, Amsterdam, 1959.
74. E. S. Machlin and W. R. Yankee, Friction of clean metals and oxides with special reference to titanium. *J. Appl. Phys.* **25,** 576–581 (1954).
75. B. Schwartz, Thermal stress failure of pure refractory oxides. *J. Am. Ceram. Soc.* **35,** 325–333 (1952).
76. R. L. Coble and W. D. Kingery, Effect of porosity on thermal stress fracture. *J. Am. Ceram. Soc.* **38,** 33–37 (1955).
77. F. P. Bowden and D. Tabor, "The Friction and Lubrication of Solids." Oxford Univ. Press, London and New York, 1950.
78. R. Scheuplein and P. Gibbs, Surface structure in corundum: I. Etching of dislocations. *J. Am. Ceram. Soc.* **43,** 458–472 (1960).
79. R. P. Steijn, On the wear of sapphire. *J. Appl. Phys.* **32,** 1951–1958 (1961).
80. A. G. King, Ceramic tool wear. *Am. Soc. Mech. Engrs., Paper* **63-Prod-11** (1963).
81. V. D. Scott and H. Wilman, Surface re-orientation caused on metals by abrasion—its nature, origin and relation to friction and wear. *Proc. Roy. Soc.* **A347,** 353–368 (1958).
82. L. B. Sibley and C. M. Allen, Friction and wear behavior of refractory materials at high sliding velocities and temperatures. *Wear* **5,** 312–329 (1962).
83. A. J. Pekelharing, A story about the cracking of ceramic tools when cutting steel. *CIRP Ann.* **11,** 25–36.
84. H. D. Moore and D. R. Kibbey, Development of accelerated testing procedures for ceramic cutting tools. *Ohio State Univ., Eng. Expt. Sta. report* **169** (1961).
85. L. Coes, Jr., unpublished research.
86. W. R. Brown, N. S. Eiss, Jr., and H. T. McAdams, Chemical mechanisms

contributing to wear of single-crystal sapphire on steel. *J. Am. Ceram. Soc.* **47,** 157–162 (1964).
87. L. Coes, Jr., Chemistry of abrasive action. *Ind. Eng. Chem.* **47,** 2493–2494 (1955).
88. M. C. Shaw, Cutting fluid theory, *in* "Machining Theory and Practice" (H. Ernst *et al.,* eds.). Am. Soc. Metals, Cleveland, Ohio, 1950.
89. M. C. Shaw, On the action of metal cutting fluids at low speeds. *Wear* **2,** 217–227 (1958/1959).
90. P. A. Beck and P. R. Sperry, Strain induced boundary migration in high purity aluminum. *J. Appl. Phys.* **21,** 150 (1950).
91. A. O. Schmidt, I. Ham, W. I. Phillips, and G. F. Wilson, Ceramic and carbide tool performance tests. Part I, *Am. Soc. Mech. Engrs., Paper* **56-A-218** (1956).
92. A. H. Cottrell, Theoretical aspects of fracture. *Conf. Fracture, Swampscott, Massachusetts, 1958.* Nat. Res. Council–Nat. Acad. Sci., Washington, D.C., 1959.
93. R. J. Stokes, T. L. Johnson, and C. H. Li, Crack formation in magnesium oxide single crystals. *Phil. Mag.* [8] **3,** 718 (1958).
94. J. Friedel, "Les Dislocations." Paris, 1956.
95. A. N. Stroh, The cleavage of metal single crystals. *Phil. Mag.* [8] **3,** 597 (1958).
96. W. D. Biggs and P. L. Pratt, The deformation and fracture of alpha-iron at low temperatures. *Acta Met.* **6,** 694 (1958).
97. M. S. Day, mgr., Ceramic cutting tool project. Personal communication, Carborundum Company, Niagara Falls, New York.
98. H. D. Moore and D. R. Kibbey, Development of accelerated testing procedures for ceramic cutting tools. *Ohio State Univ., Eng. Expt. Sta. Report* **169** (1962).
99. L. S. Williams, Fatigue and ceramics, *in* "Mechanical Properties of Engineering Ceramics" (W. W. Kriegel and H. Palmour, III, eds.). Wiley (Interscience), New York, 1961.
100. E. B. Shand, Stress behavior of brittle materials. *Am. Ceram. Soc. Bull.* **38,** 653–660 (1959).
101. W. A. Wood, Some basic studies of fatigue in metals. *Conf. Fracture, Swampscott, Massachusetts, 1958.* Nat. Res. Council—Natl. Acad. Sci., Washington, D.C., 1959.
102. L. F. Coffin and J. F. Tavernelli, The cyclic straining and fatigue of metals. *Trans. AIME* **215,** 794 (1959).
103. J. J. Gilman, Debris mechanism of strain-hardening. *J. Appl. Phys.* **33,** 2703–2709 (1962).
104. A. J. Forty, The generation of dislocations during cleavage. *Proc. Roy. Soc.* **A242,** 392–399, (1957).
105. S. Pearson, Delayed fracture of sintered alumina. *Proc. Phys. Soc.* (*London*) **B69,** 1293–1296 (1956).
106. J. A. Stavrolakis and F. H. Norton, Measurement of torsion properties of alumina and zirconia at elevated temperatures. *J. Am. Ceram. Soc.* **33,** 263-268 (1950).
107. R. J. Parker, S. J. Grisaffe, and E. V. Zaretsky, Surface failure of alumina

balls due to repeated stresses applied in rolling contact at temperatures to 2000° F. *NASA Tech. Note* **TN D-2274** (1964).
108. T. L. Carter and E. V. Zaretsky, Rolling-contact fatigue life of a crystallized glass ceramic. *NASA Tech. Note* **TN D-259** (1960).
109. H. J. Siekmann and L. A. Sowinski, What angles are best for oxide cutting tools. *Am. Machinist* pp. 113–122 (1957).
110. A. D. Makarov, "Precision and Surface Finish in Steel Turning Operations Exploying Type CM (322 Ceramic Tools." Ufa-Ordzhonikidze Aircraft Inst., 1960.
111. H. D. Moore and D. R. Kibbey, Ceramic tool geometry and preparation. *ASTE Tech. Paper* **19** (1957).
112. L. Gion and L. Perrin, French developments in sintered ceramic cutting tools. *Machinery* (*N.Y.*) **91,** (1957).
113. W. M. Wheildon and G. W. Barnes, U.S. Patent 3,152,385.
114. H. J. Siekmann, Hardened bearing races machined with cemented oxide tools. *Machinery* (*N.Y.*) (1959).
115. F. L. Bagley Jr., Turning hardened tool steels with ceramic tools. *Tool Mfg. Engr.* (1961).
116. A. G. King and W. M. Wheildon, Strength of ceramics and machining metals, *ASTE Tech. Paper* **SP63-168** (1963).
117. Information by courtesy of Vascoloy Ramet/Wesson.
118. L. Fersing, "Ceramic Tool Research." Production, 1958.
119. D. R. Kibbey and H. D. Moore, "Ceramic or Carbide Tools—Which?" Am. Machinist/Metal Working Mfg., 1960.
120. Carborundum Company, Ceramic cutting tool design and application data.
121. N. H. Cook, Self-excited vibrations in metal cutting. *J. Eng. Ind.* **81,** 183–186 (1959).
122. R. S. Hahn, Metal-cutting chatter and its elimination. *Trans. ASME, Paper* **52-A41,** 1073–1079 (1952).
123. P. Albrect, Self-induced vibrations in metal cutting. *Am. Soc. Mech. Engrs., Paper* **61-WA-195** (1961).
124. J. Tlusty, The 'why' of machine tool behavior. *Am. Machinist, Spec. Rept.* **547,** 79–94 (1964).
125. "Metal Removal Bulletin," Mfg. Res. Issue. Spring Garden Inst., Philadelphia, Pennsylvania, 1958.
126. A. A. Voronin and A. I. Markov, *Stanki i Instr.* **31,** 15–17 (1960).
127. V. N. Poduraev and Yu. E. Zakharov, Vibratsionne rezanie pri tochenii metallov. *Stanki i Instr.* **30,** 11–16 (1959).
128. H. Frommelt, Ceramics-complement of carbide. *Tooling Production* **28,** 8 (1962).
129. H. Frommelt, "Ceramic Milling," Metal Removal Bull., Issue 1, Spring Garden Inst., 1956.
130. H. J. Siekmann, Bonding ceramic tool tips to steel shanks. *Tool Engr.* (1957).
131. D. R. Kibbey and W. T. Morris, Analysis of variables in ceramic tool cutting. *ASTE Tech. Paper* **23** (1957).
132. R. Mennell and E. A. Jeffery, Evaluation of several tool-life testing techniques, RPL 23/5. Rodman Lab., Watertown Arsenal, 1958.

133. R. Mennell, The comparison type of machining test, RPL 23/7. Rodman Lab., Watertown Arsenal, 1959.
134. M. J. Moroney, "Facts From Figures." Pelican Books, Clowes, London, 1958.
135. W. W. Gilbert, Economics of machining, *in* "Machining Theory and Practice," Am. Soc. Metals, Cleveland, Ohio, 1950.
136. F. W. Taylor, On the art of cutting metals. *Trans. ASME* **28**, (1907). (1907).
137. W. W. Gilbert, Economics of Machining, *in* "Machining with Carbides and Oxides," Chapter 17. ASTME, McGraw-Hill, New York, 1962.
138. H. J. Siekmann, Application and characteristics of ceramic cutting tools, *in* "Modern Approach to Machining Problems," Coll. Eng., Ann Arbor, Michigan, Univ. of Michigan, 1959.
139. General Electric Company, Application Data (1958).
140. Carborundum Company, Engineering Data.
141. General Electric Company, Application Data (1959).
142. C. T. Ansell and J. Taylor, The surface finishing properties of a carbide and ceramic cutting tool, *in* "Advances in Machine Tool Design and Research" (S. A. Tobias and F. Koenigsberger, eds.). Macmillan, New York, 1963.
143. Cooper Bessemer Corp., Ceramic tools win tough, new jobs. *Steel* pp. 2–6 (1963).
144. Take a new look at ceramic cutting tools. *Steel* pp. 128–132 (1961).
145. G. W. Barnes, VR-97, a breakthrough in ceramic tool materials. *Grits Grinds* **V50**, 3–8 (1959).
146. General Electric Company, Application Data (1958).
147. Norton, Data Sheet (1961).
148. Carborundum Company, Case History.
149. Ceramic tools win some new and some tougher jobs. *Steel* pp. 2–6 (1963).
150. Oxide tool takes an interrupted cut. *Am. Machinist New York* p. 123 (1960).
151. General Electric Company, Application Data (1959).
152. B. A. Holmstrom, Precision boring with carbides and oxides, *in* "Machining with Carbides and Oxides" (F. W. Wilson, ed.). McGraw-Hill, New York, 1962.
153. A. O. Schmidt, J. R. Roubik, J. J. Lonergan, and G. Hug, Comparative carbide and ceramic milling tests. *Am. Soc. Mech. Engrs. Paper* **62-PROD-8** (1962).
154. E. J. Weller, written discussion of Jones *et al.* (19), April 26, 1962.
155. E. J. Krabacher, Milling, *in* "Machining with Carbides and Oxides" (F. W. Wilson, ed.), Chapter 11. McGraw-Hill, New York, 1962.
156. E. E. Hallberg, Planning with carbides, *in* "Machining with Carbides and Oxides" (F. W. Wilson, ed.). McGraw-Hill, New York, 1962.
157. I. A. Dickter, C. L. Mehl, and R. F. Kenke, Final report on high temperature machining methods, Tech. Doc. Rept. No. ASD-TDR-63-125 Cincinati Milling Co. (1963).
158. E. Meier, Oxides thread hardened steel shafts. *Am. Machinist* p. 116 (1959).
159. J. J. Gilman, Strength of ceramic crystals. *Natl. Bur. Std.* (*U.S.*), *Monograph* **59** (1962).
160. S. S. Brenner, "Growth and Perfection of Crystals." Wiley, New York, 1958.

161. R. J. Stokes, Dislocation and mechanical properties in polycrystalline ceramics. Presented at *Conf. Structure Properties Eng. Mater., N. Carolina State Coll., Raleigh, N. Carolina,* (1962).
162. H. Palmour, III, talk presented at *65th Ann. Meeting Am. Ceram. Soc., Pittsburgh, Pennsylvania, 1963.*
163. W. D. Kingery, "Property Measurements at High Temperatures." Wiley, New York, 1959.
164. Information by courtesy of G. A. Ripka and E. McTamany, Frankford Arsenal, Philadelphia.
165. Information by courtesy of E. Lott, American Manufacturing Company of Texas.

Subject Index